For :
Professor McKim Marriott
with kindest regards,
Giri Raj Gupta
March

The Social and Cultural Context of Medicine in India

Main Currents in Indian Sociology—IV

The Social and Cultural Context of Medicine in India

Edited by

GIRI RAJ GUPTA

VIKAS PUBLISHING HOUSE PVT LTD

VIKAS PUBLISHING HOUSE PVT LTD
Regd. Office: 5 Ansari Road, New Delhi 110002
H.O. **Vikas House, 20/4 Industrial Area, Sahibabad 201010**
Distt. Ghaziabad, U.P. (India)

ISBN 0-7069-0793-0

1V2G1855

Printed at National Printing Works, New Delhi 110002

CONTRIBUTORS

D. Banerji is Chairman at the Center for Social Medicine and Community Health at Jawaharlal Nehru University, New Delhi. He was associated with the National Institute of Health Administration and Education, New Delhi and the National Tuberculosis Institute, Bangalore. He received his degree in Medicine (Calcutta, 1953), and Master's degree in Anthropology (Corrr ell, 1963). His interest in social planning for health in developing countries has led him to work in the fields of formulation of health services for rural populations, formulation of a National Tuberculosis Programme for India, nutrition policy, social orientation of education and training of health workers and population planning and health planning. For this purpose, he has actively participated both as a social scientist as well as a community physician in developing an interdisciplinary approach to the study of various aspects of community health problems and has published extensively addressing himself to crucial current issues. He is the author of *Family Planning in India: A Critique and a Perspective*, Peoples Publishing House, New Delhi.

Surinder M. Bhardwaj was born in India in 1934. He received his B.A. (Honors) degree in 1955 and M.A. degree in 1958 from the Punjab University. After teaching in India for a few years he came to the University of Minnesota in 1962, where he did his M.A. (1966) and Ph.D. (1970). He joined Kent State University in 1969, where he is Chairman of the Geography Department.

Dr. Bhardwaj is the author of *Hindu Places of Pilgrimage in India: A Study in Cultural Geography*, published by the University of California Press in 1973. Dr. Bhardwaj has extensively published professional papers on modernization processes, and the attitude of rural people toward different systems of medicine in India. He is now engaged in writing a monograph on the expansion of Homoeopathy in India.

Raj Gandhi obtained his B.A. and M.A. degrees in Sociology from the Maharaja Sayajirao University of Baroda in India and Ph.D. from the University of Minnesota. In India he was the University Grants Commission scholar, and in America a Fulbright scholar. He has taught Sociology at the M.S. University of Baroda, India, San Diego State University, U.S.A. and the University of Saskatchewan, Canada. Currently he is Associate Professor of Sociology at the University of Calgary, Canada. He has presented scholarly papers at national and international conferences, and has published numerous articles in scholarly journals in India, U.S.A., Germany, France, and Canada. He is the author of *Locals and Cosmopolitans of Little India*. Major areas of research and interest include Urban and Medical Sociology, Sociology of Religion and Change, and Sociology of Family and Kinship.

Edward Montgomery was born in Manhattan, Kansas in 1941 and is currently

Associate Professor of Anthropology at Washington University in St. Louis. He received his A.B. from Stanford and Ph.D. from Columbia, both in Anthropology in 1964 and 1970 respectively. With his extensive field experience—Western Nevada (1965), India (late 1967 to mid-1970, 1974 summer) and Peru (1973 summer)—he has developed major dimensions in building Anthropology as a comparative human science and sharpening it as a contemporary, solution-directed discipline, especially by pursuing these concerns in medical anthropology, human ecology and the study of human life sequences. Exemplifying these concerns are his recent contributions appearing in *Annual Review of Anthropology*, Volume 2, 1973; *American Ethnologist*, Volume 4, 1977; *Malnutrition, Behavior and Social Organization* edited by Lawrence S. Greene, 1977; *Progress in Human Nutrition*, Volume 2, 1978; and the *Uses of Anthropology* edited by Water Goldschmidt and published by American Anthropological Association, 1978.

T.N. MADAN is currently Professor of Sociology at the Institute of Economic Growth, University of Delhi. After completing the M.A. (Lucknow) and Ph.D. (ANU), he held several coveted teaching and research assignments in India, Australia, the U.K. and the U.S.A. His areas of interest include kinship, religion, ethnicity and the professions. He has been author and editor of several excellent works and published extensively in the professional journals in India, Japan, France, the U.K. and the U.S.A. Since 1967 he has been the editor of *Contributions to Indian Sociology*. His most recent work (in collaboration with other colleagues) is *Doctors and Society: Three Asian Case Studies—India, Malaysia and Sri Lanka.*

JOANNA KIRKPATRICK obtained her A.B. degree from Stanford University in Anthropology, 1951; an A.M. in General Studies (Anthropology and Sociology) at Yale University, 1954; and her Ph.D. in Anthropology from the University of California at Berkeley in 1970, supported by NDFL fellowships in Hindi New-para, a National Institution of Health Traineeship. She is currently (1975-76) Social Science Research-cum-Teaching Consultant at the Institute of Bangladesh Studies, Rajshahi University, Rajshahi, Bangladesh, under a Ford Foundation grant to the Institute. She is on leave from Bennington College, where she is a Professor of Anthropology in the Division of Social Sciences.

Dr. Kirkpatrick's major research area is South Asia which includes field work in Lahore and Karachi, West Pakistan, in 1955-56; Ludhiana, Punjab, India in 1965-66; and Rajshahi, Bangladesh. The results of her study of social interaction and organization of a women's ward in a mission hospital are presented as her doctoral dissertation. *The Open Ward in a Closed Society: Social Interaction in a North Indian Hospital Ward.* The ethnography of medicine as a comparative study continues to be one of her major interests.

Dr. Kirkpatrick's other area of special research is the field of women's studies, and has presented several papers on this subject at annual meetings of the American Anthropological Association and elsewhere. One of her articles, "Women in Indian-English Literature: The Question of Individuation," has appeared in the *Journal of South Asian Literature*. She also writes verse and has published two poems.

PROSHANTA K. NANDI is Associate Professor of Sociology at Sangamon State University, Springfield, Illinois. Born and raised in India, his academic interests center around Sociology and Economics. He received a Fulbright Award in 1965 for graduate studies at the University of Minnesota leading to the doctorate in Sociology during the course of which he studied with, among others, Arnold M. Rose, Don Martindale, and Edward Gross. He was on the faculty of Kalyani University in India and Ohio University, prior to joining Sangamon State in 1972, and served as a Research Sociologist, under the auspices of the Ford Foundation in India, in planning for educational, health, and other systems in a Government of India Pilot Research Project in Growth Centers. His articles have appeared in *Man in India*, *International Review of Modern Sociology*, and the *Journal of Asian and African Studies*, and in other sociological monographs. His current involvement in research on Asian-Americans grew out of his social and community activities as a past President of the India Association of Springfield, Illinois, and through professional affiliation with the Asian-American Mental Health Research Center, which is supporting some of that research.

KLAAS W. VAN DER VEEN, Ph.D., studied Social Geography and Social Anthropology at the University of Amsterdam. Since 1958 he has been on the faculty of the Department of Cultural Anthropology, Anthropological Sociological Center, Keizersgracht, Amsterdam and Professor of Social Anthropology at the Vrije Universiteit Brussel, Pleinlaan 2, Brussels. He spent a year, 1963-1964, on field research on marriage and hierarchy among the Anavil Brahmans of South Gujarat. During 1970-1971, he was named as a member of an Indo-Dutch research team to study aspects of social change in Valsad District, South Gujarat. In 1975, he completed a one-year training program for nursing personnel at the Marine Hospital of the Royal Dutch Navy. In exploring the possibilities of anthropological research on the social aspects of disease control and treatment, he visited Valsad District in 1976 and 1977.

S.B. MANI, M.Sc., M.A., Ph.D. (Syracuse), is an Associate Professor of Anthropology at Slippery Rock State College, Pennsylvania, U.S.A. Dr. Mani's major areas of interest are applied anthropology and social change in India, and research interests relate to family planning, cultural aspects of interpersonal communication regarding health and family planning, decision-making process regarding male sterilization and training of indigenous midwives for the delivery of health and family planning services in rural India.

Dr. Mani has published extensively in the area of family planning communication, culture and communication, opinion leaders in family planning information, education and communication and training and utilization of indigenous midwives in Maternal and Child Health and Family Planning Programs. He spent a year, 1975-1976, as a Visiting Professor at the Directorate of Health Services and Family Planning in Tamil Nadu evaluating the training program for indigenous midwives.

MARK NICHTER received his doctorate in Social Anthropology from the University of Edinburgh in 1977. His thesis entitled "Health Ideologies and Medical Cultures of the South Kanara Areca-Nut Belt" was based on two years of field study in the rural region of South Kanara District, Karnataka State, India. Subsequently, he received a Masters of Public Health from the Department of International Health, School of Hygiene and Public Health, Johns Hopkins University.

His publications include papers on the village Indian pantheon, the semantics of illness, patterns of resort in the use of multiple therapy systems, the expression of anxiety by Grahman women, and the relationship between diet and the cultural perception of health and self. He is actively interested in the anthropology of health, the interface between anthropology and health planning, and symbolic anthropology.

DAVID G. MANDELBAUM, Professor of Anthropology, University of California, Berkeley, began his anthropological research among American Indian groups. His first work in India was in 1937-1938 and since then he has done field work in several areas of South Asia, particularly in the Nilgiri area of South India. During these four decades, his contributions have appeared in the leading journals in India, U.S.A. and elsewhere. Among his writings include a work in two volumes, *Society in India* and *Human Fertility in India*, published respectively in 1970 and 1974 by the University of California Press.

R.S. KHARE, born in 1936, is currently Professor of Anthropology and Chairman, Committee on Individual and Society, Center for Advanced Study, University of Virginia. Previously he was on the faculty of University of Wisconsin, Green Bay and Director d'Etudes, Ecole Pratigue Des Hautes Etudes, Sorbonne, Paris. He was a fellow at Institute for Advanced Study, Princeton; Indian Institute of Advanced Study, Simla; and University of Chicago. Since 1958, he has done several spells of fieldwork in Uttar Pradesh, India and is the author of *The Changing Brahmans*, Chicago, 1970; *The Hindu Hearth and Home*, New Delhi, 1976; and *Culture and Reality*, Simla, 1976. His numerous articles have appeared in distinguished professional journals in India, Europe and the United States.

EDWARD O. HENRY received his Ph.D. degree in Anthropology from Michigan State University. He is an Assistant Professor of Anthropology at San Diego State University. With the support of the U.S. Public Health Service Research Fellowships, he carried out field work in eastern Uttar Pradesh, India, during 1971 and 1972, and plans to publish several research reports. His major area of interest is ethnomusicology and social anthropology.

JAMES M. FREEMAN (Ph.D. Harvard, 1968) is a Professor of Anthropology at San Jose State University, San Jose, California, U.S.A. His research interests in South Asia are religion, urbanization, life histories, Untouchables, and humanistic aspects of change and adaptation. He has conducted two field research projects in India: (1) a 16-month study of an urbanizing Hindu temple village in 1962-1963; and (2) a 22-month follow-up study of the same village in 1970-1972. His publications on religion in India include one book: *Scarcity and Opportunity in an Indian Village* (1977), Cummings Publishing Company, Menlo Park, California; and four articles: "Religious Change in a Hindu Pilgrimage Center" in the *Review of Religious Research* (1975); "Trial by Fire" in *Natural*

History Magazine (1974); "Occupational Changes Among Hindu Temple Servants" in the *Indian Anthropologist* (1971); and "Myth and Metaphysics in Indian Thought" in the *Monist* (1966). He has recently completed a book depicting the life history of an Indian Untouchable from the same caste as the Firewalking Kalasis described in the present paper. His post doctoral research and writing on India have been supported by fellowships from the American Institute of Indian Studies (1970-1977), and the Center for Advanced Study in the Behavioral Sciences (1976-1977).

LORNA RHODES AMARSINGHAM received her Ph.D. in Anthropology from Cornell University in 1973. Her dissertation was based on a year of field work in the up-country of Sri Lanka, where she studied Sinhalese curing rituals. She is currently a post-doctoral fellow in the Laboratory in Social Psychiatry at Harvard Medical School, where she is working on a study of Indian and Ceylonese immigrants to the United States.

ACKNOWLEDGEMENTS

Numerous articles of theoretical and empirical nature in medical sociology in India have come out in the last few decades. To make the fruits of such research available in the form of this anthology, representing the current status of inquiries, is only possible through the assistance of dedicated colleagues. It has been a pleasant experience for I am greatly indebted to all the contributors for their generosity, patience and understanding, and to publishers who granted me permission to use their materials. Grateful thanks are also due to S.K. Bhardwaj, R.S. Khare, Edward Montgomery and other colleagues for incidental help and for offering comments on some of the contributions and to Charles Leslie for encouragement to pursue the project and suggesting names of contributors.

I am appreciative of the Western Illinois University Research Council, especially President Leslie Malpass and Director of Research, Dr. Myron Mustaine for continued secretarial assistance for the series and to Dr. Igolima T.D. Amachree, Chairman, Department of Sociology and Anthropology for making every effort to facilitate the work. Also, I wish to record my thanks to my friend and colleague Dr. Steven M. Cox for his unfailing support and generous advice at various stages of work. Linda Kasik and Heather Sim deserve our appreciation for their conscientious secretarial assistance.

Macomb, Illinois 61455
U.S.A.

GIRI RAJ GUPTA

EDITOR'S INTRODUCTION

Main Currents in Indian Sociology series is intended to be an outlet for ongoing research on the Indian sub-continent. Each volume is thematic, addressing the status-of-the-field, providing possible prognosis, and at least, integrating fresh areas of research. The title of this volume itself bespeaks its contents. It is intended primarily to bring together social scientists, policy makers, and men of medicine to share their ideas and perhaps put them to use for the future health and welfare of the people.

Attempts by social scientists to understand cultural conceptions of disease, prevalent preferences for prevention and cure, acceptance and rejection of a particular medical system, dependence on magical, human and spiritual agents to eliminate a disease does not have a long history. A common skepticism, which unfortunately is not healthy, still clouds the vision of the policy makers as well as the medical professionals as to the relevance of the contributions of social scientists. Medicine and sociology are perceived by many of their practioners to be two distinct domains of knowledge and scientific application. Some believe that an alliance between the two would make an odd couple. It is not only mutual mistrust, but a poor comprehension of the function of such an alliance, partly rooted in the nature of training programs where a physician is trained to find a physiological abnormality with little concern about the social and cultural conditioning and environment of the patient. Similarly, a social scientist may be at a loss to understand why a physician diagnosed a patient in the way he did, especially when the cause of the disease is rooted somewhere other than the body of the patient. This continued skepticism is not only detrimental to the people's health, but it also reinforces stagnation in this field of utmost significance for human concern.

Sociology is the study of human interaction, the social arrangement of human groups, and the latent and manifest consequences for the individuals and groups involved. Medicine is the application of technology and knowledge to the prevention and amelioration of human damage and suffering. After prolonged research, advanced technological accomplishments, drug innovations and accumulation of medical knowledge, it has been possible for humans to prevent many diseases, and avert calamities such as those disasters often caused by epidemics. The targets set by governments to improve the health of the people have often met with passive rejection, sometimes distrust and occasionally outright rebellions. Application of technology and knowledge to improve the health of human beings, their human interaction and social arrangements is not only necessary in itself, but also necessary in terms of people's investment in these resources in terms of potential return they should expect from such knowledge. Unfortunately, such realizations, if any, are rare among societies where attitudinal differences among the professionals and the populations are great and where the governments' health programs are perceived to be one of many ineffectual bureaucratic ploys. The people are often blamed for their resistance to certain programs, apathy towards well-intended preventive as well as curative measures and a general dislike for the way the government employees push schemes for the so-called "welfare of the people." Very few studies have attempted to find answers to these problems. It is therefore appropriate that sociologists examine the interaction, social arrangements, relevant cultural norms, and consequences that affect health and illness.

Medical sociologists or anthropologists are hampered in their work by a number of problems. The medical speciality of these twin sciences is relatively young compared to most other branches, and in many cases, available research tools and methods are not very sophisticated. Most social scientists, including medical sociologists, have but a layman's knowledge of medical technology, medical training, and the history of evolution of medical practice. Access to people and institutions that could provide or arrange for the collection of data is often difficult. Some physicians, like many others, are wary of individuals who claim to be able to study human interaction and social arrangements with the same rigor as is used in the studies of chemicals, atoms or cells.

In addition, in many societies the acceptance of such knowledge and its use has suffered innumerable setbacks due to cultural inhibitions. However, it would be sheer ignorance to assume that indigenous societies are slow to learn and usually are resistant to the use of medical advances since their cultural system is often in dissonance with their present ideals and values. Part of the problem relates to a set of variables besides the availability of material resources, such as: people's exposure to the medical systems; personal and cultural acceptance of the services of medical systems and what they can offer; availability of such knowledge and resources and their effective use to meet the health needs of the people; and advancement of such knowledge through further research.

Robert Straus, about two decades ago, proposed a useful distinction between sociology *in* medicine and sociology *of* medicine (Straus, 1957: 200-204). Sociology in medicine is the application of sociological knowledge techniques, concepts in attempts to delineate and analyze medical and socio-psychological problems with which medical professionals and related workers are involved. Largely in this case, sociological knowledge supplements, and occasionally complements medical knowledge in order to find solutions to what are essentially medical problems. In this instance, sociological knowledge helps explain phenomena, causes of disease and possible solutions beyond what has been explained by medical knowledge.

Sociology of medicine proposes to deal with issues related to the functioning of medical workers, their organizations and institutions and allied activities encompassing their concerns in an effort to analyze and clarify what are essentially sociological issues or questions. The approach parallels a sociological examination of other institutions or organizations such as the caste system, a political party, a religious or educational institution. Further, Patricia L. Kendall and George G. Reader have provided a helpful delineation of the above scheme (1972:1-21). I will heavily draw upon their paradigm in the following pages.

I. Sociology in Medicine

Since the uses of sociology in medicine in India have not yet taken firm roots, a general scheme may serve as a useful framework for identifying areas of research and future direction.

A. History and evolution of medical knowledge

Evolution of health concepts and treatment of disease in most societies is deeply embedded in antiquity, historical antecedents and the cultural growth of societies. Indian medicine is very ancient and the earliest concepts are spelled out in the Veda, especially the Atharvaveda which dates as far back as the 2nd millennium B.C. Dhanvantari, a king, is credited for having learned Ayurveda (science of life) from Brahma. Use of magical practices and charms was common long before the Vedic period and was popular during this age. *Carak-samhita* and *Susruta-samhita*, authored by a physician and a surgeon respectively, due to their antiquarian origins caused claims of superiority over the Greek counterpart which influenced Western medical systems. Both of these works are quite comprehensive and illustrate the three divine universal forces: the *kapha* (phlegm), *pitta* (bile) and *vayu* (air). Early Hindu writings proposed extensive diagnostic procedures and principles of prognosis. Therapeutics were primarily dietetic and medicinal. Most treatments consisted of "five procedures": the administration of emetics, purgatives, water enemas, oil enemas, and sneezing powders. The Indian materia medica consisted of vegetable drugs including milk of various animals and infrequently other parts of animal bodies; but often minerals such as gold, carbon, arsenic, lead, copper, sulfur, and sulfate. Carak was acquainted with 500 medicinal plants and Susruta 760. Modern surgery acknowledges the contributions of Susruta who recommended 20 sharp and 101 blunt instruments. Successful operations for stones in the bladder (vesical calculus), anal fistula and plastic surgery were known during the time of Susruta and in these Hindu surgeons were definitely in advance of the Greeks (Encycl. Brit., 1975: 823-841).

The observance of religious beliefs in Hindu society hygienic measures always received much importance. Religious observances were, and still are in consonance with general principles suggested in Ayurvedic medicine. Hot and cold meals, water to be drunk before and after meals, the use of condiments, texture, color and fibre of dress, exposure to sun, bathing, care of skin, cleaning of teeth, anointing of the body, use of eye washes, and bowel movements all have something to do with ritual purity and often interpreted to carry hygienic meanings.

Greek and Arabic, generally referred to as mediterranean medicine, came to India late and its impact was conspicuous by 1200 A.D. or the time of the Muslim rule. It was known as *Yunani-Tibbia* in Arabic (Greek medicine) and was initially confined to the Muslim population. Among the founders of this school of medicine were Hippocrates and Galen from Greece, Rhazes Avicenna from Persia, Abu al-Qasim (Albucasis Maimonides), a Jew from Arabia and Salerno from Southern Italy. Incidentally, all of these men advanced and used humoral theories composed of four humors: yellow bile, black bile, phlegm, and blood, which paralleled the three humors of Ayurveda. Since the principles of Ayurveda and Yunani are almost the same and laid the foundation of scientific research and professional advancement in Europe Charles Leslie (1976:4-11; also see Dunn, 1976:133-158) rejects the use of the adjectives—scientific, modern, Western medicine in Europe, the new world and elsewhere—and calls it "cosmopolitan medicine" for he asserts that objective judgments about the scientific character of medical theories and practices vary because of the multiple criteria which exists for calling them scientific. Besides, cosmopolitan medical institutions exist in every country and these institutions continue to depend upon humoral theories.

European medicine, probably, found its way to India long before the English established the East India Company in 1500; there were Dutch, French and Spanish travellers and missionaries prior to the 5th century. Alexander the Great invaded India (Punjab) as early as 327-325 B.C. The decline of the Mughal empire in the early 17th century gradually gave the English an opportunity to politically control most of India and later the whole sub-continent. The ascent to paramountcy of the British at the turn of the 19th century eventually resulted in, among several significant changes, creation of a class of professionals including physicians and surgeons who had to undergo training at approved institutions in India including some fortunate ones who were sent to England. A kind of displacement of classes occurred and those who were known to have strong allegiance to the British throne, not necessarily from the past ruling classes, reaped the rewards. In terms of the evolution of the allopathic medical system, formulation of policy and administration has ably been presented by D. Banerji.

Another system of medicine of European origin, homeopathy, came to India sometime in the 17th century. Homeopathy deals with treatment of disease by the administration of tiny doses of a drug that in healthy persons causes symptoms resembling those of the disease treated. Paracelus (Encycl. Brit., 1975: 982-984), an extraordinary man, son of a German doctor and chemist, a pioneer surgeon and chemist, is acknowledged to be the founder of homeopathy. Though homeopathy came to India with the advent of Europeans, it never gained much popularity for various reasons including the state partronage, availability of drugs, exclusion of surgical procedures and training of medical personnel. Though in many ways it remained complementary and an alternative to Ayurveda, Yunani and allopathy, it was never properly ingrained in the system like others and remained quite esoteric in its application and usage. Still, there are numerous private clinics where people obtain services as they believe homeopathy drugs are inexpensive, carry no side effects, do not require restrictions on food intake and are perhaps effective in curing diseases where other systems have failed. Bhardwaj ably records the evolution and impact of homeopathy.

B. Ecology, etiology and epidemeology

Ecology relates to that branch of knowledge which is concerned with the interrelationships of organisms and the natural cycles and rhythms of their environment. Though general concern has been shown about the incidence of certain diseases in geographical areas, sections of cities and populations, there are not many scientific studies conducted in this area. Problems of hygienic housing, nutrition, sanitation and pollution which are not restricted to urban centers have not received enough attention. Urban surveys have occasionally pointed out some of these problems, but rural areas have been mostly ignored as there are other major priority problem areas which need to be handled first.

Study of the incidence and prevalence of illnesses in society belongs within the scope of etiology. For instance, special illnesses and disabilities associated with particular occupations, age, sex, religious or food habits may be included in this category. The number of such studies carried out by individual scholars and institutions is too numerous to mention, yet they tell us enough to alarm anyone.

Another branch of inquiry deals with the incidence, distribution, determinants and control of disease called epidemeology. Just on commonsense grounds many simple correlations can be, and some have been, established. For instance, certain castes are more vulnerable to a particular disease, people living in a particular area are endangered by lung cancer or persons with a particular kind of social environment may suffer from spirit possession syndrome and/or susceptable to the displeasure of the spirit world.

C. Cultural perception of illness and societal response

What is illness and what is not is determined largely by cultural orientations of the people. Consequently what is considered illness in one society may not be viewed the same in another. Also, does a particular illness have a particular cause, like colds, coughs, minor headaches, or stomachaches or are they characteristic of certain individuals? In the latter case, what will be the best remedy? Taking some home-made medication; going to the nearest indigenous medical man, an allopathy physician, or if everything fails, to an astronomer/priest or invoking the profane or pure spirits? Relevant here are a set of diverse topics, such as: the definition of illness, public information about it, health needs, and use of various kinds of remedial measures. Again, all these may be viewed in the context of the people's beliefs about the kind of food they consume, the caste to which they belong, family history, and to an extent the kind of medication they can accept.

Rather than review what must be, by now, rather well-known literature, it is safer to say, it is of utmost importance to consider the complexity of variables which determine the course of action whether it relates to an illness or to a plan to regulate family size. For instance, the concepts of disease and the types of medical systems used by the people to cure the disease have recently received attention (see T.N. Madan, Nichter and Mani). These studies have been conducted in different settings and lead to a variety of conclusions depending upon the exposure of the people to their environment as well as various systems of medicine (see Gould, 1965:201-208). In addition, they suggest that people are not as inhibitive about the modern medicine as was reported in some of the earlier studies (Carstairs, 1956; Marriott, 1955).

In most of non-Western societies illness and disease are believed to be not only caused by exposure to adversities of environment and imbalance in the human body,but also by the spirit world which includes the spirits of the profane, spirits of the ancestors or dead members of the family and, gods and goddesses of little tradition. Therefore means used to cure disease and avoid calamities are usually consistent with these beliefs. Mandelbaum, through his brilliant analysis, introduces the concept of transcultural practices which represent the confluence of secular and religious in curing practices and influence the diagnotic procedures, functioning of therapeutic agents and procedures which are prevalent throughout South Asia, Africa, South America and parts of North America. Such beliefs are based upon early human experience and the means available to cure disease. To placate spirits, gods, goddesses and small godlings, people have used sympathetic and homeopathic magic, sacrifices, ordeals, vows, rites, ceremonies, prayers and many times extensive ritualistic procedures. Khare convincingly points out that it is not only *dava* (medicine), but *dua* (blessings) which blended together form the curing practices. Consequently, in many cases a patient not only needs the attention of a medical professional but also the assistance of human soothsayers, priests, *ojhas*, *tantrikas*, *maulvis*, *sadhus* and *sanyasins*.

Services of one of such agents, a *sadhu* (holy man) practicing *Sidha*, are commendably reported by Edward O. Henry in Eastern Uttar Pradesh. In the Sidha method of curing, magical, religious, secular and herbal elements of unknown medicinal value are combined to cause a desired result. Often, patients who could not be cured by secular medicine, or who do not believe that secular medicine has much to offer find Sidha quite acceptable. Interestingly, people believe that this system of medicine has cures for all kinds of ailments which may range from stomachache to a serious psychological problem.

Lorna Amarsingham presents a remarkable analysis of the personality, functions and goals of the Sinhalese exorcists which reflects the difference between the deflective practices of exorcists and conquest over disease by secular medical practitioners all over South Asia. The fire-walking ceremony reported by James M. Freeman from the eastern coast of Orissa demonstrates the propitiation of the goddess Kali, who is endowed with great power, and protects people against all kinds of diseases and inadversities, especially, small pox and cholera. The ceremony serves several sacred and secular objectives in addition to insulating people against disease, which cannot be isolated from other meanings implied in the ceremony.

The general orientation of all these articles reveals that South Asian medicine is transcultural, and is strongly overshadowed by the cultural system. Despite the fact that modern, Western or cosmopolitan medicine has made significant inroads, its effectiveness is impeded by the so-called professionalism or mutual alienation of the medical practitioners and the society. This process of estrangement will be further intensified as specialization in medicine advances making the medical profession a system far-removed from the needs of the masses.

D. Deviance, labelling and stigma

Illness many times is referred to as deviance and sometimes as a social problem or social pathology. Parsons (1951) characterized the sick role as a form of deviance. The underlying assumption is that socially a person is not able to perform his normal role when he is sick. Again, the meaning of normal varies from one historical and cultural context to another, yet deviance constitutes a role or set of roles and implies labelling usually reflected in commonly known epithets such as: witch-possessed, mentally ill, epileptic, among others. The Western psychoanalysts generally believe that most of the psychological problems are caused due to the repression of ideas and feelings as we already know about the causes of most of the physical illnesses. Again who is ill and what is the nature of disease is perceived to have deeper cultural meanings. For example, a person endowed with certain magical/religious qualities may be considered to be deviant by some cosmopolitan people while for his followers he may be a superior person blessed with unusual qualities. At this point it may be worth considering the ways in which the cultural context determines the nature of deviance and attendant labelling and stigma. I suggest that deviance may be classified into two categories: (1) bad deviance, and (2) good deviance. Sick role as a form of bad deviance would relate to all those situations when a person's relationships are adversely affected including his physical well-being. While good deviance will mean that his relationships are affected in a positive way entailing greater involvement of his family, kinsmen and community. For instance, a person possessed with or having seance with an evil spirit may be labelled as bad deviance, yet the same occurrence with a religious spirit will be good deviance. In view of the amount of energy expended in the study and treatment of diseases, especially mental illnesses, it is not unreasonable to expect that some of these phenomena, which are scorned off as something else, may provide enduring results.

II. The Sociology of Medicine

In this case, we are dealing with the application of sociology to the medical profession and organizations including their relationships with external institutions and agencies.

A. The recruitment of physicians

During the past three decades the process of recruitment of physicians has been influenced by democratic ideals and emphasis has been on the equal opportunity and academic accomplishments of the individuals rather than patronage favoring only certain classes of people as was common during British colonial rule. The realization that more and more doctors are needed to meet the health needs of the constantly growing population led to an increase in the number of people in the profession and by opening up the new medical institutions. Compared with the situation in the past, there is a greater awareness in the public now of the availability and use of medical services. Though most medical colleges and hospitals are run by the state and services are free of cost to the public, with the exception of large towns and cities where private clinics serve the rich and affluent, generally such services are not yet available to rural areas. According to available figures there is about one physician per 800 in the United States, 1,000 in Britain, 450 in Israel, 3,000 in Brazil, 6,000 in India, 100,000 in Nepal and Northern Nigeria. The physician patient ratio is much higher in rural areas as the concentration of medical services is usually in the cities. The statistics, incidentally, do not provide us an objective picture as there are numerous unregistered medical professionals within the field of allopathy along with Yunani, Ayurveda and homeopathy. In many cases, the quacks who pretentiously claimed to have cures for every ailment began to realize that such operations were a poor business technique and have learned the art of healing through training programs and often gained popularity as they are easily accessible and have strong local ties. Through very persuasive and critical analyses of the life histories of medical practitioners of various systems of medicine, such as, Ayurveda, Siddha, Yunani, homeopathy and allopathy, Edward Montgomery tells us about growth of public and private hospitals, training of medical practitioners and their organizations, availability and the indigenous production of pharmaceutical and chemical drugs, disease reporting and diagnostic measures and related legislation. The four biographies of the medical practitioners first of all reveal ascribed, hereditary roles through tradition and informal self-determined life experience. Their diagnostic techniques and medications are genuinely indigeneous as well as foreign in character; and their profession has the element of charity as well as business which fits in very well with the socio-cultural environment of their patients. Also an aura of hightened self-esteem and prestige marks their practice while the element of trust and confidence among the patients prevails in obtaining services.

B. The Training Program for Medical Personnel

D. Banerji points out that the history and evolution of the medical system in India has to do with its limited success and distressing failure. Pressures to do what is necessary for people's health, by and large, come from outside the profession. In contrast, pressures to maintain and promote quality medical education, setting up curriculum standards, duration of training, control of academic quality of entrants and location of institutions; administration of internships and residency training programs and to an extent appointments originate within the medical hierarchy. A frequent complaint from the medical bureaucracy is that neither the common man nor the politicians understand their science and its problems, while these people think that the medical profession is primarily accountable for its inadequacy to meet the needs of the people. Several suggestions, many conflicting in content and occasionally unworkable, have been offered by various commissions, agencies and men in politics; but nothing viable has yet been worked out. Many states have eliminated the mandatory service requirements after the completion of training, partly due to the fact that states cannot fund all the positions and partly to encourage many doctors to open up private clinics. However, this resulted in unemployment of doctors, even though they are not over abundant. The state jobs automatically provided facilities with a lucrative job while the private sector suffered from the lack of financial resources; and establishing a reasonable practice requires time, commitment and efficiency. Again, a new physician in a private clinic is not only competing with his well-established compeers if he stays in a city, but if he moves to a rural area he is competing with state-owned hospitals and clinics, where again the clients are not wealthy enough to afford his services. Rising costs of health services and ever-increasing demands on medical personnel certainly requires a critical evaluation and perhaps an overhauling.

The most serious problem at this time is not the availability of the doctors, but obtaining their services in rural areas. Besides, the absence of the amenities of urban life, small hospitals are poorly equipped, the clientele is poor, transport facilities are inadequate and the setting is not very encouraging which could offer a challenge to the young doctor. There is enough evidence to suggest that communities need more medical help of any kind and people have used all kinds of means to impress upon the administration that they are not as ignorant as they are generally believed to be and that a strong reorientation of the social and cultural aspects of the medical program is needed is hardly questionable.

The Chinese example may not be an appropriate model for India, where conflict exists not only between the people and the politically influenced medical bureaucracy which has to deliver the goods, but also among the medical systems: Allopathy, Ayurveda, Yunani and Homeopathy. Can all these systems work together? Can a person be trained in all these systems of medicine? How much training is necessary? What will be the most cost-effective system? Would the people accept what is offered to them? The answer to the last question will certainly be in the affirmative as long as the system does the job (see Madan). Still some other possibilities can be identified. These are: (1) reduce the number of years in medical college and create an intermediate degree for a doctor; similar steps may be taken for other personnel; salaries should be matched with qualifications; personnel should be assigned to jobs according to their qualifications; (2) research institutes should be created to explore the possibilities of synthesizing medical knowledge irrespective of the systems involved. This attempt, hopefully, will not only cut the costs of expensive medicine but also help in standardizing indigenous medicine, including home-made remedies which are usually scorned by the sophisticated; (3) emphasis should be placed upon social-cultural aspects of the patients personality, for example, diagnosis of psychosomatic disease; (4) a program for community involvement should be planned in which decision-making and material in-put may be considered as valuable as the state's participation. Rather than supervisory jobs being assigned to district and division or state authorities, a review board should be composed of local state and professional representatives.

C. *The relations of medical personnel to others in various role-sets*

The hierarchical structure of a hospital, depending upon the extents of services offered, is usually composed of a District Medical Officer, senior specialists, physicians, surgeons, housemen/residents, interns, under-training undergraduate medical students, matrons, nurses, nurse's assistant, ward attendants, janitorial and custodial staff. There are others who temporarily become part of the system, such as: patients visiting relatives, friends and private attendants. Research in this area is almost absent. The role of the medical staff is well defined, yet what a patient must know from the medical professional about his health problems is considered to be irrelevant to him and his relatives. Though disease is, largely, clearly defined, a great amount of mystification of information prevails, generally leading to the mechanistic role-playing of medical staff. The latter assert that most people have little knowledge about disease and medication and often acquainting them about either or both of these leads to problems as cultural barriers start working against the patient role. van der Veen and R.S. Gandhi, citing numerous relevant studies, bring out very clearly that besides the cultural context of illness, health and medicine it is the network of relationships among the patient's social world and the place of the practitioner in it which determines the use of the services of the latter. van der Veen, from his research in the Gujarat state suggests that due to a lack of understanding among medical personnel, in spite of facilities provided by the state, services are under utilized. The ill-functioning of the Public Health Centers remains a difficult task to handle since there is no working relationship between the centers and the public whom they are supposed to serve. Mark Nichter reaches the same conclusions from his South Kanar study in South India and questions the suitability of bio-medical model without recognizing the socio-medical needs of the people.

The dilemma of hospital systems is characterized by yet another serious problem. While new knowledge in the field of medicine is moving the system towards internationalization and responsiveness to professional growth, it is at the same time straying away from the understanding of local needs. The continuity between the patient and the practitioner is lost as the latter advances in his field leading to greater alienation from his own patients, the community and those he serves. Joanna Kirkpatrick comes out with such conclusions by analyzing the health delivery system in the north Indian city of Ludhiana. Yet another aspect adversely affecting professionalization among the nursing services, which are largely manned by women, is presented by P.K. Nandi. The basic tenets of nursing ethics, which he measures with Western standards, he believes are poor. But comparing the evolution of the system in a historical perspective he finds that it is not the profession, but other socio-cultural variables which have deterred the growth of professionalism.

Various systems of medicine in India have existed for centuries. The systems exchanged knowledge though their principles were occasionally conflicting. For instance, *Tibb* is a hybrid of Muslim-Hindu or Yunani and Ayurveda systems (Basham, 1974 : 39). Such amalgamation of knowledge is certainly prevalent in almost all the systems today. The plurality of the systems is valuable to the systematic advancement of medical knowledge and meeting the needs of the people.

Emphasis in this volume has been on the socio-cultural dimension. There are, of course, many other significant topics which need to be researched to gain a complete knowledge of the subject. There is much to be done. The valuable contributions in this work present a variety of approaches to the theme, but are not indicative of all of the disagreements which have led to major debates on significant issues. Rather, many problems have been highlighted enough to motivate researchers to look at them in depth and critically and to offer us insights to gain better understanding of the systems not only in India or South Asia but elsewhere as well.

REFERENCES

BASHAM, A.L.

1976 "The Practice of Medicine in Ancient and Medieval India" Charles Leslie (ed.), *Asian Medical Systems*. Berkeley: University of California Press.

CARSTAIRS, G. MORRIS

1956 *The Twice-Born*. Bloomington: Indiana University Press.

DUNN, FRED L.

1976 "Traditional Asian Medicine as Adaptive Systems" Charles Leslie (ed.), *Asian Medical Systems*. Berkeley: University of California Press.

ENCYCLOPAEDIA, BRITANICA

1975 "History of Medicine." II:823-841.
"Paracelus." 13:982-984.

GOULD, HAROLD A.

1965 "Modern Medicine and Folk Cognition in Rural India." *Human Organization* 24:201-208.

KENDALL, PATRICIA L. AND GEORGE G. READER

1972 "Contributions of Sociology to Medicine" H.E. Freeman, S. Levine and L.G. Reeder (eds.), *Handbook of Medical Sociology* (Second Edition). Englewood Cliffs, N.J.: Prentice-Hall.

LESLIE, CHARLES
1976 "Introduction" Charles Leslie (ed.), *Asian Medical Systems*. Berkeley: University of California Press.

MARRIOTT, MCKIM
1955 "Western Medicine in a Village of Northern India" B.D. Paul (ed.), *Health, Culture* and *Community*. New York: Russell Sage Foundation.

PARSONS, TALCOTT
1951 *The Social System*. New York: Free Press.

STRAUS, ROBERT
1957 "The Nature and Status of Medical Sociology." *American Sociological Review* 22:200-204.

CONTENTS

PART THREE

INDIGENOUS SYSTEMS OF HEALING AND CURING

PART ONE

HISTORY, EVOLUTION AND APPROACHES TO THE HEALTH SERVICES SYSTEM

D. BANERJI

*HISTORICAL AND SOCIO-CULTURAL FOUNDATIONS OF HEALTH SERVICES SYSTEMS**

ABSTRACT. India has a long history of health services systems. However, during the colonial era, especially during the British rule, though the services were systematized they generally never reached the masses.

After Independence, the new leadership of the health services system readily committed itself to providing good health services to the vast masses of the Indian people, but for this it did not consider it necessary to bring about any basic changes in the system. The colonels of the Indian Medical Service, by then greatly depleted by the withdrawal of the British, and the Brown Englishmen were assigned the very much more challenging task of building the new health services system for India.

Medical colleges grew very rapidly and poured out large numbers of physicians who were mostly alienated from the masses. A number of hospitals were opened in urban areas. Of the limited resources that were made available for providing preventive services for rural areas, the colonels, with strong "persuasion" from foreign consultants, set aside large amounts for running mass campaigns against specific diseases—malaria, population growth, small-pox, leprosy, trachoma and filariasis.

Not only have these campaigns hindered the development of a permanent health services system in the rural areas but almost invariably they have also failed to achieve the set goals. The country was persuaded in the late fifties to invest about Rs 1,010 million to eradicate, malaria by 1966, but after an investment of over Rs 3,500 million the possibility of doing so even by 1979 does not appear to hold.

*This is a revised and extended version of an article "Social and Cultural Foundations of Health Services System" appeared in *Economic and Political Weekly* 20 (Special Number, August) 1974: 1333-1345.

The campaign against population growth has turned out to be a similar costly blunder.

Social scientists and health educators from abroad helped the colonels to divert attention from the basic malady of the system by raising the bogey of resistance of the villagers to acceptance of the Western system of medicine. Following that reference model, their counterparts in India dutifully echoed their findings and a large number of positions were created to accommodate such professional health educators and social scientists within the system.

Finding of a carefully conducted empirical study of the health behavior of rural populations of India have, however, underscored the fact that there is considerable active interest among villagers in acquiring both curative and preventive services. Mostly, it is the services which have let the people down, rather than the reverse. Not only are the rural health services very much below what the Bhore Committee's short-term program had in 1946 described as the "irreducible minimum requirements" and much below the actual demands of the people, but even these very limited services are working at an alarmingly low level of efficiency—one of the main causes for this being the alienation of the health workers and of the institutions for education and training of such workers from the masses of the people.

THE WELL-MEANING GOVERNMENT AND THE HEALTH SERVICES AGENCIES have often failed to impress upon the masses the significance of their ideas and policies so as to make the people aware that what they have in mind is the people's interest. Due to various reasons such policies fail to take account of what people think for themselves. As a consequence the peoples' money is wasted in those programs which the policy makers consider the most viable means of serving the people.

Every community has a health culture of its own—its own cultural meaning of its health problems, it health practices and its corps of practitioners. As a component of its overall culture, the health culture of a community is shaped by the interplay of a number of social, political, cultural and economic forces (Galdston, 1961). The history of the health services system in India provides an account of the influence of such forces in giving shape to it. Henry Seigerist (Marti-Ibanez, 1960) has drawn attention to this important aspect by contrasting the manifestly high standards of environmental sanitation of the Indus Valley period with the level of sanitation that exists in India today.

HEALTH PRACTICES IN ANCIENT INDIA

Describing the five-thousand-year old planned city of Mohenjo Daro, (Marshall, 1931) has remarked that the public health facilities of the city was superior to those of all other communities of the ancient Orient. Almost all households had bathrooms, latrines, often water closets and carefully built wells. The elaborate nature of the Indus Valley public health organization provides an indication of the extent of health consciousness among the ancient Indian people. It is difficult to conjecture the nature of the health problems of those days, but the great emphasis on the preventive aspects of disease indicates a fairly mature attitude of the society towards the health problems that might have been prevailing at that time.

The Vedic medicine that developed after the advent of the Aryans to the Indus Valley (during the second millenium BC) had begun to show a tendency to develop rational methods of approaching health problems at quite an early stage. Even in the purely religious Vedic Samhitas are found reflections of anatomical, physiological and pathological views which are neither magical nor religious, and there are references to treatments which are impressively rational.

Furthermore, there exists the famous decree of Emperor Ashoka Maurya (279-236 BC) in his second Rock Edict (257-236 BC) "celebrating the organization of social medicine shaped by the Emperor along the lines of Buddhist thought and kindred ethics (dharma)" (Zimmer, 1948). The works of the famous Charaka of the first century AD and of Susruta of the fourth century AD laid the foundation of the highly developed science of medicine which flourished in the tenth century after Christ—a period of all-round social and economic progress, often called the age of Indian Renaissance. There is also epigraphical evidence indicating that social medicine was practiced in medieval South India (Zimmer, 1948).

During the subsequent centuries, a series of political, social, and economic changes profoundly disrupted the ecological balance in Indian society. Perhaps the lowest point of this ecological crisis was reached during the decline of the Mughal Empire, a situation which set the stage for the British conquest of India. Even during this period the system of Indian medicine had retained some fragments of its past heritage; for example, the surgeons of the British East India Company learned the art of rhinoplasty from Indian exponents of surgery (Basham, 1954: 500). It is noteworthy that during the early period of British rule in India, the Western system of medicine, which was still dominated by such procedures as purging, leeching, scarification and blood-letting, could not be considered as superior to the prevailing methods of the Indian systems of medicine.

HEALTH PRACTICES DURING THE BRITISH RULE

The social, cultural, economic and political changes that followed the introduction of British rule in India dealt an almost fatal blow to the practice of the Indian systems of medicine. With the imposition of the British rule, almost every facet of Indian life, including the medical and public health services, was subordinated to the commercial, political and administrative interests of the Imperial Government in London. In developing health services for certain limited purposes (for example, for the army), the patronage was shifted from the Indian systems of medicine to the Western system. The decision to make this shift appears to be amply vindicated by the spectacular advances in the different branches of Western medicine during the nineteenth and twentieth centuries. As a result of these changes the already stagnant Indian systems of medicine got caught in a vicious circle: its very neglect accelerated its further decline and the decline, in turn, made it increasingly difficult for it to compete with the highly favored and rapidly flourishing Western system in capturing the imagination of the educated population of India. Incidently, in most colonial nations the power and authority of the invading ruler being superior also gave people to think that whatever they offered in other areas of human life was always superior. Accepting the cultural modes of the ruler has always been viewed as status enhancing. In the long run, therefore, not only did the profession of the Indian systems of medicine get infiltrated by various kinds of quacks, but the very basis of the sciences got considerably eroded by forces of superstition and beliefs in supernatural powers and deities (Basham, 1954: 500).

The British had introduced Western medicine in India in the latter half of the eighteenth century principally to serve their colonial aims and objectives. Medical services were needed to support the British army and British civilian personnel living in India. Later on, medical services were made available to a very tiny selected segment of the native population. At the time of Independence, only the affluent and the ruling classes could get adequate medical services. Of the rest, constituting more than 90 per cent of the population, only a small fraction could get some form of medical care from hospitals and dispensaries run by government agencies, missionaries, philanthropic institutions and private practitioners (Government of India, Health Survey and Development Committee, 1956). Similarly, public health services consisted of some form of environmental sanitation in a few big cities. For the rest, some public health services were provided only when there was an outbreak of massive epidemics of diseases such as plague, cholera, and small-pox. Because of these conditions, in spite of the availability of knowledge from the Western system of medicine, there was widespread prevalence of such easily preventable diseases as malaria, tuberculosis, leprosy, small-pox, cholera, gastro-intestinal infections and infestations, trachoma and filariasis; India was among the countries of the world with the highest infant and maternal morbidity and mortality and gross death rates. In addition, there was enormous problem of undernutrition and malnutrition. India was among the lowest per capita calorie consuming countries in the world (*Ibid.*, 1956).

At the time of Independence, British India (population 300 million) had 17,654 medical graduates, 29,870 licenciates, 7,000 nurses, 750 health visitors, 5,000 midwives, 75 pharmacists and about 1,000 dentists (*Ibid.*, 1956).

The colonial character of the health services had also profoundly influenced almost all aspects of medical education in India—in shaping the institutions, in developing the course content and, perhaps most important of all, in shaping the value system and the social outlook of the Indian physicians. The first medical college in India was established way back in 1835. It was quite natural that British teachers should have nurtured such institutions in their infancy. However, along with the "scientific core" of medical sciences (which was a most welcome diffusion of a cultural innovation from the Western world), there came certain political, social and cultural overcoatings which were definitely against the wider interests of the country (Banerji, 1973d: 485-488).

Also, opportunities for medical education in these institutions were made available to the very privileged upper class of the society. Additionally, the Medical Council of India accepted the British norms of medical education in order to gain recognition of the Indian medical degrees from the British Medical Council. This enabled some of the physicians, who were, "the select among the select" to go to Britain to get higher medical education. Acquiring Fellowships or Memberships of the various Royal Colleges was generally considered to be the pinnacle of achievement in their respective fields.

These four considerations—the colonial value system of the British rulers, class orientation of Indian physicians, their enculturation in British modeled Indian medical colleges and a more thorough and more extensive indoctrination of future key leaders of the Indian medical professions in the Royal College—provided a very congenial setting for the creation of what Lord Macaulay had visualized as "Brown Englishmen" (Banerji, 1973d: 485-488). These Brown Englishmen acquired dominant leadership positions in all the facets of the health services in India. This arrangement proved convenient to both parties. To the Indian physicians it ensured power, prestige, status and money at home. Their mentors from foreign countries retained considerable influence on the entire health service system of the country by ensuring that the top leadership of the medical profession in India remained heavily dependent on them.

EVOLUTION OF EXISTING HEALTH SERVICES SYSTEMS

Profile of Policy Formulators and Health Administrators

After Independence, the health services system of the country was shaped by the two key political decisions of the new leadership. Following the political commitments made during the struggle for Independence, provision of plank of the Directive Principles of the people—particularly to those living in rural areas—was made an important plank of the Directive Principles of State Policy of the Constitution (Basu, 1971: 230-235). The other political commitment, which turned out to be even more sacred and of overriding importance, was to bring about the desired changes in the health services system without making any basic changes in the then existing machinery of the government.

The personnel of the Indian Medical Service of the British days and the "Brown Englishmen" were called upon by the Indian leadership to provide the initiative in shaping the proposed new health services system for India. These personnel, like those of the Indian Civil Service, belonged to the elite class of administrators. They were former officers of the British Indian Armed Forces who had opted for civilian work. They were also trained in the traditions of the Western political independence brought to the fore two additional issues which profoundly affected the cadre of the Indian Medical Service. Firstly, the withdrawal by the British officers after Independence caused a sudden vacuum in their ranks. This came as a windfall to a number of not-so-competent officers who were catapulted into positions of key importance simply because they happened to become senior in the cadre as a result of the very large number of vacancies caused by the departure of the British. Secondly, in adhering strictly to the seniority rules when the health services were expanded very rapidly to meet the requirements of the newly formulated health programs, the administration drew more and more from the relatively small group of people who had entered the services in, say, 1930-35, 1935-40, or 1940-45 to meet the very rapidly increasing manpower needs for key posts. As a result, a large number of the key posts in the health services got filled by persons, who, even by colonial standards, were not considered to be bright.

Such a massive domination of the organization by men who were trained in the colonial traditions and whose claim to a number of vital posts in development administration was based merely on their being senior in the cadre, led to a virtual glorification of mediocrity, with all its consequences (Banerji, 1971). What was even worse, such a setting was inimical to the growth and development of the younger generation of workers. Often these young men had to pay heavy penalties if they happened to show enterprise, initiative and imagination in their work. Conformism often earned good rewards and this ensured perpetuation of mediocrity within the organization.

Because of their being inadequate for the job, these Brown Englishmen went out of the way to appeal to foreign experts for help and the latter have generously responded to such entreaties. A large number of foreign experts were invited to play a dominant role in almost every facet of the health services system of the country (Banerji, 1973c).

Medical Colleges, Teaching Hospitals and Other Medical Care Facilities in Urban Areas

Two divergent forces in the country—availability of relatively very much larger amounts of resources for the health sector and perpetuation by the technocrats, the bureaucrats and the political leadership of the old privileged class and the Western value system of the colonial days—gave shape to a health service system which had a strong urban and curative bias and which favored the rich and the privileged.

It is significant that when the country had only about 18,000 graduate physicians and about 30,000 licenciate physicians, (Government of India, 1956a) one of the first major decisions of the popular government of India in the field of health was to abolish the three-year post-matriculation licenciate course in medicine. While recognizing "the great lack of doctors," the very large majority of the members of the Health Survey and Development Committee (Bhore Committee), probably "strongly influenced by the recommendations of the Good-enough Committee in the United Kingdom," (*Ibid.*, 1956b) asserted that resources maybe concentrated "on the production of only one and that the most highly trained doctor," (*Ibid.*, 1956b). The Committee had made elaborate recommendations concerning the training of what it termed as the "basic doctor" and stressed that such training should include "as an inseparable component, education in community and preventive aspects of medicine" (*Ibid.*, 1856b).

The Medical Council of India, a direct descendant of the Medical Council of Great Britain, which is the statutory guardian of standards of medical education in India, has issued repeated warnings against reviving the licenciate course. The Health Survey and Planning Committee of 1961 (Mudaliar Committee) has also emphatically rejected the idea of reviving such a short-term course because they were "convinced that the proper development of the country in the field of health must be on the lines of what we consider as the minimum qualification for a basic doctor" (*Ibid.*, 1961: 349). It went on to state: "India is no longer isolated and is participating in all problems of international health. The WHO has laid down certain minimum standards of qualifications. In view of India being an active member, participating in all public health measures on an international basis, we think it will be unfortunate if at this stage once more the revival of a short-term medical course is to be accepted" (*Ibid.*).

One of the saddest ironies of the medical education system in India is that resources of the community are utilized to train doctors who are not suitable for providing services in rural areas where the vast majority of the people live and where the need is so desperate. By identifying itself with the highly expensive and urban and curative-oriented system of medicine of the West, the Indian system actively encourages the doctors to look down on the facilities that are available within the country, particularly in the rural areas, and they look for jobs abroad and thus cause the so-called brain drain. As if that is not enough, till recently these foreign-trained doctors have been pressurizing the community to spend even more resources to attract some of these people back to the country by offering them high-salaried prestigious positions and making available to them very expensive super-sophisticated medical gadgets. These foreign trained Indian specialists, in turn, actively promote the creation of new doctors who also aspire to "go to the States" to earn large sums of money and to specialize. Emphasis on specialization, incidentally, causes considerable distortion of the country's health priorities, thus causing further polarization between the haves and have-nots.

Those who are unable to go abroad, attempt private practice in urban areas, often linking their practice with honorary or full-fledged jobs in urban health institutions run by the government. Only, some government jobs are non-practicing. As a result of such considerations, a desperately poor country like India finds itself in a paradoxical position in relation to the distribution of the doctors in the country: the urban population, which forms 20 per cent of the total, accounts for 80 per cent of the doctors.

Pretending to follow the recommendations of the Bhore Committee, soon after Independence upgraded departments of preventive and social medicine were created in medical colleges, at the instance of the government and of the Medical Council of India, to act as spearheads to bring about social orientation of medical education in India. However, as in the case of so many other ambitious and morally lofty government programs, concurrently it was also ensured that the very spirit of this program was stifled, if not totally destroyed, by actively discouraging in various ways its actual implementation. For instance, instead of mobilizing the finest brains in the profession to bring about social orientation, most of the positions in the departments of preventive and social medicine were filled by the discards, who were often found intellectually inadequate to get into the highly competitive and prestigious clinical disciplines, or even the paraclinical disciplines. This gave enough opportunities to the threatened foreign trained super-specialists to ridicule the entire discipline of preventive and social medicine and bring it down almost to the bottom of the prestige hierarchy of disciplines in the medical college (Ramalingaswami and Neki, 1971:204-209). Significantly, the political leadership—the ministers and legislators, who are beholden to these super-specialists for their personal needs of various kinds—winked at this systematic desecration of the philosophy of social orientation of medical education in the country (NIHAE, 1966).

Along with the rapid proliferation of expensive teaching hospitals for medical colleges, each having a number of specialities and super-specialities, a number of general hospitals were established in urban areas. The number of hospital beds shot up from 113,000 in 1946 (Government of India, 1961) to the present figure of 300,000 (*Ibid.*, 1973). There has also been a rapid increase in the number of dispensaries for providing curative service to urban populations. There were over 1,807 urban dispensaries in 1966 (*Ibid.*, 1968). The development of medical colleges, teaching and other hospitals, and medical care facilities has accounted for a large chunk of the investment in health services in the country's Five-Year Plans (*Ibid.*, 1961). The recurring cost for these institutions accounts for over three-fourths of the annual health budget of a State (West Bengal, 1971).

MASS CAMPAIGN AGAINST SOME MAJOR HEALTH HAZARDS

The fact that despite their obvious overriding importance, preventive services have received a much lower priority in the development of the health service system of India provides an insight into the value system of the colonels of the Indian Medical Service, the British trained bureaucrats of the Indian Civil Service and, above all, the value system of the political leadership of free India. The colonels did not appear to relish the prospects of dirtying their hands—getting involved in problems which required mobilization of vast masses of people living in rural areas. The rural population raised in the minds of these decision makers the spectre of difficult accessibility, dust and dirt,... superstitious, ignorant, ill-mannered and illiterate people. Therefore, when they were impelled to do some preventive work in rural areas, characteristically, they chose to launch military style campaigns against some specific health problems.

Undoubtedly, because of the enormous devastation caused by malaria till the early fifties, this disease deserved a very high priority. But the program became a special favorite of the colonels not only because it required relatively much less community mobilization, but it also provided them with an opportunity to build up an administrative framework to launch an all-out assault on the disease in a military style—in developing preparatory attack, consolidation and maintenance phases, in having "unity of command," and surprise checks and inspections and in having authority to "hire and fire." Some of the followers of the colonels in fact went so far as to compare the malaria campaign with a military campaign (Ramkrishna, 1960: 3-4). Another enthusiast for military methods has written an entire book (Borkar, 1961) with a preface by the late Prime Minister Jawaharlal Nehru describing the saga of the growth of the health services in independent India as if he were describing a military campaign.

Experience of implementation of India's National Tuberculosis Program bring sharply into focus the limitations of this military approach to developing a health service system for the people of this country. On the basis of a series of operational research studies, (Banerji, 1971b: 9-25), it was demonstrated that it is possible to offer facilities for diagnosis and treatment to over a million and a half of sputum positive cases who are known to be actively seeking help for their illness from over 12,000 to 15,000 health institutions in various parts of the country. But because of the failure of program administrators to develop a sound health delivery system on a permanent basis for the rural populations of the country, more than a decade after the launching of the program, less than one-fifth of these sputum positive cases, who have an active felt need, are being dealt with by the program organization. This provides an example of how the militaristic urban privileged class value system has come in the way of building a health service system to meet even some of the very urgently felt needs of the people of the country.

After some pilot projects, a National Malaria Control Program was launched with the help of the United States Technical Cooperation Mission, the World Health Organization and the United Nations

International Children's Emergency Fund in 1953 to cover all the Malarious areas of the country, then involving a population of 165 million (Borkar, 1961). It achieved a phenomenal success; for instance, the number of Malaria cases for every 100 persons visiting hospitals or dispensaries declined from 10.2 per cent in 1953-54 to 4.0 per cent in 1958-69 (*Ibid.*). This success emboldened the administrators to think in terms of totally eradicating the disease from the country, once and for all. The danger of the mosquitos developing resistance to the main weapon for malaria control, DDT, was given as an additional reason for embarking on the eradication program. Besides, pressure was also put on India by foreign consultants from WHO and elsewhere to embark on the eradication program as it was to become a part of the global strategy propounded by the WHO *(Ibid.)*.

It was also stated, to give economic grounds for the decision, that while the control program was estimated to cost about Rs 270 million in the Second Five-Year Plan (1956-1957 to 1960-1961) and Rs 350 million during the Third Plan (1961-1962 to 1966-1967) and thereafter would continue to remain a heavy item of expenditure, "the cost for the eradication program was estimated to be Rs 430 million in the last three years of the Second Plan and Rs 580 million for the entire Third Plan with the annual expenditure becoming negligible thereafter." The immediate successes of the National Malaria Eradication Program were even more spectacular, but a disastrous snag developed in implementing the maintenance phase of the program (Government of India, 1973). It turned out that, among other factors, because of the preoccupation of the administrators with specialized mass campaigns against malaria and other communicable diseases, they had not paid adequate attention to building a permanent health service system—the so-called health infrastructure—strong enough to carry on the malaria surveillance work effectively at the village level. This has been responsible for a series of setbacks to the National Malaria Eradication Program, resulting in the reversion, at a very considerable cost, of large segments of the maintenance phase population on to consolidation or attack phases. Instead of getting rid of malaria once and for all by 1966, as it was envisaged in the late fifties, 40 per cent of the population is still to reach the maintenance phase *(Ibid.)*. The National Malaria Eradication Program thus continues to drain huge quantities of scarce resources even today, thus making it even more difficult to find resources to develop the health services infrastructure.

During the last four years, for instance, less than 3 per cent of the additional population (9.4 units) has entered the maintenance phase *(Ibid.)*. Meanwhile, the country is forced to set aside huge chunks of its very scarce resources to prevent the program from sliding still further. As against the envisaged expenditure of Rs 1,015 million, the National Malaria Eradication Program has thus far used over Rs 2,500 million. In addition, Rs 967 million have been set aside for it for the next five years *(Ibid.)* and even this allocation might have to be raised still further. In spite of this, the chances of eradicating malaria in the foreseeable future do not appear to be very bright. So the country will be compelled to keep on pouring resources into this program to see that the disease does not recur in epidemic form as has happened in some other countries.

Also, following the model of the NMEP, a specialized military style campaign was launched in 1963 to eradicate small-pox within three years (Borkar, 1961). Once again the campaign conspicuously failed to achieve the objective of eradication. Only recently (1973-74) yet another campaign has been launched to eradicate small-pox "once and for all" (Government of India, 1973).

A mass campaign to provide BCG vaccination for the entire population of the country, and to continue to do so periodically, was the first effort to deal with the problem of tuberculosis in India as a public health problem *(Ibid.)*. This program has also failed to yield the desired results (Banerji, 1971b: 9-25).

Special campaigns have also been launched against leprosy, filariasis, trachoma and cholera with even more discouraging results (Government of India, 1973).

The health service system of the country had hardly recovered from the consequences of the very costly failures of the mass campaigns against malaria, small-pox, leprosy, filaria and trachoma, when a large bulk of investment in health was cornered by another specialized campaign—this time it was against the rapidly rising population of the country. The Fourth Plan investment in family planning was Rs 3,150 million as against Rs 4,500 million for the rest of the health sector of the country (Banerji, 1971a). This involved deployment of an army of 125,000 persons *(Ibid.)*. All of them were specially earmarked for doing family planning work only. Significantly, once again, this program was also developed by officers belonging to the Indian Medical Service—the colonels, with strong backing from foreign consultants from various agencies. Predicably, once again, this campaign also failed to attain the demographic objectives, with disastrous consequences, both to the programs for socio-economic development as well as the development of a sound infrastructure of health services for the country *(Ibid.)*.

Recognizing, at long last, the weaknesses of the campaign approach, recently the Government of India has veered round to the idea of providing an integrated package of health, family planning and nutrition services with particular emphasis on the weaker sections of the community (Government of India, 1973b). This package, in turn, is a part of a bigger package of the Minimum Needs Programs of the Fifth Five-Year Plan (1974-1979) which is meant to deal with some of the very urgent social and ecomomic needs of the rural populations of the country (*Ibid.*, 1973a).

DEVELOPMENT OF A PERMANENT INTEGRATED HEALTH SERVICE SYSTEM FOR RURAL AREAS

The Health Survey and Development Committee, (1946) which was set up by the British Indian Government in 1943 to draw a blueprint of health service for the post-War British India, had shown exceptional vision and courage to make some very bold recommendations. These included development of an elaborate health service system for the country, giving key importance to preventive aspects with the "countryside as the focal point" *(Ibid.)*. To forestall any criticism of practicability, pointing out the achievements in health in the Soviet Union within a span of 28 years (1931-1941), it asserted that its recommendations are quite practical, in fact relatively very modest, provided there was the will to develop the health services of the country (*Ibid.*). Unfortunately, however, the leaders who took over from the British did not show this will. They had quoted, often out of context, the recommendations of the Bhore Committee to justify abolition of the licenciate course and to establish a very large number of medical colleges with sophisticated teaching hospitals in urban areas. They also invoked the Bhore Committee to justify setting up an even more sophisticated All-India Institute of Medical Sciences in New Delhi on the model of the Johns Hopkins Medical Center of the USA (*Ibid.*, 1961). A number of other postgraduate centers for medical education were also set up in due course. It, however, took them over seven years even to start opening primary health centers to provide integrated curative and preventive services to rural populations of the country (Dutt, 1965). These primary health centers were a very far cry from what was suggested by the Bhore Committee: they did not have even a fourth of "the irreducible minimum requirements" of staff recommended by the Bhore Committee for a given population (and that too only as a short-term measure) (Government of India, 1946). Furthermore, it took more than 10 years to cover the rural populations in the country even with this manifestly rudimentary and grossly inadequate type of primary health centers.

The entry of the National Malaria Eradication Program into the maintenance phase and concurrent development of an extension approach to family planning provided a transient impetus to integrated health and family planning services through multipurpose male and female workers (*Ibid.*, 1963). But the clash of interests of the malaria and the family planning programs again led to the formation of unipurpose workers for both (*Ibid.*, 1966). Even worse was the application of intensive pressure on various workers of primary health centers to attain certain family planning targets. This led to the neglect of whatever health services were earlier being provided by the PHCs, thus causing a series of further setbacks to different health programs (Banerji, 1971). Maternal and child health services, malaria and small-pox-radication, environmental sanitation and control of other communicable disease, such as tuberculosis, leprosy and trachoma, are examples of the services which suffered as a result preoccupation of health workers with achieving the prescribed family planning targets.

Very recently, following the recognition of the fact that a unipurpose, high-pressure military-type campaign approach which does not ensure a concurrent growth and development of other segments of health and nutrition services (and growth and development in other socio-economic fields) will not be able to yield the desired results, as pointed out above, decisions have already been taken to integrate malaria, family planning, maternal and child health, small-pox and some other programs and thus provide an entire package of health, family planning and nutrition services to the community through male and female multipurpose health workers (Government of India, 1973a and b).

Indian Systems of Medical Services

There are three major indigenous systems of medicine in India: Ayurveda—the Hindu medical system; Unani—the Greek system of medicine which was brought to India from West Asia by the Muslim rulers of India; and the Siddha system, which can be considered as a specialized branch of Ayurveda. After Independence, these systems were subjected to two contradictory pulls: their firm roots in the culture for centuries and their rich heritage evoked considerable admiration and even a certain degree of emotional attachment from a large section of the population. At the same time, long neglect of these systems of medicine led to a very sharp deterioration in the body of knowledge, in their institutions for training and research in their pharmacopia and drug industry and in their corps of practitioners. Therefore, while the leaders of independent India build almost the entire health services on the lines of the Western system, they have, from the very beginning, shown sympathy for the Indian systems of medicine and have made available some grants for conducting research in these systems, for supporting educational institutions and for providing some services to the community.

Present State of the Health Services

Considering the size of the population and the staggering nature of its health problems, the existing health services are grossly inadequate. Furthermore, the bulk of the expenditure is earmarked for curative services which are predominantly situated in urban areas and are more accessible to the privileged sections of society. The privileged population has the additional advantage of being able to pay to avail of private nursing home services and services of private practitioners who are located almost entirely in urban areas. Of the total number of doctors in India 53 per cent are in private practice; another 7 per cent are employed in the private sector, (IAMPR and NIHAE, 1966); the community spends about Rs 100,000 for the training of one doctor.

India has barely half a bed per thousand population, while the corresponding figure is over 10 for the industrialized countries (Government of India, 1973e). Of these beds, 90 per cent are located in cities and towns where only one-fifth of the population lives. Even the 10 per cent of the beds which are primarily meant for rural populations are ill-staffed, ill-equipped and ill-financed. The expenditure for curative services is about three times as much as for preventive services (West Bengal, 1971). Again, in terms of the preventive services, while over 90 per cent of the urban population is provided with some degree of protected water, only 4 per cent of villages get piped water supply; while about 40 per cent of the urban population has a sewerage system, it is almost non-existent for the rural population (Government of India, 1973d).

Primary health centers and their sub-centers form the sheet anchor of rural health services in India. There are over 5,195 PHCs in the country; there are 32,218 sub-centers attached to these PHCs (*Ibid.*, 1973e). Each PHC and its sub-centers are expected to provide integrated health, family planning and nutrition services to a population of about 100,000. Provision of medical care, environmental sanitation, maternal and child health services, family planning services, eradication or control of some of the communicable diseases and collection of vital statistics are some of the functions of a PHC (Dutt, 1965). However, both quantitatively as well as qualitatively the resources made available at a PHC are grossly inadequate for serving the population assigned to it (The Johns Hopkins School of Public Hygiene and Public Health, 1970; NIHAE, 1972; GOI, 1973a; 1974a).

There are now 103 medical colleges which have an annual admission capacity of over 13,000. The number of doctors available in India has now increased to 137,930. There are 88,000 trained nurses, 32,000 sanitary inspectors and 54,000 auxiliary nurse midwives (Government of India, 1973e).

The government is at present financing about 9,000 dispensaries and 195 hospitals which offer the services according to the Indian systems of medicine. There are 44,460 institutionally qualified and 111,371 non-institutionally qualified Ayurvedic registered practitioners in the country; the corresponding figures for the Unani and the Siddha systems are 6,013 and 18,507 and 625 and 14,785, respectively (*Ibid.*, 1974b). The government runs two postgraduate colleges in Ayurveda and one in Unani; there are also 91 Ayurvedic, 10 Unani and one Siddha undergraduate colleges (*Ibid.*, 1974b).

That the present health services system of India needs considerable improvement is dramatically brought home by the fact that in the year 1974 India happens to be one of the few countries in the world which has not yet succeeded in eradicating small-pox. Much remains to be done before it will be possible to control such apparently easily controllable diseases as tuberculosis, leprosy, trachoma and filariasis (Government of India, 1972). The fact that the National Malaria Eradication Program continues to be a very heavy drain on the very limited resources even today, instead of being eradicated by 1966, also provides an indication of the serious weaknesses in the system.

COMMUNITY AND HEALTH SERVICES SYSTEMS

Health administrators sought to secure some degree of social legitimacy for their actions by getting some not very well defined or even relevant social, cultural and psychological considerations raised by social scientists and health educators. Their appeal was particularly directed towards the then dominant group of social scientists which was engaged in generating social science knowledge to legitimize the existing social structure and social relations (Valentine, 1969: 48-127; Andreski, 1972: 59-154). The response was generous. Eminent social scientists from the West, such as McKim Marriot (1955), Morris Carstairs (1955), Morris Opler (1962), H.A. Gould (1957), and E. Wood (1960) came out to draw attention to certain basic cultural and social factors which mitigate against acceptance of modern medical practices in the mostly tradition-bound, caste-ridden, rigidly hierarchical, illiterate and superstitious rural communities of India. Their Indian disciples dutifully carried on the refrain by drawing similar conclusions on the basis of their own "studies." Studies of Hasan (1967), Dhillon (1963), Khare (1963), Kakar (1972), and Prasad (1961) offer examples of such Indian workers.

The report on the Conference on Social and Cultural Factors in Environmental Sanitation (Government of India, 1956) represents an instance of the collective wisdom on this subject of a group of eminent Indian social scientists which was brought together by the Ford Foundation. Ignoring the vital necessity of "distinguishing between the true clinical core of scientific medicine and the surrounding folklore, magic, custom, and faddism that are included in our institution of medicine," (Foster, 1958) they went on to find ways of overcoming the cultural resistance of villagers to installation of sanitary latrines. They overlooked some basic epidemiological, clinical, social, economic and even cultural issues which ought to have called into question the very rationale of selling such latrines to rural populations (Banerji, 1964, Foster, 1958). Their deep seated bias, which perhaps contributed to their inability to take a holistic view of the social, cultural and technological interaction in the sanitation program, made them behave more like salesmen than like scientists who possess the competence to use the conceptual and methodological rigor of their discipline to make an objective analysis of the situation (Banerji, 1973a: 145-147).

The profession of health education also came in very handy to health administrators in giving a facade of legitimacy to the health service system built by them. As practitioners of social science knowledge which was generated by scholars like Marriot, Carstairs, Hasan and Khare, the administrators found it convenient to assign them the task of "educating" the community to pave the way for acceptance of the Western system of medicine. When the administrators in India, with strong backing from consultants from abroad, launched a country-wide family planning program which required acceptance of family planning practices in a poverty-stricken population, with very poor health services, extensive unemployment and social injustice, they once again found it convenient to call upon the health educators to sell this brand of family planning to the masses. It is significant that the leaders of the health education profession, both in India as well as from other countries, willingly Allowed themselves to be identified with a program which involved motivating individuals to accept family planning practices by using persuasion, administrative coercion and material enticements (*Ibid.*, 1972: 2067-2074).

A carefully conducted sociological study of tuberculosis patients in a rural district in South India (*Ibid.*, 1973a: 145-147; 1971b: 9-25), revealed that more than half of these cases visited a government institution of modern medicine, where they were almost invariably dismissed with a bottle of cough mixture. These findings were diametrically opposed to what was forecast by social scientists like Marriot and Carstairs. Again, a number of studies of treatment default among tuberculosis patients getting domiciliary treatment revealed that by far the most important causes of default were attributable to limitations at the technical level and in the field of administration of the services, rather than to the patients' own behavior (Anderson and Banerji, 1963: 685-689; Banerji, 1967: 156-172; Singh and Banerji, 1968: 157-164). Yet, despite these very clear-cut findings, health educators and community health workers have kept harping on the need for "educating" the public about tuberculosis (SHEB, UP, 1968; Mitra and Gupta, 1965). They could not think of "educating" the program administrators to take into account the community health behavior and accordingly formulate suitable services. They have written numerous accounts as to how the villagers in India refused small-pox vaccination because of their superstitious faith in the goddess Sitala, but they could not take note of the very glaring fact that a much larger number of persons remain unvaccinated because nobody has cared to offer facilities of vaccination to them (NIHAE, 1972).

A Recent Study of Health Behavior of Rural Populations in India

Taking note of the limitations in social science studies in health fields in India, an attempt was made by the author to narrow this gap by considering the activities of the primary health center as a purposive intervention to change for the better some aspects of the pre-existing health culture of the community served by it. A research study was designed to examine the current status and the nature of this interaction between the health services that are introduced through the PHCs and the pre-existing culture of rural populations in India. A report of this study has already been published in a journal (Banerji, 1973b: 2261-2268). Only the broad outline of the study design and the principal findings are being summarized here to draw attention to some aspects of the health behavior of rural populations which appear to be of significance in shaping the future pattern of the health services system of the country.

In order to get data on health behavior of rural populations under relatively more favorable conditions, a deliberate effort was made to select, in the first instance, PHCs and villages which are much above the average. The study has been completed in 16 villages, 19 of which also serve as the headquarter village of a PHC. These PHC are from seven states of the country, belonging to seven regions. Considerable attention was paid to developing a methodological approach that is specially tailored for studying the health behavior of villagers (including their behavior in relation to the PHC services) against the background of the total village culture. Research investigators lived in these villages for three to five months. Apart from making special efforts to get themselves accepted by all the segments of the village community and collecting data through village informants, the investigators identified informants and some "ordinary" members from each segment of the village community and made observations and conducted depth interviews to understand the health culture of each segment of the village against the background of its total culture. They also prepared case reports to provide a deeper insight into the response of the different segments to health problems in the fields of medical care, family planning, maternal and child health, communicable diseases, environmental sanitation, etc. Documents have been prepared to enable all the investigators to cover uniformly all the major areas in relation to these problems. Their stay in the village also enabled them to make direct observations, followed by depth interviews, of the actual behavior of the villagers when they encountered certain specific health problems. They could also study the interaction between the PHC personnel and the villagers, both when the former visited the village and when the villagers visited the PHC. Apart from these efforts to ensure that in-depth qualitative data were obtained from all the segments of the entire village community according to well-defined work procedures and checklists, a quantitative dimension was given to the main qualitative data by framing an unstructured interview schedule on the basis of these data and administering it to a 20 per cent stratified random sample of the village households.

As an additional safeguard, after completion of the fieldwork in the villages of a PHC, some of the data concerning the health behavior of the community were cross-checked with personnel at the level of the corresponding seven State Directorates of Health Services. An additional three states were added to the original seven to examine how far the findings from these seven were applicable to the others. These ten states covered 77.8 per cent of the population of the country. Recognizing that the complex nature of the subjects of this study called for a new and rather exacting methodological approach, special safeguards were adopted to ensure that the data collected by all the investigators were of a minimum acceptable quality.

Taking into account the social and economic status of the people, the epidemiology of health problems and the nature of the health services available, it is not surprising that problems of medical care should be by far the most urgent concern among the health problems in rural populations. But the surprising finding is that the response to the major medical care problems is very much in favor of the Western (allopathic) system of medicine, irrespective of social, economic and occupational consideration. Availability of such services and capacity of patients to meet the expenses are the two major constraining factors. On the whole, the dispensary of the PHC projects has a very unflattering image. Because of this and because of its limited capacity it is unable to satisfy a very substantial proportion of the demand of the villagers for medical care services. This enormous unmet felt need for medical care services is the main motive force in the creation of a very large number of the so-called Registered Medical Practitioners (RMPs) or "quacks." The RMPs are thus in effect created as a result of the inability of the PHC dispensary or other qualified practitioners of Western medicine to meet the demands for medical care services in the villages. It is worth noting that all these RMPs use allopathic medicines rather than ayurvedic or unani medicines. When these RMPs prove ineffective, depending on the economic status of the individual and the gravity of his illness, villagers actively seek help from government and private medical agencies in the adjoining (or distant) town and cities.

There are, however, numerous instances of adoption of healing practices from qualified or non-qualified practitioners of the different Indian systems of medicine and homeopathy and from other non-professional healers. But among those who suffer from major illnesses, only a very tiny fraction preferentially adopted these practices, by positively rejecting the facilities of the Western system of medicine which are more efficacious and which are easily available and accessible to them. Usually these practices and home remedies are adopted (1) side by side with Western medicine; (2) after Western medicine fails to give benefit; (3) when Western medical services are not available or accessible to them due to various reasons; and, (4) most frequently, when the illness is of a minor nature.

Another very significant finding of this study is that the family planning program has ended up in projecting an image which is just the opposite of what was actually intended. The image of the family planning workers in rural areas is that of persons who use coercion and other kinds of pressure tactics and who offer bribes to entice people into accepting vasectomy or tubectomy. Because of the failure of family planning workers to develop a rapport with the villagers, sometimes the villagers are unable to meet their needs for family planning services. There are several instances of mothers who, failing to get suitable family planning services from the PHC, took recourse to induced abortions to get rid of unwanted pregnancies. This not only points to the failure of the program to meet their needs for the services but also draws attention to the failure of the program to offer suitable abortion services to mothers with unwanted pregnancies, despite the abortion bill.

Another significant finding of this study is that there is considerable unmet felt need for the services of the Auxiliary Nurse Midwife (ANM) at the time of childbirth. Villagers are keen to have the ANM's services because they consider her to be more skilled than the traditional *dai*. Whenever the ANMs have provided the services, the *dai's* role has become less significant. The overall image of the ANM in villages, particularly in North India, is that of a person who is distant from them—meant only for special people or for those can pay for her services. She is not for the poor. She can be called only when there are complications and then also she has to be paid. Because of the inaccessibility of the ANMs, the majority of the deliveries even in the villages where the PHC is located are conducted by *dais* and relatives and neighbors. In villages with no PHC, their sway is almost complete. As in the case of the Registered Medical Practitioners, confinement by relatives and friends by any indigenous *dais* is popular among the villagers not because of their intrinsic superiority but because in the absence of suitable services from the ANM/Lady Doctor, they are compelled to settle for something which they consider to be inferior but which is all that is available and accessible to them. They actively seek more specialized services either from the PHC or from the towns and cities when the *dais* are unable to tackle complicated cases.

The only two programs which can be stated to have reached the grassroots level in the villages are those concerning malaria and small-pox. Despite several complaints regarding the sincerity of these workers, there is almost a universal agreement among the villagers that these workers do visit the community. A significant finding is that these workers do not encounter any major obstacle in getting participation of the community in these programs. Except when there are understandable compulsions, such as the prospect of a poverty-stricken mother losing wages for 4-5 days in the peak agricultural season due to the child's vaccination reactions and some cases of orthodoxy, there is general acceptance of small-pox vaccination in village communities. The number of children who are left unvaccinated due to lapses on the part of parents appear to be a very small fraction of those who remain unvaccinated due to lapses on the part of vaccinators and their supervisors.

Patients suffering from tuberculosis, leprosy and trachoma get very little service from the corresponding national programs. It is remarkable that despite this, these actively seek help from elsewhere—from nearby towns or even big cities. Such help is not only much more expensive and bothersome but it is also much less efficacious, both clinically as well as epidemiologically. Other preventive measures, of course, are almost non-existent.

Extensive prevalence of abject poverty, as a result of which more than half the population is unable to meet even the minimum dietic calorie needs and appalling conditions of sanitations, water supply, housing, and education present an ecological setting which is conducive to widespread prevalence of various types of health problems in the community. These health problems form only a small component of the overall gloomy picture of the way of life in Indian villages. Ignorance, superstition, suspicion, apathy and fatalism should thrive in such a milieu. It is, therefore, a tribute to the strength of the culture of the rural populations that, despite these overwhelming odds, their health behavior has retained so much of rationality.

Because of their urban orientation, workers of rural health and other developmental agencies generally have a strong distaste for rural life. This distaste is for the entire way of life and not simply for the very poor facilities available there. Health workers tend to keep a distance from the rural population as a whole. However, as they are required to work for rural populations, they take advantage of the village power structure and confine themselves, as far as possible, to satisfying the privileged gentry of the village. In doing so they (*a*) win approbation and rewards from the so-called community leaders who have the ear of their superior officers and of the political leaders at the higher levels; (*b*) deal with the least disagreeable segment of the village community; and (*c*) get a free hand to "tackle" the rest of the community.

The findings of this study bring out some of the key issues which are of far-reaching significance for the future development of the health services system of the country:

1. It brings out clearly that there is no significant cultural resistance to acceptance of modern medicine as long as they are efficacious and are available and accessible to the people. This finding, therefore, seriously calls into question the belief of a very significant section of health administrators, social scientists and health educators that there is considerable cultural resistance to the acceptance of modern medical practices in rural populations in India.

2. The existing health services are working at a grossly low level of efficiency, which has led to considerable underutilization. Priority should, therefore, be given to ensuring that this problem is overcome. (Government of India, 1974a.)

3. There is also considerable scope for bringing about qualitative improvements in the existing health services system in rural areas by bringing it more in tune with the social and cultural setting of the village communities.

4. Finally, after ensuring a reasonable level of utilization of the existing capacities quantitatively and after bringing about qualitative changes, there is a strong case for making quantitative expansion of the health services to meet the requirements of rural populations. This will imply rectification of the existing imbalance in allocation of resources, requiring a shift in investment from urban to rural areas, from curative to preventive and from the privileged to the underprivileged.

Summary

There has been a cumulative increase in the knowledge of the medical sciences which has at times grown almost at an exponential rate. However, that actual application of this knowledge to societies is determined by a number of political, social, cultural, economic and technological factors. In ancient India, when these factors were favorable, despite the very rudimentary nature of the available knowledge, the people enjoyed a much higher level of health services than what is available at present. In fact these favorable conditions created a setting which enabled the society to make significant contributions to the body of medical knowledge—through Charaka and Susruta, for instance. The decline of the society in the subsequent centuries saw a decline in the health service system. Colonization of the country by the British, when every facet of its activities was subordinated to the interest of the Imperial Government in London, dealt almost a fatal blow to the still active Indian systems of medicine. The entire health service system of the country was purposively developed to provide the Western system of medical services to a small privileged group—the armed forces, the British civilians and the Indian gentry. Medical colleges were opened to prepare Brown Englishmen, medical institutions were established to serve the gentry living in urban areas and officers of the armed forces medical services were brought in to administer the health services.

With the advent of Independence, the new leadership readily committed itself to providing good health services to the vast masses of people of the country, but for this it did not consider it necessary to bring about basic changes in the system. The colonels of the Indian Medical Service, by then greatly depleted by the withdrawal of the British, and the Brown Englishmen were assigned the very much more challenging task of building the new health services system for India. Medical colleges grew very rapidly and these colleges poured in a large number of physicians who were mostly alienated from the masses of the people. A number of hospitals were opened in urban areas. Out of the limited resources that were made available for providing preventive services for rural areas, the colonels, with strong "persuasion" from foreign consultants, set aside big chunks for running mass campaigns against specific diseases—malaria, population growth, small-pox, leprosy, trachoma and filariasis. Not only have these campaigns hindered the development of a permanent health services system in the rural areas but almost invariably they have also failed to achieve the set goals. The country was persuaded in the late fifties to invest about Rs 1,010 million to eradicate malaria by 1966, but, even after an investment of over Rs 3, 500 million, the prospect of doing so even by 1979 does not appear to be particularly bright. The campaign against population growth has turned to be a similar costly blunder.

Social scientists and health educators from abroad helped the colonels to divert attention from the basic malady of the system by raising the bogey or resistance of the villagers to acceptance of the Western system of medicine. Following that reference model (Singh, Y. 1973: 14-28), their counterparts in India dutifully echoed their findings and a large number of positions were created to accommodate such professional health educators and social scientists within the system. Findings of a carefully conducted empirical study of health behavior of rural populations of India have been presented to underscore the fact that already there is considerable active interest among villagers in acquiring both curative and preventive services. Mostly it is the services which have let the people down, rather than the reverse. Not only are the rural health services very much below what the Bhore Committee's short-term program had called in 1946 the "irreducible minimum requirements" and much below the actual demands of the people, but even these very limited services are working at an alarmingly low level of efficiency—one of the main causes for this being the alienation of the health workers and of the institutions for education and training of such workers from the masses of the people of the country.

REFERENCES

ANDERSON, S. and D. BANERJI

1963 "A Sociological Enquiry into Urban Tuberculosis Programme in India." *Bulletin of the World Health Organization* 29:685-689.

ANDRESKI, S.D.

1972 *Social Sciences as Sorcery*. London: Andre Deutsch.

BANERJI, D. and S. ANDERSON

1963 "A Sociological Study of Awareness of Symptoms Suggestive of Pulmonary Tuberculosis." *Bulletin of the World Health Organization* 29:665-684.

1964 "Health Problems and Health Practices in Modern India: A Historical Interpretation." *The Indian Practioner* 22:137-143.

1967 "Behaviour of Tuberculosis Patients Towards a Treatment Organization Offering Limited Supervision." *Indian Journal of Tuberculosis* 14:156-172.

1971a *Family Planning in India: A Critique and a Perspective*. New Delhi: Peoples' Publishing House.

1971b "Tuberculosis: A Problem of Social Planning in India." *National Institute of Health and Education Bulletin* 4:9-25.

1972 "Prospects of Controlling Population Growth in India." *Economic and Political Weekly* 7:2067-2074.

1973a "A Critical Review of the Role and Utilization of Social Scientists in Promoting Social Science Research in Health Fields in India." *Journal of the Medical Association* 60:145-147.

1973b "Health Behaviour of Rural Populations: Impact of Rural Health Services." *Economic and Political Weekly* 8:2261-2268.

1973c Population Planning in India: National and Foreign Priorites. *International Journal of Health Services* 3:428-437.

1973d "Social Orientation of Medical Education in India." *Economic and Political Weekly* 8:485-488.

BASHAM, A.L.
1954 *The Wonder that was India*. London: Sidgwick and Jackson.

BASU, D.D.
1970 *Shorter Constitution of India*. Calcutta: S.C. Sarkar.

BORKAR, G.
1961 *Health in Independent India*. New Delhi: Ministry of Health.

CARSTAIRS, G.M.
1955 "Medicine and Faith in Rural Rajasthan." In B.D. Paul (ed.), *Health, Culture, and Community*, pp. 107-134, New York: Russel Sage Foundation.

DEPARTMENT OF INTERNATIONAL HEALTH
1970 *Functional Analysis of Needs and Services*. Baltimore: The Johns Hopkins University School of Hygiene and Public Health.

DHILLON, H.S. and S.B. KAR
1963 "Behavioral Sciences and Public Health." *Indian Journal of Public Health* 7:19-24.

DHIR, S.L.
1971 "Malaria Eradication Programme and Integration of Mass Eradication Campaigns in General Health Services." *The Journal of Communicable Diseases* 3:1-12.

DUTT, P.R.
1965 *Rural Health Services in India: Primary Health Centers*. New Delhi: Central Health Education Bureau.

FOSTER, G.M.
1958 *Problems of Intercultural Health Programmes*. New York: Social Science Research Council.

GLADSTON, IAGO
1961 *Doctor and Patient in Medical History*. The Seventh Annual Max Danzis Lecture. Newark, New Jersey: The Newark Beth Israel Hospital.

GOULD, H.A.
1957 "Implications of Technological Change for Folk and Scientific Medicine." *American Anthropologist* 59: 507-516.

HASAN, K.A.
1967 *Cultural Frontiers of Health in Village India*. Bombay: Manaktalas.

INDIA, GOVERNMENT OF
1946 *Health Survey and Development Committee Report*. Volume 2. Delhi: Manager of Publications.
1956a *Conference on Social and Cultural Factors in Environment Sanitation in Rural India*. New Delhi: Publications Division.
1956b *Health Survey and Development Committee Report*. Volume 1. Delhi: Manager of Publications.
1961 *Health Survey and Planning Committee Report*. Volume 1. New Delhi: Ministry of Health.
1963 *Committee on Integration of Health Services Report*. New Delhi: Ministry of Health.
1966 *Committee on Basic Health Services Report*. New Delhi: Ministry of Health and Family Planning.
1968 *Ministry of Health, Family Planning and Urban Development Report*.

New Delhi: Ministry of Health, Family Planning and Urban Development.

1972 *The Fourth Plan: Mid-term Appraisal.* Volume 2. New Delhi: Planning Commission.

1973a Draft Fifth Five-year Plan: 1974-79. Volume 1 & 2. New Delhi: Planning Commission.

1973b *Memorandum of Centrally Sponsored and Purely Central Schemes for the Fifth Five-Year Plan.* New Delhi: Ministry of Health.

1973c *Ministry of Health and Family Planning Report* 1972-73. New Delhi: Ministry of Health and Family Planning.

1973d *Pocket Book of Health Statistics.* New Delhi: Central Bureau of Health Intelligence, Directorate of General Health Services.

1974a *Committee of Utilization of Public Health Centers Beds in India-Report.* New Delhi: Ministry of Health and Family Planning.

1974b *Indian System of Medicine and Homoeopathy-Agenda.* Item No. 6. New Delhi: Central Council of Health, Ministry of Health.

INSTITUTE OF MANPOWER RESEARCH

1966 *Stock of Allopathic Doctors in India-Report.* No. 2. 1966. New Delhi: Institute of Applied Manpower Research.

KAKAR, D.N., S.K. SRINIVAS MURTHY and R.L. PARKAR

1972 "Peoples Perception of Illness and Their Use of Medical Care Services in Punjab." *Indian Journal of Medical Education* 11:286-298.

KHARE, R.S.

1963 "Folk Medicine in a North Indian Village." *Human Organization* 22:36-40.

MARRIOTT, MCKIM

1955 "Western Medicine in a Village in Northern India." In B.D. Paul (ed.), *Health Culture and Community*, pp. 239-268. New York: Russel Sage Foundation.

MARSHALL, J.H.

1931 *Mohenjo Daro and the Indus Valley Civilization.* London: A. Probstheim.

MARTI-IBANEZ, F.

1960 *Henry Seigorist on History of Medicine.* New York: M.D. Publications.

MITRA, A.C. and B.P. GUPTA

1965 "Peoples' Knowledge and Attitude Towards Tuberculosis." *Health Centre Journal*, Punjab (September).

NATIONAL INSTITUTE OF HEALTH ADMINISTRATION AND EDUCATION

1966 *Report and Recommendations of the Conference on the Teaching of Preventive and Social Medicine in Relation to Health Needs of the Country.* New Delhi: National Institute of Health Administration and Education.

1972 *Study of District Health Administration, Rohtak (Phase 1).* Research Report No. 7. New Delhi: National Institute of Health Administration and Education.

OPLER, M.E.

1962 "Cultural Definition of Illness in Village India." *Human Organization* 21:32-35.

PRASAD, B.G.
1961 "Some Common Beliefs and Customs in Relation to Health and Disease in Uttar Pradesh." *The Antiseptic* 58:225-238.

RAMAKRISHNA, S.P.
1960 "An Examination of Resemblance and Divergence Between War and Malaria Eradication." *Bulletin of the National Society of India for Malaria and Other Mosquito Borne Diseases* 8:3-4.

RAMALINGASWAMI, P. and K. NEKI
1971 "Studies' Preference of Specialities in an Indian Medical College." British Journal of Medical Education 5:204-209.

SINGH, M.M. and D. BANERJI
1968 "A Follow-up Study of Patients of Pulmonary Tuberculosis Treated in an Urban Clinic." *Indian Journal of Tuberculosis* 15:157-164.

SINGH, YOGENDRA
1973 "The Role of Social Sciences in India: A Sociology of Knowledge." *Sociological Bulletin* 22:14-28.

STATE HEALTH EDUCATION BUREAU
1968 *Attitude Towards Tuberculosis*. Lucknow: State Health Education Bureau, U.P.

VALENTINE, C.A.
1969 *Culture and Poverty: Critique and Counter-Proposals*. Chicago: University of Chicago Press.

WEST BENGAL, DIRECTORATE OF HEALTH SERVICES
1971 *Health on theMarch, West Bengal* 1948-1969. Calcutta: State Health Intelligence Bureau.

WOOD, E.
1960 "Rural Health Promotion." *Kurukshetra* 8:23-26.

ZIMMER, H.R.
1948 *Hindu Medicine*. Baltimore: Johns Hopkins University Press.

SURINDER M. BHARDWAJ

HOMOEOPATHY IN INDIA

ABSTRACT. Homoeopathy, a medicine system of German origin, is intensively practiced and officially recognized in India even though it has greatly declined or virtually disappeared from most Western countries. Attempt has been made here to briefly outline the spread of homoeopathy in India since its introduction to India in the nineteenth century. It is argued that homoeopathy passed through a process of "naturalization" in the Indian socio-cultural milieu particularly in metropolitan Calcutta and the neighboring area of Bengal.

A strong commitment of Indian homoeopathic physicians to the homoeopathic "law of similars" and their efforts to harmonize other fundamental principles of homoeopathy with Indian, particularly Hindu, ideas helped to maintain the identity of this system. The apparent simplicity of the principles of homoeopathy opened the profession to people with poor professional medical training and helped its spread among the moderately educated Indians who adopted this as a symbol of modernity. Once Indianized, the survival of homoeopathy was insured at the political level, culminating in its official recognition by the Government of the Republic of India. It is suggested that the Bengali physicians played a significant role in the spread of homoeopathy in the Ganges Valley in North India.

INDIA IS PERHAPS THE ONLY MAJOR COUNTRY WHERE HOMOEOPATHY, A medicine system of Western origin, is extensively practiced and officially recognized. An official report, based on the Census of India, placed the number of homoeopathic practitioners at over 27,000.[1] The spread of homoeopathy in India has not been the subject of much sociological-historical inquiry. There is no study about homoeopathy in India comparable to Martin Kaufman's

[1]According to the available census data, the number of various types of physicians in India is: (*i*) Allopathic-96, 458; (*ii*) Ayurvedic-73, 382; (*iii*) Homoeopathic-27, 468; (*iv*) Others Unani, Nature cure, etc.-45,605 (see Institute of Applied Manpower Research, 1967).

Homoeopathy in America, 1971. In this essay, an atttempt has been made to briefly outline the spread of homoeopathy in India by emphasizing the process of its "naturalization" in the Indian socio-cultural environment.

THE SYSTEM IN BRIEF

The homoeopathic system of medicine traces its origin in the professional sense from Dr Samuel Hahnemann of Saxony (1755-1843). The system is based on a number of "principles," the most fundamental of which is the *law* of homoeopathy, i.e., *Similia, Similibus, Curantur*—let likes be cured by likes. This law is also alternatively referred to as the law of similitude or, popularly, the law of *simila.*[2] In practice, this law maintains that a given cluster of symptoms in a sick person can be remedied by a drug capable of producing in a healthy person the same symptoms. Other principles of homoeopathy developed by Hahnemann included the use of single remedy—often termed as "*simplex*," *individualization* emphasizing the individual characteristics of each sick person as well as the drug to be prescribed, and the famous principle of *infinitesimal* doses of the remedy.[3] Homoeopaths maintain after Hahnemann that the smaller the dose of the remedy, the greater is its effect in energizing the vital forces of the body itself thus effectuating cure (see Dhawle, L.D. 1954).

THE EARLY PHASE

Homoeopathy, probably as an amateur's hobby, was practiced in

[2]These principles of homoeopathy within a longer medical-historical context have been presented by Dr Diwan Harish Chand, "History of Medicine and the Contribution of Hahnemann," paper presented at the Jubilee Congress of International Homoeopathic Medical League, Rotterdam, 1975. See also, English Homoeopathic Association, "Homoeopathy in India," pp. 192-194; English Homoeopathic Association, "Medical Prejudices," p. 140; Anonymous, 1866: 52-53; Indian Correspondent, 1969: 266; *First Half Yearly Report of the Calcutta Native Homoeopathic Hospital* (Calcutta: Printed by P.S. D'Rosario and Co., 1852, pp. 18-19; Anonymous, 1852: 19-52.

[3]See for example Mohammad Masood (ed.), *Directory of Homoeopaths of India, Burma and Ceylon*, Lahore, 1938, p. iv. Masood calls Honigberger "A Renowned Homoeopath." One of the very few copies of this directory is available in the Lloyd Library at Cincinnati, Ohio. See also, Mathews, 1965, pp. 34, 358, and Honigberger, 1852, p. vii.

India by some of the Europeans before the mid-nineteenth century and must have been known to their Indian associates before its first institutions emerged in India. One of the earliest references to the beginnings of homoeopathy in India points to the establishment of a hospital by the then Raja of Tanjore in which the new system was to be adopted (English Homoeopathy Association, 1847: 192-194). A Madras Presidency surgeon, Dr. Samuel Brooking, after his retirement in 1846 probably found it worthwhile to continue his medical work in the employment of the Raja of Tanjore. There is also some indication that homoeopathic treatment was used by doctors in the General Military Hospital at Bombay, particularly in the treatment of cholera (*Ibid.*, 1847:140). There is evidence that some missionaries adopted the novel and inexpensive system and made it part of their do-good ethic. A missionary in 1866 reported in the *Homoeopathic World* thus:

> having studied the rudiments of the system before leaving England, we were soon called to put our knowledge to the test, for there being no medical men in that part where we resided, the natives always apply to the missionary for cure in all their maladies. Thus we had the honour of introducing Homoeopathy into those parts (1866:52-53).

Similarly the Indian correspondent of the *Homoeopathic World* reported from the Nilgiris in 1869 that he was "often called upon to act the doctor out here, where most people are compelled to depend very much, at present, on non-professional assistance, when they prefer Homoeopathic treatment" (1869:266).

It is not clear how significant a part the amateurs and the missionaries played in preparing the groundwork for the spread of homoeopathy before the 1850's. One of the tangible evidence of this interest was the emergence of the shortlived Calcutta Native Homoeopathic Hospital in 1852. A list of the subscribers and donors of this hospital shows that a majority of them were European, including the patron, Major General Sir J. H. Littler (1852:18-19). The Europeans included civil as well as military servants as shown by their ranks and titles, and probably also missionaries and traders. The Indian donors included both Hindu and Muslim gentlemen, although the former showed more interest as indicated by their much larger number. The superintendent medical officer of this homoeopathic hospital was a French doctor C. Fabre Tonnerre.

The developing interest in Homoeopathy during the 1850's is also to some extent reflected in literary journals published in Calcutta. The *Calcutta Review*, for example carried a lengthy article on homoeopathy in 1852. From that article it appears that although Homoeopathic medicines were appreciated by many people in Calcutta, it had probably little adherence in the *Mofussil.* The same article claimed that "The system has been extensively practiced by amateurs, in the civil and military services, and by other gentlemen. ...There is perhaps scarcely a large district in India, in which such an amateur has not for years been diffusing blessing around him.... The author of the article then makes an optimistic prognosis about the growth of homoeopathy in India. If even non-professional people, he argues, can achieve good results with homoeopathy medicine, there should be no doubt about the good that will result when professional men begin to practice this system.

In the early phase of homoeopathy in India Dr. Honigberger's name figures prominently. Some influential homoeopathic physicians consider Honigberger to be responsible for introducing this medical system into India (Masood, 1938). Many homoeopathic physicians of note today in India consider Honigberger a homoeopath (Mathews, 1965: 34, 358). Honigberger himself claims somewhat differently:

> I do not profess myself a votary of Hahnemann's system... and I am bound to confess, that, in the majority of cases, the results I obtained from homoeopathy, were not favourable (1852: VII).

Honigberger pointed out that his system was the "medium-system." He tried to steer clear of being branded either as an "allopath" or as a "homoeopath" because he did not believe that physicians should "infatuated by their own system drag their patients over gulfs and precipices" (*Ibid.*, 1852: IX-X). It is true that he learned the principles of homoeopathy from Hahnamann—the founder of the system—but really did not wholeheartedly become a sectarian homoeopath himself.[4] Honigberger had learned about the new

[4]Honigberger does not make any lengthy statements about his learning homoeopathy from Hahnemann. It appears from his narration that he learned only the fundamentals of homoeopathy from Hahnemann. He seems to have spent a short time in Paris where Hahnemann, in his later years had established his practice.

system while traveling in Russia. Of his encounter with Hahnemann he says: "The magnanimous old man and his lovely young wife received me in the most friendly manner, and I must not omit to mention, that the open and good-natured Homoeopathist made many interesting revelations to me respecting his new methods of curing. After traveling through several countries, Honigberger settled at Lahore (Punjab) where he was one of the physicians in the court of Maharaja Ranjit Singh, during the late 1830's. While at Lahore, he used to dispense homoeopathic remedies. Ranjit Singh himself sought Honigberger's homoeopathic treatment and was cured.[5] Whether or not Honigberger called himself a homoeopathic doctor is really not important. It is of interest from the viewpoint of the history of homoeopathy in India that a trained physician did practice homoeopathy in India at about the same time when this system of medicine was beginning to spread rapidly in the European countries and the U.S.A. Homoeopathy, however, spread more slowly in India than in the Western countries.

What happened to homoeopathy in Punjab, after Honigberger left Lahore and went to Calcutta, is not known but it is doubtful that this system attracted any professional or popular following. Perhaps one of the main reasons was that homoeopathy was, after all, a Western medical system in an area in which direct Western influence was not yet established. Pre-British Punjab (before 1849) had either indigenous medicine, *Ayurveda* or *Unani Tibb*. In fact we learn from Honigberger's descriptions that there was considerable suspicion of Western medicine. Maharaja Ranjit Singh, it is claimed, never himself used the medicines prescribed to him by English doctors. It appears that the kind of social and intellectual medium that was to be useful for the spread of developed homoeopathy in Bengal did not occur in the Punjab. The fact remains that homoeopathy during the nineteenth century probably did not make any significant impact in the Punjab. The impulses for the early expansion of homoeopathy ensued most consistently from Bengal. It is not my purpose here to list the names of individual doctors who practiced homoeopathy in Bengal. It is, however, interesting to explore why Bengal became important for the further diffusion of homoeopathy in India.

[5]Honigberger got a handsome reward for this from Ranjit Singh. However, a few days later Ranjit Singh got ill again, was administered medicines by his other court physicians (hakims), but died in 1839.

After Honigberger left Punjab, he sought his fortunes in Calcutta which in the India of 1850's was probably the center where most intensive social, commercial, political and cultural interaction between India and the West was then going on. Perhaps, within this type of intercourse the reasons for the spread of homoeopathy in India are to be searched. We should also not ignore the possible relationship between the propagation of homoeopathy and certain specific diseases prevalent in Bengal during the mid-nineteenth century.

BENGAL—THE HOMOEOPATHIC HEALTH IN INDIA

During the 1850's and 60's it appears that several physicians of European origin established their practice in Calcutta. We have already referred to Dr. Tonnerre of French origin. Later, Dr. Salzar of the University of Vienna and Dr. Berigny from France carried on their new healing art at Calcutta (Mathews, 1965: 34-35). To these of course we must add Dr. Honigberger of Transylvania who, along with his "medium system" also dispensed homoeopathic remedies. It is of some interest to note here that none of the above "famous" homoeopathists were of British origin. It seems curious that in the capital city of India, Calcutta, ruled by the British, there was no notable British homoeopath and this despite the fact that in Britain there was a substantial number of such physicians.[6] The reason lies, at least partly, in the offical policies of the British Government and of the East India Company. Until the late 1850's the British surgeons came to India either as the employees of the East India Company or as medical officers in the British army. It was to be expected that such medical doctors would be trained in the officially accepted system of medicine. The East India Company usually accepted surgeons trained at the well known British institutions and subjected the candidates for employment to professional examination for the job. In 1822 one of the chief requirements for appointment to the post of Assistant Surgeon in the E.I.C.'s service was a diploma from the Royal College of Surgeons of London and a few other prestigious colleges. Several regulations existed for the competitive examinations to join the medical service (Crawford,

[6] *The British and Foreign Homoeopathic Directory and Record*, 1853. In London alone sixty-six homoeopaths were named. This directory provides a county-wide list of the homoeopaths in Britain.

1914: 48-49, 488-528). The point is, that British medical practitioners came to India essentially as the representatives of the officially recognized medicine and not that of any sectarian system of medicine such as homoeopathy. Homoeopathy, in addition, was under severe attack in Britain during the 1850's and some of the well known Universities were refusing to recognize the new system. There are indications however, as previously noted, that certain physicians in the service of the E.I.C. probably had an inclination towards homoeopathy. The Calcutta Medical College, one of the only three contemporary medical colleges in India, also followed the official British lines of medicine and surgery in which there was no room for homoeopathic medicine.

Thus, while British and Indian homoeopaths were relatively few through the 1850's, nationals of several other Western countries perhaps filled this deficiency in Calcutta. Since Calcutta was the major focus of the Indian-European trade, the presence of many nationalities was only to be expected. Moreover, Calcutta had a substantial European population as well as some Americans, and Calcutta was growing.[7] The *Calcutta Review,* (1858: 305), described the City in glowing terms:

> As the capital of our Indian Empire, the grand emporium of the Asiatic commercial world, the seat of European civilization in Asia; she has fairly eclipsed all her rivals in that mighty continent, which in natural treasures is the fairest portion of the globe.

By the 1850's homoeopathy appeared in many cities of Europe as shown in Table 1. This spread is further substantiated from the German homoeopathic sources of the 1860's (Table 2).

Because of the inevitable omissions and possible selectivity it is not desirable to strictly compare the nineteenth century British and German sources of data, but the fact remains that homoeopathy was an established system of medicine over most of Europe. It was therefore to be expected that some European physicians would find it attractive to move to those parts of the world where European trading communities had been established such as in Calcutta.

[7]For a description of Calcutta in 1850's by an American see Robert B. Minturn, Jr., *From New York to Delhi by Way of Rio de Janeiro, Australia and China*, New York: D. Appleton and Company, 1858, pp. 96-120. See also, Anonymous, 1858: 305, and Meyer, 1860.

TABLE 1

NUMBER OF HOMOEOPATHIC PHYSICIANS: CA. 1850 IN SELECTED CITIES OF EUROPE

City	*Number*	*City*	*Number*
London	66	Berlin	11
Paris	55	Turin	8
Vienna	51	Gratz	8
Madrid	17	Prague	7
Dresden	13	Pest	7
Leipzig	12	Marseilles	6
		Genoa	6

SOURCE: George Atkin (ed.), *The British and Foreign Homoeopathic Directory and Record,* London: Aylott & Company, 1853, pp. 24-35 and 105-122.

TABLE 2

NUMBER OF HOMOEOPATHIC PHYSICIANS AND SURGEONS: CA. 1860 IN SELECTED CITIES IN EUROPE

City	*Number*	*City*	*Number*
London	72	Turin	17
Paris	109	Gratz	11
Vienna	50	Prague	14
Madrid	26	Pest	13
Dresden	11	Marseilles	7
Leipzig	7	Genoa	7
Berlin	11	Moscow	12
		Petersburg	12

SOURCE: Dr. V. Meyer, *Homopathischer Führer Für Deutschland und das Gesammte Ausland,* Leipzig: Eduard Mayner 1860, pp. 32-127.

Once the seeds of homoeopathy were planted in Bengal, its further propagation depended mostly on the "conversion" of *indigenous* physicians to the new concept in the healing art. It is important therefore, to understand the circumstances which favored such conversion, and the further spread of homoeopathy in India.

NATURALIZATION PROCESS OF HOMOEOPATHY IN INDIA

The adoption of homoeopathy by Indian physicians and the way in which it became domiciled in India without much competition from the *Ayurvedic*, and the *Unani*, and despite opposition from the Western system of medicine may be termed as the process of naturalization. It appears that this process came about due to several reasons, which have to do in part with the nature of homoeopathy and partly with the Indian socio-cultural milieu. It is not possible within the scope of this essay to delve into the details of either the philosophy of homoeopathy or the Indian milieu. We can refer only to the broader aspects of each insofar as they seem to bear on the question of expansion of this system of medicine.[8]

During the later part of the nineteenth century, certain philosophical bases of homoeopathy must have appealed to a segment of the modern, newly emergent and Western-influenced Indian elite. The Western influence in India had been represented through many streams of Western thought such as the commercial philosophy of the East India Company, the religious zeal of the Christian missionaries, the scholarly, secular and scientific attitudes of the British Orientalists, and the emphasis on a strictly ordered pattern of social and civic relationships brought by the Civil Service bureaucracy.[9]

The first regular medical college in India was established at Calcutta in 1835 but it was not until 1881 that the first surviving homoeopathic college was established, although the latter too was to be in Calcutta. During the same time period, however, several Indian homoeopathic physicians had emerged, some converted from the regular Western system (alternatively termed as "allopathic")

[8]This question has been addressed in S.M. Bhardwaj, 1976.

[9]Several scholars have studied the nature and impact of Western influences in nineteenth century India. Among the best, both for theoretical clarity and rigour of analysis, is Kopf, 1969. See also A.F. Salahuddin Ahmed, *Social Ideas and Social Change in Bengal 1818-1835*, Leiden: E.J. Brill, 1965.

and others joining their ranks without professional degrees and diplomas. The conversion of allopathic physicians to homoeopathy was, of course, not novel in India, for such conversions had been going on in the European countries—generally after the 1840's.[10] Perhaps the most significant conversion in India from the allopathic system of medicine to homoeopathy was that of Dr. Mahendra Lal Sircar, a graduate of Calcutta Medical College who earned his M.D. in 1863. Dr. Sircar's status as a recognized individual of scientific distinction in Bengal is evident from Buckland's salutary remark:

> No one in Bengal has held a higher position in Science than Dr. Mahendra Lal Sircar, a position which he has fairly won for himself by ability and labour (Buckland, 1902: 1066).

Trained in the allopathic tradition of his day, Dr. Sircar was, originally, vehemently opposed to the homoeopathic medicine, not unlike most similarly trained allopathic physicians of Europe. However, between 1863 and 1867 his views regarding homoeopathy changed to the extent that he finally espoused its principles. His declaration of faith in homoeopathy was made in an address at the annual meeting of the Medical Association in February, 1867.[11] In order to propagate his views regarding homoeopathy he started *The Calcutta Journal of Medicine*, in 1868. Reading through the first volume of his journal one gets the impression that Dr. Sircar was disillusioned by the closed minds of those who claimed that only the official Western medicine had the key to cure and that any other philosophy of medicine was *ipso facto* irrational. Sircar's attitude toward contemporary medicine are well expressed in the following quote:

> As matters stand at present, practically we cannot, and we ought

[10]Most of the well known homoeopathic physicians of the mid-nineteenth century had their regular M.D. degrees from the recognized medical colleges and only later converted to the new creed. For a concise history of homoeopathy see Ameke, 1885. Also see Kaufman 1971, and Buckland, 1902:1066. For some episodes of conversion from the orthodox practice of medicine to the homoeopathic creed see Kett, 1968: pp. 132-155.

[11]Mahendra Lal Sircar, "On the Supposed Uncertainty in Medical Science and on the Relation Between Diseases and Their Remedial Agents." Address read at the annual meeting of the Bengal Branch of the British Medical Association, February, 1867, see also Sircar, 1868: 1-4.

> not to be wedded to any particular system of treatment. Even if convinced that a certain law is the absolute law of cure, still from our inability to apply it in all cases, we must not sacrifice the interests of our patients, simply because we cannot get hold of a remedy to work according to the law.[12]

Sircar's espousal of homoeopathy was perhaps the most significant landmark in the propagation of this system. He had the then best available allopathic medical training in India, he had a recognized status in science and in the contemporary Bengal elite, and he obviously had the courage to adopt a system that was officially scorned and declared non-scientific. He proved himself enlightened enough to begin inquiry into the indigenous Ayurvedic system both as an open-minded scientist and as an individual aware of the richness of the national heritage in the field of medicine. He thus, perhaps, became a symbol which made it possible for several other *Indian* allopathic practitioners to turn to homoeopathy more openly.

Opposition to homoeopathy in general and to Dr. Sircar in particular continued in the official medical circles and in their publications. In 1878, the *Indian Medical Gazette* tried to make a strong case for removing Dr. Sircar from the medical faculty of the University of Calcutta. The *Indian Medical Gazette* recognizes him as "gentlemen of amiable character, of considerable natural ability, belonging to the progressive school in matters of education and social culture among his fellows,...possessing, moreover, a good position and considerable influence in the native community. However, the *Gazette* declared homoeopathy as "system of absurd transcendentalism, tinctured largely with positive quackery." It then appealed that "it is incumbent on the profession in all parts of the world to set its face uncompromisingly against a system which, even according to its more honest adherents, is false and impracticable." The *Gazette* further observes that "this is all the more necessary in India where national medicine is young and is displacing another system of false doctrine and irrational practice, not unlike homoeopathy in its

[12]Sircar, *op. cit.*, p.3. the "law" referred to above, of course, is the fundamental homoeopathic law: *similia similibus curantur*, i.e., let likes be cured by likes. See also, *The Indian Medical Gazette*, 1878: 158-160. The "another system" referred to above is, most probably the Ayurvedic system.

spirit and method."[13]

Dr. Sircar's conversion to homoeopathy, his attitude to medicine and the attitude of the official Western medicine toward homoeopathy and indigenous Indian systems of medicine represent in fact part of the broader ferment in which Western influences were penetrating the India of the latter half of the nineteenth century.

While there is ample evidence of hostility toward homoeopathy from the allopathic profession, the nature of opposition from the indigenous systems, *Ayurveda* and *Unani*, is not clear. It appears, however, that reaction from the *vaidyas* and *hakims* was probably neither strong, nor well articulated. Factors, such as the following, may have contributed to this accomodation: (*a*) most *hakims* and *vaidyas*, by the very nature of their respective system of medicine, were not schooled in the English language. Therefore, they could not have articulated opposition to homoeopathy in either the vernacular press or literary and professional journals; (*b*) The allopaths were opposed to homoeopathy *as well as* to the Indian system, rejecting both of them as non-scientific. However, the primary conflict of the homoeopaths was with the allopaths who characterized them as quacks. On the contrary the homoeopaths not only did not oppose the indigenous systems, but made positive efforts to reconcile their principles with those of *Ayurveda*. Therefore, potential opposition from the Ayurvedic system may have been minimized. (*c*) Both *Ayurvedic* and the *Unani* system were spatially rural because they had been long prevalent and had acquired a distribution closely associated and commensurate with the distribution of population. Homoeopathy, on the contrary, was new, and had urban orientation in its early phase in India; not having had time to spread into the vast rural milieu. As a result of this spatial separation of the respec-

[13]Sircar, *op. cit.* From time to time other homoeopathic physicians have tried to harmonize homoeopathy with Hindu medical philosophy. See for example, Kaistha, 1909: 355-361. Also see Bhattacharyya, 1956:57. There are some indications now that the physicians of Indian "indigenous" systems, such as ayurveda and siddha, are beginning to express their opposition to homoeopathy and vice versa, in order to achieve expressly separate identity. See Parliament of India, Rajya Sabha, *The Indian Medicine and Homoeopathy Central Council Bill, 1968. Report of the Joint Committee* (New Delhi: Rajya Sabha Secretariat, November, 1969), pp. vii-viii. For detailed lists of graduates, alumni and faculty of homoeopathic institutions in the United States, see King, 1905.

See also, Majumdar, 1895: 34-36. Details of the curriculum are provided by the editor, *Indian Homoeopathic Review*, Vol. 6, 1896, p. 100, and Bhaduri, 1897: 12-13. See *Indian Homoeopathic Review*, vol. 16, No. 4 (April), 1907, pp.99.

tive systems it seems that there was very little competition, hence little opposition to each other.

Homoeopathy from its early days in India faced many problems of professionalization. Conversions from the professionally trained allopathic physicians and addition from the foreign trained Indians constituted the chief source of homoeopathic physicians up to about the 1880's (King, 1905).

The Calcutta Homoeopathic School and Hospital was one of the typical schools in India which trained homoeopathic physicians. Established in 1883 it began with four students and Dr. P.C. Majumdar, its founder, as the only lecturer. By 1894, this school had over one hundred students. The graduates of this school were, of course, not accepted by the government for official employment. Consequently, most of the indigenously trained Indian homoeopathic physicians found private practice as the main source of their employment. Some of the trainees of the Calcutta Homoeopathic School "entered private service, under some landlords or other rich people" (Majumdar, P.C., 1895:34-36).

It is important to note that the very first Indian indigenous schools of homoeopathy de-emphasized dissections of human body. In the three-year curriculum, surgery occupied a minor role. Two circumstances seem to have been responsible for the neglect of surgery by the Calcutta Homoeopathic School. First, the founder of this school was himself not a trained M.D. but rather a licentiate of medicine and surgery indicating fewer years of rigorous training at the Calcutta Medical College. Second, and perhaps the more important, reason was that the students of the homoeopathic school could have had very little opportunity to practice surgery in view of the fact that the school had no hospital attached to it for almost a decade since its start. The hospital was formally opened in 1892, while the school had started in 1883. Although the above two reasons for the neglect of surgery by the Calcutta Homoeopathic School are somewhat obvious, there was also general disregard of surgery by the homoeopaths. This disregard for surgery was not admitted by most homoeopaths and was admonished by some thoughtful partisans, yet the force of the dictum, *similia similibus curantur* emphasized finding an appropriate *medicine* for a malady rather than the lancet. A prominent homoeopath of Calcutta accused the contemporary American homoeopaths of perfoıming "dreadful operations, where internal administration of medicines could have more safely cured the disease" (Bhaduri, C., 1897: 12-13).

Whereby even the Western homoeopaths in general emphasized medicine rather than surgery, in India religious prejudice against touching a corpse may have fortified aversion to dissection. In essence, the beginning of homoeopathic professional training in India, by generally disregarding surgery, added to the differentiation between homoeopathic physicians and the allopaths. By the same token they would attract a class of students who (*a*) did not have adequate level of education for admission to the regular medical college; (*b*) came from the relatively orthodox families; or (*c*) felt that with some homoeopathic medical training, which appeared relatively simple yet was claimed to be "modern" by its proponents, would enable them to earn a living without investing large sums of money. It seems that homoeopathy in the last part of the nineteenth century occupied a position intermediate between the official, allopathic system and the *Ayurveda-Unani.* It was most probably this intermediate status that allowed its wider expansion in India without official support.

Towards the end of the nineteenth century, the number of schools of homoeopathy increased, but instead of imparting rigorous professional medical training, they emphasized the sale of diplomas and certificates. This situation reached alarming proportion in the early part of the twentieth century. In an editorial the *Indian Homoeopathic Review* issued a desperate call to the profession: "Let us for once, for the sake of homoeopathy, wake up and do something to unite all schools and have a good one in place of half a dozen rotten schools that are hastening the ruination of homoeopathy in this country" (1907:99).

The flow of converts from the allopathic system seems to have come to an end by the last decade of the 19th century partly because of the government support cosmopolitan medicine and the medical colleges, but largely because by then allopathy had given up the concept of heroic doses, blood letting and other pre-nineteenth century methods that were long attacked by the homoeopaths. In other words, allopathy was no longer subject to a fundamental criticism once levelled against it. On the other hand, the kind of homoeopathic schools that existed in Bengal did not command the respect of even the Indian homoeopaths. Thus, it no longer was respectable for a trained M.D. of, say, Calcutta Medical College to declare himself a homoeopath and yet claim to be scientific medical practitioner. In other words, time had already passed when a scientist of the stature of Dr. Sircar could espouse the cause of homoeopathy in good conscience.

At the same time that homoeopathy, probably effectively sealed itself from new converts from allopathy (and failed to develop bettei standard of training for its own students), it continued to fortify its belief in the central principle *similia similibus curantur*, to the point where it became accepted as a self-evident, infallable law. Hahnemann, the promulgator became almost deified in India. The editor of the *Indian Homoeopathic Review* called Hahnemann as "Our great master" and declared, "It is our duty to propagate his method of cure for the good of humanity at large and our mother country in particular."[14]

The deification of Hahnemann and the total belief in the law of similitude may have helped rather than hindered homoeopathy's propagation. It probably ensured that homoeopathy would remain distinct from allopathy so long as scientific developments were not allowed to undermine the fundamental homoeopathic law. The allopathic medicine had no single law comparable to the homoeopathic "law of similars." Its appeal was therefore direct to the laymen and the newly educated elite. Several other factors however must have contributed to the spread of homoeopathy.

Since homoeopathy was a non-official system, it was by the same token free from any association with British Imperialism or colonialism. In fact, most of the opposition to homoeopathy seems to have come from the practitioners of allopathy who were either of foreign origin or if Indians, were taught in a foreign language mostly by the British physicians and surgeons. The homoeopaths, with the exception of a few, were Indians. In the absence of any rigorous curriculum in the homoeopathic colleges, most of the "training" probably came from either reading the *materia medica*

[14]Dr. G. Hering, a homoeopath of London had argued in favor of some aspects of allopathic medicines, such as pleasant taste, attractive coloration, in the *Homoeopathic Recorder*. This argument was countered by the editor of the Indian Homoeopathic Review by a declaration of faith: "We must steer clear by the help of Hahnemann's Organon, and everything will be all right." To some homoeopaths in India today Hahnemann is a god! See Beni Prasad Gupta *Encyclopaedia of Homoeopathy*, New Delhi: Homoeopathic Agency 1971. The dedication of which reads, "I dedicate Encyclopaedia of Homoeopathy to the Trust in the memory of Lord Samuel Hahnemann, the founder and inventor of Homoeopathic Medical Science...."

in English or its translations into Bengali. Some of the earliest professional homoeopathic journals (e.g., the *Indian Homoeopathic Review*) published articles in English as well as in Bengali. The process of naturalization of homoeopathy could only have been helped when it used a flourishing Indian language (Bengali) as its medium. For example, a pharmacists' manual widely used in Bengal in the 1890's contained English and Bengali in parallel columns.[15] The majority of the Indian homoeopaths of the latter part of the nineteenth century, except those who could read English well, must have read the principles of homoeopathy in Bengali or other regional languages. Perhaps such a process contributed towards a schism between the homoeopaths and the allopaths, the latter being associated with the colonial British.[16] Later, in the twentieth century some of India's prominent leaders such as Mahatma Gandhi, V.V. Giri, and others were to consider homoeopathy as a superior system.[17]

In the process of naturalization of homoeopathy some of its basic characteristics and principles may have played a useful role. It is not possible to document the importance of specific "principles" of homoeopathy that may have helped in its propagation but nor can their implicit significance be ignored. The fundamental diagnostic method of homoeopathy is to "take into consideration the apparent state of the physical constitution of the patient, ...the disposition, occupation, mode of life, habits, social relations, age.." (Hahnemann 1833: 106-107). In essence, the homoeopathic physician emphasizes the individualization of treatment rather than only curing a given disease. This attitude of the homoeopathic physician, set in the framework of nineteenth-century medicine in India, assumed added significance. The allopathic doctors in India, were usually derived from relatively wealthy urban families or belonged to the

[15]See a review of *Pharmaceutist's Manual*, published by M. Bhattacharji in *Indian Homoeopathic Review*, Vol. 4 (November), 1891, p. 112.

[16]The association of allopathy with the force of the British Rulers is brought out in a letter by D.H. Banerjee, dated Calcutta, September 11, 1894, written to the *Homoeopathic Recorder*, Vol. 9, (November), 1894, pp. 551-552. Banerjee remarks: "but we are obliged or rather compelled to accept this art of healing simply for the vast introduction of Allopathy by our rulers."

[17]Mahatma Gandhi's opinion about the greatness of homoeopathy has been used as a testimonial by the Indian Homoeopathic Directory 1965: "Just as my non-violence will never fail Homoeopathy never fails...." Attributed to Mahatma Gandhi, 30 August 1936. See also Hahnemann, 1838.

rural landed aristocracy, the *zamindars*. This was to be expected, because in order to get admission to the Calcutta Medical College, education in the English medium was compulsory and this type of education was not within the reach of the masses. The allopathic doctors, therefore, most likely had elitist attitude not unlike the attitude of many doctors even today. Their essentially Western mores and demeanour further kept them at a social distance from the common folk. The requirement of the homoeopathic diagnosis and the educational and social characteristic of the homoeopathic physicians perhaps made him more accessible than the allopathic counterpart.

The mid-nineteenth-century "native doctor" (allopath), trained at the Calcutta Medical College, had little empathy with the Indian medicine. Although the British had originally hoped that the Calcutta Medical College would help acquaint the students with Indian *materia medica*, the results were apparently disappointing. The *Calcutta Review* lamented that "the professors in the college pay very little attention to making the students acquainted with the native *materia medica*."[18] Under such circumstances the field was wide open for medical practitioners with an orientation towards the indigenous systems. Although homoeopathy was not an indigenous system, its practitioners were closely empathetic with the Indian ethos.

Homoeopathy, from its very conception by Hahnemann, had an aura of mysticism and spiritualism about it. Hahnemann speaks of energies such as "vital powers," "dynamic powers," and "moral powers." These beliefs were not lost on the Indian homoeopathic physicians. Many of them consciously tried to bring in Hindu ideas into homoeopathy. Dr. A.C. Bhaduri claimed that according to the *Vedanta* philosophy minute doses are best suited for the cure of diseases (1897:11). Attempt to reconcile homoeopathy with Hindu beliefs sometimes resulted in ridiculous logic.[19] Whether the logic of harmonization between Hinduism and homoeopathy was faulty or not is not the issue. It is important that the homoeopaths saw no

[18]The Review admitted that several European doctors such a Royle, Ainsilie, O'Shaughnessy had written on Indian drugs, but "their discoveries are little brought into practice." See Anonymous, "English Ideas, Indian Adaptation," *The Calcutta Review*, No. 59, (March), 1858, p. 30. Also, Bhaduri, 1897: 11.

[19]See for example Ghosh, 1901: 201. "His (Hahnemann's) recognition of the Divine Providence enabled him to discover this law of cure." In a subsequent issue of the same journal Ghosh declared that "The healer of the sick...is not so until he is a philosopher, an *Astrologer*, a scientist."

conflict between their system of medicine and their religious and cultural beliefs even though the system was clearly imported from the West.

Through most of the 19th century the allopathic system, despite its many achievements in the European countries, did not seem to have an impressive record in India. The death rate of admitted patients in the hospitals of Bengal, including the Calcutta Medical College Hospital was very high (Tables 3 and 4).

In some of the dispensaries the death rate of patients was higher than 300 per thousand. The Alipore dispensary of Calcutta had a

TABLE 3

DEATHS AS *PER CENT* OF ADMITTED HOUSE PATIENTS IN THE CHARITABLE DISPENSARIES OF BENGAL, 1868

Disease	*Died as Per cent of admission*
Tetanus	63.63
Cholera	53.53
Dropsies	43.33
Dysentery and Diarrhea	43.13
Pleurisy and Pneumonia	30.16
Spleen Diseases	13.07

SOURCE: Bengal, *Report on the Charitable Dispensaries Under the Government of Bengal, for the Year 1868* (by J. Murray), Calcutta, Superintendent of Government Printing, 1869.

TABLE 4

DEATH RATE OF ADMITTED PATIENTS IN THE CALCUTTA MEDICAL COLLEGE HOSPITAL, 1872

Death Rate Per 1000

Year	*Europeans*		*East Indians*		*Natives*	
	Males	*Females*	*Males*	*Females*	*Males*	*Females*
1869	76.26	36.49	97.48	84.28	260.07	239.24
1870	70.11	42.01	79.92	55.24	210.11	185.18
1871	45.51	45.87	57.30	50.80	190.54	176.07
1872	53.20	12.70	79.60	41.10	177.90	149.50

SOURCE: Calcutta, Medical Department. *Report on the Calcutta Medical Institutions of the Year 1872*, J. Campbell Brown, Calcutta, 1873, p.11.

mortality rate of 319.3 per thousand in 1875.[20] The point of presenting the above data is that even though the allopaths characterized the homoeopaths, the *hakims* and the *Kavirajs* as quacks, their own system was not demonstrably superior. Therefore, the homoeopaths and the indigenous Indian physicians had simple room in the medical profession.

The homoeopathic medicines were usually very inexpensive in comparison to the allopathic drugs. It is interesting to note that the low cost of homoeopathic treatment has been considered as a factor in favor of homoeopathy by the Homoeopathic Enquiry Committee.[21] This characteristic of homoeopathy may have induced many poor people to patronize the homoeopath. On the other hand, the allopathic doctors of the Calcutta Medical College used to charge handsome fees which probably excluded most common folks from their treatment. The *Calcutta Review* tersely summed up the situation: "The rich Babu may have medical assistance from the native doctors (allopaths) of the Medical College, but unless four rupees a visit are paid, the poor man, who must live on two rupees a month, can get little aid."[22] Through its comparative cost advantage homoeopathy not only was able to maintain its distinctiveness from allopathy but also became "popular" as the homely medicine. During the 1860's popular works on homoeopathy were beginning to be available in India.

In the process of naturalization of homoeopathy, the Indian ideas of avoidance of certain foods may have played a less obvious but perhaps a significant role. Accordintg to Honigberger, who had learned the principles of homoeopathy from Hahnemann himself the latter had prohibited the use of tea and coffee for patients while under homoeopathic treatment, (1852:VII-VIII). Whether Hahnemann prohibited the use of meat and spirituous liquors is not known, but it is clear that the Indian homoeopathic practitioners were not in favor of meat and liquor. Commenting on the prescribed diet by one Dr. William E. Leonard, an Indian homoeopath observed that in

[20]For comparison with other hospitals of Calcutta,see India,Medical Department. J. Fullerton, *Report on the Calcutta Medical Institutions* for the Year 1875, Calcutta 1876, p. 3 of "Resolution" in Appendix to the Report.

[21]See Government of India, Ministry of Health. *Report of the Homoeopathic Enquiry Committee 1949*, Delhi: Manager of Publications, 1949, p. 2.

[22]*The Calcutta Review*, March, 1858, p. 30. See the advertisement of Lanne's Homoeopathic Domestic Medicine in *The Indian Lancet*, March 15, 1860, p. 15. Also, Honigberger, *op. cit.*, p. vii-viii.

India meat was not really necessary, that it was "preferable that a very small quantity of fish or meat may be selected according to the nature of the disease."[23] D.N. Banerjee stated the case more emphatically: "Allopathy may be suited for cold climates and for those who are also accustomed to flesh and wine" (1894:55). Hindu aversion to the use of animal products in Western medicine, even in the form of vaccine is indicated by a Bengali gentleman in the following words: "and moreover they were ever averse from nature of the prejudice of caste, to insert the purulent matter from the body of a beast into that of a human being, and therefore they particularly abominate the vaccine virus to the present day...."[24]

THE SPREAD

By the end of the nineteenth century homoeopathy seems to have been naturalized in India. Whereas in most Western countries it began to suffer a rapid decline, in India it was gaining popularity.

Due to the paucity of numerical data, it is not possible here to conjecture about the number of homoeopaths in Bengal at any time during the nineteenth century, but indications are that they were widely spread by the end of the century.[25] It is evident that Bengal, through the latter part of the last century, served as the domicile of homoeopathic profession and from Bengal, homoeopathy spread up the Ganges valley. This expansion moreover, initially at least, was carried on by the Bengali physicians. A Bengali gentleman by the name of Baboo Loke Nath Moitra is credited with the establishment of the first homoeopathic hospital in Banaras.[26] Two Bengali homoeopathic physicians, C.C. Ghosh

[23]This observation was made by S. Dey in *Report of theCalcutta Homoeopathic Charitable Dispensary for the Year 1888-1889*, Calcutta (printed by) Thacker, Spink and Co., 1889, p. 7.

[24]Baboo Radha Kant Deb, "Vaccination," *The Indian Journal of Medical Science*, Vol. 1, No. 1 (January), 1834, p. 34. Also see, Baboo Kanny Loll Dey, "Hindu Social Laws and Habits Viewed in Relation to Health," an address delivered at the third anniversary of the Bengal Branch of the British Medical Association, *Indian Annals of Medical Science*, No. 20, 1866, pp. 467-495.

[25]See the *Indian Homoeopathic Review*, Vol. 19, No. 6, (June), 1910, p. 165. "Not only in large cities and towns but also in all thriving villages there are numbers of homoeopathic practitioners...."

[26]Surinder M. Bhardwaj, "A Western Medical System in Indian Cultural Setting" (forthcoming) Proceedings of the 30th International Congress of Human Sciences in Asia and North Africa. The author is in the process of

and S.B. Chatterjee established *The Indian Homoeopathician*, a periodical published from Lucknow in 1899.

The main regions of concentration of homoeopathy at present are Bengal, Bihar, parts of Assam, followed by Orissa, Tamil Nadu, U.P. and Kerala. The Western states have a paucity of homoeopathic practitioners. In general homoeopathy has an urban rather than a rural concentration.

This regional distribution, however, does not bear any relationship to the growth or spread of quality homoeopathic training in India. The Homoeopathic Inquiry Committee's report clearly brings out that in spite of the widespread practice of this medicine, most of its practitioners unfortunately are very poorly trained in the medical profession. The above report tried to estimate the number of practitioners from various sources. Since it was hard to define a practitioner of this system the estimate was subject to considerable error. The committee nevertheless estimated "that the number of homoeopathic practitioners in India would exceed 2 to 300,000 possibly including all categories, whereas the number of homoeopathic practitioners who have received some sort of institutional training is not likely to exceed 5,000."[27]

CONCLUDING REMARKS

Through the latter half of the nineteenth century, Bengal served as the domicile of homoeopathy. The schism and antagonism between the modern Western medicine and sectarian homoeopathy, present in Europe and the United States, was reflected in India, particularly in Bengal because of the latter being the region of most intimate contact between Europe and India. Bengali physicians espoused homoeopathy with remarkable, even religious zeal soon after its introduction by a few European laymen, physicians and missionaries. The almost religious attachment to Hahnemannian law by the homoeopaths and the repudiation of the same "law" by the Indian allopaths resulted in the recognition of the "new art of healing." Homoeopathy was gradually but surely Indianized.

Throughout its existence during twentieth-century India, the

writing a monograph on the socio-spatial dimensions of Homoeopathy in India. See *The Homoeopathic World*, Vol. 4, No. 44, 1869, p. 171.

[27]India, (Dominion), Ministry of Health, *Report of the Homoeopathic Enquiry Committee*, New Delhi: Manager of Publications, 1949, pp. 34-35.

homoeopathic profession has swelled its ranks but largely with poorly trained practitioners. It has also through various political means tried to seek national recognition. At the same time the more articulate members of the profession have argued for legislative measures to rid the profession of incompetent individuals in an effort to gain professional stature for this art of healing. It is a tribute to the political efforts of the sympathizers of homoeopathy, that finally the Indian Parliament passed a law for the establishment of a council of homoeopathy in 1973. This is a unique situation in the world. However, the establishment of this council, the attendant research facilities, and the resultant scientific scrutiny that this system will inevitably come under, seems to pose both problems and opportunities for profession. Whether homoeopathy will be able to maintain its identity through the vindication of its most fundamental "law of similars" remains to be seen. There is little doubt however that due to continuing shortage of physicians in India, there will be a demand for homoeopaths, as in fact for othei systems of healing. Like the "ambiguities" of the relationships between the "Western" medical system and the indigenous ones discussed by Charles Leslie, homoeopathy too has problems of modernization to contend with.[28] Whether scientific or sectarian, homoeopathy has at least achieved national recognition in India, a status it had sought all along. Whether it will help its spread, consolidation of decline is not as yet clear.

REFERENCES

AMEKE, WILHELM

1885 *History of Homoeopathy, Its Origin, Its Conflicts*; *With An Appendix of the Present State of University Medicine.* London: Gould.

ANONYMOUS

1852 "Homoeopathy, and its Introduction into India."*The Calcutta Review* 28: (March) 19-52.

ANONYMOUS

1858 "English Ideas, Indian Adaptation." *The Calcutta Review* 59:30.

ANONYMOUS

1858 "The Armenians in India: Physically Considered." *The Calcutta Review* 60:305.

ANONYMOUS

1866 "The Missionary and Homoeopathy." *The Homoeopathic World* 1: 52-53.

ANONYMOUS

1907 *Indian Homoeopathic Review* 16: (April) 99.

[28]On this issue see Leslie, 1974: 69-108.

BANERJEE, D.N.
1894 "Letter September 11, 1894." *Homoeopathic Recorder* 9: (September) 551.

BHADURI, A.C.
1897 "Homoeopathy and Homoeopaths." *Indian Homoeopathic Review* 7:11-13.

BHARDWAJ, SURINDER M.
1976 "A Western Medical System in Indian Cultural Setting." Proceedings of the 30th International Congress of Human Sciences in Asia and North-Africa (Forthcoming).

BHATTACHARJI, M.
1891 "Pharmaceutist's Manual." *Indian Homoeopathic Review* 4: 112.

BHATTACHARYYA, BENOYTOSH
1956 *The Science of Tridosha: The Three Cosmic Elements in Homoeopathy.* New York: Gothmam Book Mart.

BRITISH AND FOREIGN HOMOEOATHIC DIRECTORY
1853 *The British and Foreign Homoeopath Directory and Record.* London: Aylott and Company.

BUCKLAND, C.E.
1902 *Bengal Under the Lieutenant-Governors.* Calcutta: Kedarnath Bose.

CALCUTTA HOMOEOPATHIC HOSPITAL
1852 *First Half Yearly Report of the Calcutta Native Homoeopathic Hospital.* Calcutta: P.S. D'Rosario and Co.

CRAWFORD, D.G.
1914 *A History of the Indian Medical Service—1600-1913.* London: W. Thacker.

DEB, RADHA KANT
1834 "Vaccination." *The Indian Journal of Medical Science* 1:34.

DEY, KANNY LOLL
1866 "Hindu Social Laws and Habits Viewed in Relation to Health." *Indian Annals of Medical Science* 20:467-495.

DHAWALE, L.D.
1954 *Homoeopathy; Its Principles and Tenets,* Bombay: published by the author.

ENGLISH HOMOEOPATHIC ASSOCIATION
1847 "Homoeopathy in India." *The Progress of Homoeopathy: A Series of Papers Illustrative of the Position and Prospects of Medical Sciences,* pp. 192-194, London: Samuel Highley.
1847 "Medical Prejudices: Cholera and its Treatment." *The Progress of Homoeopathy: A Series of Papers Illustrative of the Position and Prospects of Medical Science,* p. 140, London: Samuel Highley.

FULLERTON, J.
1876 *Report on the Calcutta Medical Institutions* for the year 1875. Calcutta: Medical Department.

GHOSH, C.C.
1901 "Exposition of Organon." *Indian Homoeopathician* 2:201, 264.

HAHNEMANN, S.
1833 "Organon of the Healing Art." *The Homoeopathic Medical Doctrine,*

pp. 106-107, Dublin: W.F. Wakeman.

HONIGBERGER, JOHN MARTIN
1852 *Thirty-Five Years in the East.* Calcutta: R.C. Lepage and Co.

INDIAN CORRESPONDENT
1869 "Homoeopathy in India." *The Homoeopathic World* 4:266.

INDIA, GOVERNMENT OF
1969 *The Indian Medicine and Homoeopathy Central Council Bill, 1968, Report of the Joint Committee.* New Delhi: Rajya Sabha Secretariat.

INDIAN MEDICAL GAZETTE
1878 *The Indian Medical Gazette* (June 1).

INDIA, MINISTRY OF HEALTH
1949 *Report of the Homoeopathic Enquiry Committee, 1949.* Delhi: *Manager of Publications.*

INSTITUTE OF APPLIED MANPOWER RESEARCH
1967 *Stock of Doctors of Non-Allopathic Systems of Medicine.* New Delhi: Institute of Applied Manpower Research.

KAISTHA, D.S.
1909 "Some Traces of Homoeopathy in the Ancient Hindu Medicine." *The Indian Homoeopathic Review* 18:355-361.

KAUFMAN, MARTIN
1971 *Homoeopathy in America: The Rise and Fall of a Medical Heresy.* Baltimore: Johns Hopkins University Press.

KETT, JOSEPH F.
1968 *The Formation of the American Medical Profession: The Role of Institutions.* New Haven: Yale University Press.

KING, WILLIAM HARVEY
1905 *History of Homoeopathy.* New York: Lewis Publishing Co.

KOPF, DAVID
1969 *British Orientalism and the Bengal Renaissance: The Dynamics of Indian Modernization.* Berkeley: University of California Press.

LESLIE, CHARLES
1974 "The Modernization of Asian Medical Systems." In Poggie, John J. and Robert N. Lynch (eds.), *Rethinking Modernization: Anthropological Perspectives*, pp. 69-108, Westport, Connecticut: Greenwood Press.

MAJUMDAR, P.C.
1895 "The Report of the Calcutta Homoeopathic School and Hospital." *India Homoeopathic Review* 5:34-36.

MATHEWS (Dr.)
1965 *All India Homoeopathic Directory.* Chowghat: The India Homoeopathic Gazette.

MEYER, V.
1960 *Homoeopathischer Führer Für Deutschland and Gesammte Ausland.* Leipzig: Eduard Mayner.

SIRCAR, MAHENDRA LAL
1868 "Our Creed." *The Calcutta Journal of Medicine* 1:1-4.

VANNIER, PIERRE
1970 *L'Homoeopathic.* Paris: Presses Universitaires de France.

RAJ S. GANDHI

AN INTERACTIONIST APPROACH TO THE SOCIOLOGY OF ILLNESS AND MEDICINE AND ITS RELEVANCE TO THE INDIAN SITUATION

ABSTRACT. An interactionist approach to the sociology of illness and medicine, as we have advocated in this essay, rejects the typological tradition of Western sociology as it exhibits ideological as well as theoretical bias. Rather than dichotomizing tradition and modernity, we emphasize the interactions between the contrasting types as they obtain in the Indian empirical situation. We have further expanded the meaning of interactionist approach to characterize the meaningful interactions between those who are culturally defined as "ill" or "sick" and the modern, Western, scientific medical practices and their practitioners. Unlike the Parsonian paradigm of the professional medical practice as it is found in the Western culture, we do not locate the field of sociology of illness in the area of deviant behavior and social control, but, we consider it to be an interactive process in the area of socialization. Illness is viewed as a socialization to the indigenous social and cultural institutions of the community. Both, the ill and the medical practitioner are considered to be the active agents initiating new social activities and defining, re-defining, and modifying the situation together. Since illness is viewed as a part of the interactive process of socialization, it is always conditioned by culture in which it is taking place. Thus, the magico-religious ideas and supernatural beliefs as explanations of diseases among the simple people of India reflect the cultural definition of illness given by the people in village India and it is dependent upon their socialization to the social and cultural institutions of village communities. With the change in the type of community, its institutions of socialization also undergo change, and the definition of illness also changes. Similarly, medicine also is emancipated from magico-religious interpretation.

THE TYPOLOGICAL TRADITION IN WESTERN SOCIOLOGY HAS CREATED a typical bias, both ideological as well as theoretical. Paradoxically, sociology in the West would not have received impetus without this typical ideological bias and it has to date remained a part and parcel of Western sociology. Being infused with the idea of evolution and progress on the one hand, and revolution and change on the other, the ideological overtones are inevitably found in favor of "progress," "modernity" and "change" and they are embedded in such devices as the dichotomies, typologies, contrasts, continua and ideal Types. To be sure, not all of them represent one and the same thing; but, they have one thing in common: the underlying assumption that while one and of the scale or the side of dichotomy (usually the left) represents the lack of "modernity," traditionalism, and hence the lack of "progress" or change, the other end (the right) reflects rationalism, "modernity," "progress" and change. The latter somehow is assumed to be desirable and at times appears in the theoretical disguise of the "direction of change."

To be sure, there have been, recently, some correctives to the above exaggerations (see Gusfield, 1967; Rudolph and Rudolph, 1972; Kothari, 1970). However, various subfields within sociology, notably, urban and medical sociology find it difficult to do without the use of the typologies and dichotomies or contrasts and continua under the implicit assumption that they are perhaps the inevitable instruments of comparison. Be that as it may, many times, the comparative analysis with the use of such instruments curtails an important empirical reality: the interactions between tradition and "modernity," traditionality and rationality (Weber, 1947), sacred and secular (Becker, 1950: 248-80), *Gemeinschaft* and *Gesellschaft* (Tönnies, [1887] 1957), folk and urban (Redfield, 1969), mechanical and organic solidarity (Durkheim, [1893] 1964), status and contract (Maine, 1963) or familistic and contractural relations (Sorokin, 1947). Our purpose in pointing out all these is threefold: (1) To point out how the dichotomies disguise ideological bias (see Gandhi, 1974); (2) In spite of the variations in dichotomies and the different labels emphasizing different themes, most theories have only two contrasting types, and; (3) The two contrasting types do not indicate the interactions between the two. Of these, the special importance attaches to the latter as the lack of this interactionist approach obscures an important empirical reality which is of great significance in its relevance to sociology of illness and medicine in India, particularly in examining its socio-cultural context. However, we not only use the label "interactionist approach" to characterize the interactions between the "traditional" and the "modern," but, the meaningful interactions between those who are culturally defined as "ill" or "sick" and the modern, Western, scientific medical practices and their practitioners. Thus, the label "interactionist approach" is used to emphasize these dual meanings. This is further critically elaborated below.

The Patient, Professional Medical Practice and the Parsonian Pattern Variables

The typological tradition in Western sociology has culminated into the Parsonian pattern variables (Parsons, 1962: 76-91). But even before the pattern variables were "invented" by Parsons, his essay, "The Professions and Social Structure" (Parsons, 1964a:34-49) analyzes the role of a professional. He is characterized as possessing "disinterestedness" or "impersonality" in dealing with his patients or clients. The professional man is collectivity-oriented; he exhibits "rationality" as opposed to "traditionalism" and he is characterized by "specificity of function"; the basis of his decision is "universalistic" rather than particularistic. Throughout his essay the illustration of the role of a doctor as a professional *par excellence* is present. The doctor, in performing his services for a patient, as per the Parsonian picture of pattern variables, is impersonal, rational, collectivity-oriented, specific and universalistic. Nowhere in this essay is theie any mention that this is the "Ideal Type" construct of the role of a doctor nor is it said here that the pattern variables are "Ideal Constructs" (though it is mentioned later in his *Theory of Action*, 1962); nor does the "patient" enter very much into the picture. He is considered as though he is a passive instrument to be dealt with by the doctor. The whole problem of meaningful interactions between the patient and the doctor is missing.

But the patient who has been very much hiding from Personian perspective in his earlier essay on professions reveals himself in his so-called classic analysis of the case of modern medical practice (Parsons, 1964b: 428-479). However, the picture is further complicated by the fact that this analysis is now to be understood within the "structural-functional" framework. Further, the influence of L.J. Henderson's essay, "Physician and Patient as a Social System"

(1935: 819-23) is very much in evidence (see also, Sigerist, [1891] 1960). Illness is defined as deviant behavior and hence dysfunctional for the efficient functioning of the social system. The functional setting of medical practice is examined as well as the roles of the physician and the patient "the sick role"; but the latter is "deviant," to be "brought back into line." He is not considered to be an active partner in the process nor is his role placed within the specific historical or socio-cultural context. Of course, the attention is exclusively focussed on the highly distinctive "cultural tradition" of modern scientific medical profession. But here again, the interpretation becomes one-sided and highly selective. As usual, the physicians are characterized with achievement orientation, universalism, affectivity-neutrality, functional-specificity, and collectivity-orientation. Illness is one mode of response to social pressures, one way of evading social responsibilities. But it may also have some positive functional significance. An ill person moves into the sick role, which consists of "a set of institutionalized expectations and the corresponding sentiments and sanctions." Its characteristics are: (1) a sick person is exempt from normal social responsibilities. This is his duty as well as right; (2) he cannot be expected to take care of himself. Someone must help him; (3) his state is undesirable. He should want to get well and others should make him well as soon as possible; (4) he should, and is obliged to, seek competent medical advice and help and cooperate with medical experts to get himself out of sickness (see Frankenberg, 1974: 418; Robinson, 1971:10).

Frankenberg (1974:412-26) is correctly critical of the class-period specificity of Parsons's whole analysis. Quoting at length from Karl Marx's descriptions of socially created diseases (as found in his *Capital*) he convincingly argues that what seems remote and historical in the prosperous parts of Western industrialized countries still represents reality in other countries. To this, Asia and especially India is no exception. He sarcastically but surrealistically reveals Parsons's devotion to the sacredness (in Durkheimian sense) of the physician who is expected to share the values and pattern variables with the profane patient: "The patient is controlled, ignorantly uncertain, the object of the death process. The physician controls, is wisely uncertain, is intimate with death." So sacred is the physician's position that he has "privileged access to secrets and secret places; the vagina and the rectum are specifically mentioned by

Parsons's as places where, in Parsons's world, even one's best friends are not admitted." Only in such manner, perhaps, the complimentary role structure of the sick person as patient becomes articulated with that of the physician. Thus, at last, in this sense and in this way, the "interactional" aspect of the patient and physician is revealed. But what is also revealed by Parsons's analysis is his typical ideological bias in favor of the physician who is expected to control and "correct" the deviance of the patient, a historical and culturally confined one-sided interpretation of the situation of medical practice which is of course empirically extremely limited as he cannot see the specific dimensions of social stratification, class, status (or caste) and power as well as the specific socio-cultural factors playing their dynamic role in meaningful interactions between the patient and the physician. In this process of interaction neither patients nor their social and cultural traditions are considered to be passive objects or "things." They actively enter into interaction with physicians and their medical practice, and in the process transform both the native traditions, traditional practices, indigenous structures and attitudes, and the newly introduced institutions and ideas. In what follows we shall emphasize the "interactionist approach" as used in dual sense, to the sociology of illness and medicine, critically re-examine and reinterpret some case studies in this area with special relevance to the Indian situation.

Illness as Socialization to the Indigenous Social and Cultural Institutions

Traditionally, functionalists have located a sociology of illness within the field of social control as illness is conceived to be "dysfunctional" for the social system, upsetting its equilibrium. It is the function of a given social system to restore the balance of control. We can at once realize here the basic problem with the functional approach in treating sociology of illness as a matter of social control. This basic problem is the ideological bias of the functionalists. Their historical outlook and class-period specificity are responsible for their lack of appreciation of the socio-cultural contexts within which the interactions between the ill and the healthy take place. To treat the former as the "deviants" to be "controlled" reflects the character of functionalists as the spokesmen for social strata that had newly come to power in industrialized society.

In contrast, an interactionist approach to illness does not only attend to the negative features of illness. While illness may impair some on-going social activities, it may also provide an occasion for initiating new social activities or it may become an opportunity for cultural innovation which would not otherwise occur at all. By the same token, the role of a medical practitioner or physician is perceived not only as a "controller" of the situation but as an innovator, and so is the role of patient. Both together define the situation and in the course of meaningful interactions, each may learn from the other and at times re-define or modify the situation.

Briefly, an interactionist account of the theory of socialization is found in the writings of G.H. Mead (1934). Mead rejected the traditional mind-body dualism (note the direct significance of this for the sociology of illness and medicine) and postulated the formation and socialization of the human self within on-going society as a social process. By not treating self simply as a bodily organism, Mead noted the uniqueness and peculiarity of the human self in its quality of reflexiveness. Through this capacity, it becomes both subject as well as object. Thus, the patient is not only the object for the doctor but also becomes an active agent acting towards himself while interpreting the interactional situation and the cultural context within which his treatment is taking place.

When interaction mediated by gestures is transmuted into communication in terms of significant symbols, a reconstruction of biological into social individuality is inevitable. When interaction is mediated by significant symbols, a world of universal meanings opens to both parties of the act. The symbol can call out a specific response not only to the one to whom it is communicated, but to anyone who understands it. The symbol evokes in the person producing it the same meaning he conveys to others. Thus symbols involve the sharing of meanings in situations in which individuals take the role of the other (see also, Martindale, 1966: 406). It would now be realized that understood in this way, the doctor-patient interactions which constitute an important part of the sociology of illness assumes a different meaning from the typical analysis given by the functionalists in general, and Parsons in particular.

It should also be clear from the underlying emphasis of the interactionists that the socialization of an individual is not only confined to family but notably to other groups as well. We specifically draw attention to the socializaton of individuals in the system of stratification, particularly the caste system in the case of India, and a variety of subcultures produced by various strata. Vera Rubin (1960: 785) has stated that, "...between man as the host and the micro-organisms of disease there intervene socio-cultural patterns and individual psychological processes as well as organic factors."

Thus if we view illness as a part of the interactive process of socialization, and the latter as conditioned by the culture in which it takes place then it makes sense to find that the folklore of simple people in India consists of magico-religious ideas which describe diseases as caused by supernatural powers. A survey in connection with smallpox in North India (Bharara, 1961) revealed a variety of beliefs regarding the cause of this disease.

TABLE 1*

PERCEIVED CAUSES OF SMALLPOX IN NORTH INDIA AND ACTION TAKEN

Cause	*% Believing*	*Action Taken*†	*% People*
The goddess (of smallpox	55.8	Stopped all frying of food and taking of condiments	67.5
Unseen living organism	19.2	Stopped combing hair	66.8
Unknown	16.7	Stopped shaving hair	48.5
Evil spirits	3.6	Worshipped goddess in the village	56.1
Foul smells	3.3	Worshipped the goddess in home	44.3
		Made sacrificial offerings to goddess	22.7
		Stopped all work	37.6
		Gave no treatment to the patient	41.2

*Adapted from Bharara (1961) quoted in Margaret Read (1966:34).

†Action was taken by the people in the same area, 45.4 per cent of whom had the experience of smallpox in their own homes.

It is noteworthy that although a variety of beliefs regarding smallpox obtain among the simple people in India, the highest proportion is that of the people who believe that the disease is caused by the goddess of smallpox. Similarly, although a variety of actions are taken by the people as a consequence of direct or indirect experience with the disease, in general, the action seems to follow the belief.

Altogether, the largest proportion of people resort to the worship of goddess for the cure of the disease. It should also be noted that 41.2 per cent of the people gave no treatment to the patient. This should not be interpreted as lack of action. In this case, giving no treatment itself is an action oriented towards the belief. One may passively and patiently wait for the wrath of goddess to pass away. Taking action against it may further provoke the anger of goddess and it may prove to be fatal. Illness, in this sense, is accepted as inevitable. The cultural definition of illness given by the people in the villages of India is thus dependent upon their socialization to the social and cultural institutions of villages. Among the causes of disease, as reported by Opler (1963) and Khare (1963), are (1) lack of harmony with the supernatural, (2) activity of ghosts, and (3) deities. Thus, in their separate articles, both Opler as well as Khare report that these factors are brought into play by violation of moral, economic or religious codes. They find that among the villagers, supernaturalism seems to have major significance in disease causation and treatment. However, there are variations. The degree to which supernaturalism functions varies within a group and the extent of variation is based on social hierarchy, the particular disease and the extent of formal education. We shall return to the problem of variation of the interpretation of disease given by the simple people in India, particularly, as it relates to *social hierarchy* and *a particular disease*. However, the latter relates to smallpox, as it appears to be the recurrent theme in the literature on sociology of illness and medicine in India, and the former revolves around the hierarchically arranged groups, the recurrent theme of *homo hierarchicus*, (Dumont, 1970) especially as it relates to the family, kin, and the caste system as found in India. But, at this juncture, it should be noted that the supernatural interpretation of health and disease not only relates to social hierarchy, the type of disease encountered or experienced by people and their formal education, but, *the type of community*. It is well known that even in traditional India, the urban communities experienced the beginning of emancipation of medicine from magico-religious interpretation. It is in the early, pre-industrial urban communities of India that we first find the systematic philosophico-scientific explorations in Indian medicine in the name of Ayur Veda. The origins of this science of diagnosis and cure are attributed to Dhanvantri by his later successor. Sushruta, a professor of medicine at the University of Benaras, in the fifth century B.C. Charka, who lived in the sixth century A.D., systematized all his knowledge into a *Samhita*, an encyclopedia of medicine, and gave it to his disciples (see, Motwani, 1947: 80-81). Needless to mention that true to the diffusion of knowledge from the Great Tradition to the Little Tradition, (see Singer, 1972:250-71) villagers of India, along with their magico-religious beliefs are quite familiar with these philosophico-scientific developments which took place in the large ancient urban centers of India. This is found sometimes in the explanations of the causes of ordinary diseases with the help of the *tridosha* theory in the villages of India. The Table 2 explains the correspondence between the type of community and the health and welfare as a part of the institutions of socialization.

TABLE 2*

CORRESPONDENCE BETWEEN COMMUNITY TYPE AND HEALTH AND WELFARE INSTITUTIONS

Community Type	*Health and Welfare*
Pre-cultivating tribes, 15,000-10,000 B.C.	Magico-religious notions of health and disease. Mutual sharing by family and kin
Pre-city peasant village, 10,000-3,500 B.C.	Magico-religious notions of disease Increase in surgical and herbal knowledge. Joint family primary welfare agency
City, 3,500 B.C.	Beginning of emancipation of medicine from magic and religion Specialized welfare institutions
Feudal manor, 900 A.D.	Some continuity with civil traditions. Mainly magico-religious concepts of disease†
Nation-State, 1,700 A.D.	Specialized public and private health institutions Scientific medicine

*Adapted from Martindale (1966:454).

†In the case of India, this was found mixed with philosophico-scientific concepts.

Although the Table 2 gives a rough correlation between the two, in the case of India, interaction between the Great and Little Tradition should never be underemphasized.

INTERACTION BETWEEN TRADITIONAL AND RATIONAL

As pointed out above, one should not think of all the ideas and actions of simple people in India guided by supernatural forces when it comes to the interpretation of health and disease. Nor are their actions always purely traditional as opposed to rational. To begin with, interaction between magico-religious and philosophico-scientific concepts has been a common feature of Indian life. Further, most of the common diseases are interpreted as a "fault in the physical system" and are treated with herbal medicines or modern drugs obtained from a dispensary. People seem to resort to ritual practices when diagnosis becomes difficult, (this could happen even in modern hospitals surrounded by professionally qualified specialists) and the disease is persistent. This was found by S.C. Dube (1955: 127) in a study of Indian village life in Hyderabad State:

> ... Common colds, headaches, stomach ache, scabies, gonorrhea and syphilis are regarded as natural diseases, and an effort is made to cure them with medicines. But persistent headaches, intermittent fevers, continued stomach disorders, rickets and other wasting diseases among children, menstrual troubles, repeated abortions, etc. are attributed to supernatural forces. *In such cases medicinal cures as well as propitiation of the "unseen powers" are attempted simultaneously*... (emphasis added).

It is important to recall that in describing the role of traditional ideas in the process of socialization to sickness, the interaction between the "traditional" and the "rational" is present. First of all we must note the protective significance of the ritual:

> Many standard rites are in fact precautionary ceremonies in which a deity is regularly honored, so that he will bear his worshippers good will only. For example, just before the season when smallpox is likely to erupt, a rite in honor of the Smallpox Goddess is carried out in each household, in the course of which she is fed, honored and ceremonially led from vicinity (Opler, 1963:35).

Further, one must remember the cultural context within which the interaction between doctor and patient is taking place. It would be difficult to achieve mutual understanding when doctor and patient behold each other through different kinds of cultural glasses. In addition, structural context is equally important. Just as we find it everywhere in the world, the people of rural India interpret sickness as much a moral as a physical crisis. Similarly, definitions of health contain ethical components that rest on value systems. Since the days of Marx and Durkheim, all sociologists have recognized the structural context of morals and values. Thus the people may suffer from organic diseases without assuming the sick role and conversely, persons who have no organic disease or impairment may be assigned the role of sickness (contrast this with the Parsonian position on sick role as "deviant behavior"). "Values and social structure account for much of the lack of correspondence between the existence of organic disease, of illness, and of the sick role" (Susser, 1974:541). Carstairs correctly considers the people of rural India as conceiving the roots of illness extending into the realm of human conduct as well as cosmic purposes. As a consequence they look for relief to ritual reassurance as well as to mundane medicines.

Sacred and Secular Interaction Between Folk and Scientific Medicine

An excellent demonstration of interaction between sacred and secular is found in Carstairs' account of the treatment of snake-bites in the village he studied:

> All snakes, but especially the black cobras, were believed to be the embodiment of powerful godlings....[E]very plot of cultivated field had a protector-god....Should anyone trespass or otherwise offend the god, he would get bitten....(T)here were priests of the snake-god whom the sufferer might consult. They would become 'possessed,' suck out the poison, and be placated with an offering (1955:126).

Carstairs further notes that he had in his stock of medicines a set of dried polyvalent antivenin serums for intravenous injection for use in cases of snake-bite. Although he made it known to the villagers that this medicine was available, no one asked for the medicine. This, Carstairs confesses, was on account of the close association of the illness and the god. However, the non-acceptance of the Western medicine was due to disregard for the all-important divine agent which could not inspire confidence among the villagers in treating this condition. Here, the physician is expected to take the role of the villagers and understand their own beliefs concerning sickness and cure. The villagers have a different conception of the role of the physician. Only after learning it, he can expect to disseminate scientific knowledge.

Similarly, an empirical illustration of a successful role-taking is found in Harold Gould's account of success in spreading contemporary medicine in Sherupur (pseudonym for the village he studied). Gould (1969:320) maintains that the primary variable responsible for his popularity as a "doctor" was the personal relationship with the village people and the patients (contrast this with Parsonian emphasis on "impersonality" of a professional practitioner). He not only, through primary relationships, successfully took the role of the villagers, but his typical role with the kind of powers and resources at his disposal became an aspect of the structure of village medicine. Once he became trusted and accepted, people suffering from severe physical problems who usually sought relief through scientific medical procedures, preferred to use him as an intermediary between themselves and scientific medicine. Gould singles out villager's preference for personal relationships as the single most important factor in gaining their confidence; but, this does not necessarily result into changing the belief structure of the village; rather it results into an active interaction between the scientific and folk medicine:

> ...(M)y medicine and I had become integral parts of certain disease situations. In this sense, the acceptance of scientific medicines from me and from doctors too for that matter, resulted in no material changes in basic folk cognitive structure. These experiences were filtered through the screen of this cognitive system and converted into meanings which did no violence to it. One therefore wonders whether it is correct to say that the villagers accepted modern technology or that they converted modern technology into folk medicine (Gould, 1969: 329).

However, in his observations on the smallpox case Gould witnessed how the medical beliefs and practices of the villagers were found to be well integrated with the religion and morality of the group; and yet, how the power and strength of personal relationship succeeds in overriding religious sanctions. He shows how both in folk medicine as well as scientific medicine there are always problems about correct diagnosis and how the strength of the pragmatic impulse of the villagers could be utilized in modifying their religious resistance, and once modified, *both* religious rites *and* scientific medicine could be utilized for the treatment.

The case relates to Balaka Ram, the ten-year-old son of a poor low-caste family in Sherupur. His high fever was interpreted by his parents as the attack of smallpox, and hence, abstaining from eating and performance of religious rites were found to be only suitable courses of action. No doctor should be allowed to intervene. His inference would further anger Bhagoti Mai (the goddess of smallpox) and consequently she would kill Balaka Ram:

> ...At one point, after Balaka Ram's grandmother repeated her conviction that this was an exclusively supernatural matter, I countered by asking her how she could be so certain that God works only in one narrow way. Here I was quite consciously attempting to awaken in her rustic mind some of the implications of Hindu pantheism. Is it not true, I asked her, that God is to be found in everything and that he acts in many different ways?... may he not also live in the doctor and work through his medicines?...*Would it not be wise to do the religious rites and then also let the doctor and me help through medicines?* (Gould, 1967: 328), (emphasis added).

Needless to say that this argument proved to be convincing and it was agreed to let the doctor's medicines be tried on Balaka Ram. Meanwhile the rituals were performed too. Balaka Ram recovered. It matters little whether Bhagoti Mai got the credit or modern medicine. Once again, much like Carstairs's experience, we are clearly able to witness here the interaction between the sacred and the secular. We can see why people in Sherupur preferred to get medicines from an anthropologist. The medicine in the village was integrated into patterns of social interaction which the people understood and which did not drain from them every ounce of their self-respect (see symbolic interactionist theory of formation of self) as the price for being benefitted by what modern medicine has to offer (Gould, 1969: 334). The difference lies in empathy and appeal to the belief system of culture in which interaction takes place for adaptation and change and in the process modifies both—the agent of change and the system under the impact of change.

THE MODERNITY OF TRADITION IN INDIAN MEDICINE

Those who would like to paint an idyllic picture of rural India still think of the dominance of the *Gemeinschaft* way of life in the Tönnies' sense of the term. It is based on *Wesenwille* (natural will) as opposed to *Kürwille* (rational will). They could not conceive of the interaction between the two. But the empirical facts precisely point out how the "natural" and the "rational" interact:

> ...(T)he chief health officer of Jodhpur State, turned upon a judicious use of showmanship. This doctor, an Irishman and a famous athlete included in his retinue one of those emaciated beggars, blind and pockmarked.... When he came to a village he would summon everyone with his stentorian voice. 'Take a good look at him,' he would bellow, 'that is what Mataji (the goddess of smallpox) does for you! And now look at this: this is what vaccination does to you!' He would then strip to the waist and display not only his vaccination scars but also his muscular torso. The demonstration was convincing. (Carstairs, 1955: 108).

It was Henry Sumner Maine who thought of traditional societies as based on status rather than contract. Parsons's depiction of interaction between doctor and patient within the Western cultural milieu rests on the assumption of contract-dominated society. But even in Western society the capitalistic class is generally more contact-oriented than the other. When we look at the changing society of India, what is more obvious is the interaction between tradition and modernity. In fact what is happening is the modernity of tradition. Gould's experience in Sherupur convincingly demonstrates the interaction between folk and scientific medicine. Carstairs relates the patient's expectations to the general cultural climate of the Indian community. Individuals acting in conformity with the demands of culture may suppress or restrain almost any biological need, and even pain, rather than violate the demands (see Miner, 1956; Zborowski, 1952). Those who live by socially prescribed eating codes will starve before partaking of foods identified as profane. In this sense, food is certainly a part of culture and accordingly some general dietary restrictions may be followed in case of illness. D.B. Jelliffe (1969) has given an interesting account of the extent to which socio-cultural factors influence maternal and child health practices in village India, especially, rural West Bengal. Jelliffe in his study was concerned with identifying the "cultural blocks" which were felt to be harmful with regard to protein nutrition in the young child. Though he is appreciative of certain aspects of local domestic culture of the West Bengal village (for example, prolonged breast feeding), he finds that the village mothers have their own ideas of the etiology of disease and the following may at different times be thought to be responsible: (1) evil spirits; (2) divine intervention; (3) evil eye (*nazar*); (4) effect of climate (i.e., physical cold or heat). For instance, if the child is found to be continually ill, then the mother according to the *garam-tonda* classification may restrict the child's diet. This may result in underfeeding and malnutrition. In short, Jelliffe observes that in rural West Bengal there is a direct relationship between the cultural blocks to nutrition and traditional concepts of prestige and social class, food, hot-cold food, rice-feeding ceremony (*mukhe bhat*), social status and mixed-feeding practices.

However, the presence of scientific methods in Indian villages itself induces an updating of practices of the folk curers. Further, where there is no disharmony between scientific practices and the existing cultural structure, the former seem to be more easily accepted.

The Structural Context

In addition to the role of the cultural context in interaction between doctor and patients as well as the acceptance of scientific medicine in India, the structural context is of similar significance. This is found in three main principles of Indian social structure, viz. family, kinship, and socio-economic status or caste. The term "family," however, is to be understood in the wider sense of the term, as the so-called "nuclear family" has not become a characteristic of urban communities, let alone villages of India (see Desai, 1964; Shah, 1974). Since the norm of joint family guides the beliefs and actions of people in India, it is understood to represent a complex of mutual obligations and services. The wider kin-group is found to take the responsibility for a sick person. It includes "classificatory" fathers, mothers, brothers, grandparents, and so on, and constitutes a social group in a rural or urban community which eludes the customary definition of family.

In a study of the difficulties met by an exploratory clinic in Kishan Garhi, a village in Northern India, McKim Marriott (1969) finds the social world of the villagers consisting of three concentric realms. Using social structure as the main frame of reference, he considers the structural context of village to be more directly relevant than the cultural context as directly referred to by Bharara, Carstairs, Gould and Jelliffe. The three concentric realms mentioned by Marriott are, family, with its further extension into kinship, caste and internal kinlike connections throughout the village.

For a period of fourteen months during 1950-1952, Marriott lived in Kishan Garhi for the anthropological study of the village. When approached by the peasants for a variety of physical ailments and problems, he enlisted the cooperation of a young English physician who was then in the area. His experiences vividly demonstrate the structural context of interactions between the patients and the doctor. In addition to the utter disregard for the "contractual" nature of the relationship between the doctor and the patients (refusal to make payment in advance for medicines), it was difficult for the doctor to remove the patient for purposes of individual examination as the latter was many times surrounded by anxious family members. Moreover, the family members carried more weight than the doctor, which fact is clearly reflected in the following experience:

> ...One Brahman girl... was suffering the chills and fevers of acute malaria during the doctor's visit. The girl's father and her father's brothers came repeatedly to beg that the doctor give her quinine. The doctor... discovered three days later that none of the quinine had been permitted to reach the girl. An old widowed aunt who ruled the women of that family had voiced objections, and the whole matter of Western treatment was dropped. (Marriott, 1969: 243).

Interpreting further the difficulties encountered by the exploratory clinic in the village, Marriott believes that the reasons did not lie in villagers' apathy, nor in objections to scientific techniques nor in high costs but rather in the system of interpersonal relationships. In other words, interactions between the sick people, the other villagers and the external medical practitioner should take into account the structural context of the village. Moreover, trust, responsibility, charity, power, and respect—the ethical values within the structural context—are of crucial significance. The success or failure of Western medicine and the medical practitioner would depend on the degree to which they find an acceptable social place in the village. Further, representatives of each social realm command varying degrees of trust; and different degrees of trust are appropriate in dealings among members of groups of the three realms. First, it is within the context of the family that specialized medical services are always rendered. The families extend into kinship groups in the village and they, in turn, merge into caste groups which are rank-ordered. "The larger family in the village...does what in Western society would be done respectively by receptionist, lawyer, nurse, orderly secretary, and bondsman" (pp. 250-51). Any doctor in the village, to be successful, has to recognize the significance of this joint family orientation.

Secondly, all persons and kinship groups in a village ought to be placed in a system of hierarchy and the Western medical practitioner, especially if he is an outsider, is no exception. Whether he is identified as belonging to a high, middle or low position determines the way in which he will be treated by the people. His wealth and power may also depend on the position he occupies. In turn, lines of power within village families and among different castes also affect the utilization of medical treatment. Thus, in spite of good medicines and good intentions, the Western medical practitioner may be distrusted or suspected so long as the villagers identify him as an "outsider" and place him in a low position in village social structure.

This brings us to the consideration of the way in which the villagers deal with strangers. The attempts of the former may be to classify the latter as pseudokinsmen or try to trace more specific kinlike connections. When villagers have to deal with the outsiders who are more powerful than themselves, their relations tend to extend upward in a castelike form. Thus, Marriott believes that so long as the Western medicine in the village exists beyond the realm of family, caste, and village, it may be interpreted as one of "contrived dependency and fundamental distrust." Here, one can do no better than quote Marriott (1969:266):

> Western ideas of personal privacy, of individual responsibility, of the dignity of certain techniques, and of the democratic nature of interpersonal trust are not intrinsic parts of scientific and medical practice but are cultural of accretions upon it. These

> ideas are not compatible with the traditional social organization of such an Indian village as Kishan Garhi. Not being supported by the social experience of villagers, such ideas tend to weaken or disrupt any medical approach that attempts to base itself upon them.

This certainly is a far cry from the Parsonian paradigm of doctor-patient relationship.

CONCLUDING REMARKS AND IMPLICATIONS

An interactionist approach to the sociology of illness and medicine, as we have advocated in this essay, rejects the typological tradition of Western sociology as it exhibits ideological as well as theoretical bias. Rather than dichotomizing tradition and modernity or traditionality and rationality, sacred and secular, status and contract, etc., we emphasize the interactions between the contrasting types as they obtain in the Indian empirical situation. We have further expanded the meaning of interactionist approach to characterize the meaningful interactions between those who are culturally defined as "ill" or "sick" and the modern, Western, scientific medical practices and their practitioners. Unlike the Parsonian paradigm of the professional medical practice as it is found in the Western culture, we do not locate the field of sociology of illness in the area of deviant behavior and social control, but we consider it to be an interactive process in the area of socialization. Illness is viewed as a socialization to the indigenous social and cultural institutions of the community. Both the patient and the medical practitioner are considered to be active agents initiating new social activities and defining, re-defining, and modifying the situation together.

Further, following G.H. Mead, we do not artificially separate self, society, and culture. Rather, they are always found to be fused together in empirical reality and hence we do not abstractly remove self or interaction between selves from its socio-cultural context. Only in this way the interactions between the sick, the healthy, and the medical practitioner become empirically more meaningful and realistically analyzable within the cultural and social structural context.

Since illness is a part of the interactive process of socialization, it is always conditioned by the culture in which it is taking place.

Thus, the magico-religious ideas and supernatural beliefs as explanations of diseases among the simple people of India reflect the cultural definition of illness given by the people in village India and it is dependent upon their socialization to the social and cultural institutions of village communities. With the change in the type of community, its institutions of socialization also undergo change, and the definition of illness also changes. Similarly, medicine also is emancipated from magico-religious interpretation. In any case, the empirical situation of illness and medicine in India is further complicated by the interactions between the Great Tradition and the Little Tradition.

Thus, in further elaborating our interactionist approach, in emphasizing interactions between types of traditions, we do not consider the ideas and actions of simple people in India as irrational. There is, in fact, interaction between traditional and rational as both are simultaneously used by them in interpreting diseases as well as cures.

While the studies of Opler, Khare, Jelliffe, Bharara, Carstairs and Gould explain the cultural context of illness, health, and medicine as well as the interaction between scientific and folk medicines in India, Marriott also draws our attention to social structural context and points out family, kinship, hierarchical order and the internal integration of village social organization as significantly affecting the interactions between the village people, the patient, and the modern medical practitioner. Moreover, one must also bear in mind the structural context of morals and values of the people and the sick. The successful role-taking of the medical practitioner is mainly dependent upon his adaptability to this socio-cultural context.

REFERENCES

BECKER, HOWARD
1950 *Through Values to Social Interpretation.* Durham: Duke University Press.

BHARARA, S.S.
1962 *Pilot Health Education and Reorientation Training.* Lucknow: Health Education Bureau.

CARSTAIRS, MORRIS G.
1955 "Medicine and Faith in Rural Rajasthan." In Benjamin D. Paul (ed.), *Health, Culture and Community*, pp. 107-34. New York: Russell Sage Foundation.

DESAI, I. P.
1964 *Some Aspects of Family in Mahuva*. London: Asia Publishing House.
DUBE, S.C.
1955 *Indian Village*. London: Routledge and Kegan Paul.
DUMONT, LOUIS
1970 *Homo Hierarchicus*. Chicago: The University of Chicago Press.
DURKHEIM, EMILE
1964 *The Division of Labor in Society*. Translated by George Simpson. New York: The Free Press.
FRANKENBERG, RONALD
1974 "Functionalism and After? Theory and Developments in Social Science Applied to the Health Field." *International Journal of Health Services* 4:412-27.
GANDHI, RAJ S.
1974 "Ideology, Theories of Urban Society and Social Change." *International Journal of Contemporary Sociology* 11 (April-July): 130-43.
GOULD, HAROLD A.
1969 "Modern Medicine and Folk Cognition in Rural India." In L. Reddick Lynch (ed.), *The Cross Cultural Approach to Health Behavior*, pp. 316-36. Cranbury: Associated University Press Inc.
GUSFIELD, JOSEPH R.
1967 "Tradition and Modernity: Misplaced Polarities in the Study of Social Change." *American Journal of Sociology* 72 (January): 351-62.
HENDERSON, L. J.
1935 "Physician and Patient as a Social System." *New England Journal of Medicine* 212 (May): 819-23.
JELLIFFE, DERRICK B.
1969 "Social Culture and Nutrition: Cultural Blocks and Protein Malnutrition in Early Childhood in Rural West Bengal." In L. Reddick Lynch (ed.), *The Cross-Cultural Approach to Health Behavior*, pp. 296-315. Cranbury, J.J.: Associated University Presses, Inc.
KHARE, R.S.
1963 "Folk Medicine in a North Indian Village." *Human Organization* 22 (Spring): 36-40.
KOTHARI, RAJNI
1970 "Introduction." In Rajni Kothari (ed.), *Caste in Indian Politics*, pp. 3-25, New York: Gordon and Breach.
MAINE, HENRY SUMMER
1963 *Ancient Law*. Boston: Beacon Press.
MARRIOTT, MCKIM
1969 "Western Medicine in Northern India." In Benjamin D. Paul (ed.), *Health, Culture and Community*, pp. 239-68. New York: Russell Sage Foundation.
MARTINDALE, DON
1966 *Institutions, Organizations, and Mass Society*. Boston: Houghton Mifflin Company.
MEAD, GEORGE H.
1934 *Mind, Self, and Society*, Charles W. Morris (ed.), Chicago: University of Chicago Press.

MINER, HORACE

1956 "Body Ritual Among the Nacirema." *American Anthropologist* 58:503-507.

MOTWANI, KEWAL

1947 *India: A Synthesis of Cultures*. Bombay: Thacker and Co.

OPLER, MORRIS E.

1963 "The Cultural Definition of Illness in Village India." *Human Organization* 22 : 32-35.

PARSONS, TALCOTT

1962 "Categories of the Orientation and Organization of Action." In Talcott Parsons and Edward A. Shils (eds.), *Toward a General Theory of Action*, pp. 53-109. New York: Harper and Row.

1964a *Essays in Sociological Theory*. New York: The Free Press.

1964b *The Social System*. New York: The Free Press.

READ, MARGARET

1966 *Culture, Health and Diseases*. London: Tavistock Publications.

REDFIELD, ROBERT

1969 "The Folk Society." In Richard Sennett (ed.), *Classic Essays on the Culture of Cities*, pp. 180-205. New York: Appleton Century-Crofts.

ROBINSON, DAVID

1971 *The Process of Becoming Ill*. London: Routledge and Kegan Paul.

RUBIN, VERA

1960 "Preface." In Franklin N. Furness (ed.), *Culture, Society, and Health*, pp. 787-88. New York: Annals of the New York Academy of Sciences.

RUDOLPH, LLOYD I. and SUSANNE H. RUDOLPH

1972 *The Modernity of Tradition*. Chicago: The University of Chicago Press.

SHAH, A.M.

1974 *The Household Dimension of Family in India*. Berkeley: University of California Press.

SIGERIST, HENRY E.

1960 *On the Sociology of Medicine*. M.I. Roemer (ed.). New York: M.D. Publications.

SINGER, MILTON

1972 *When a Great Tradition Modernizes*. New York: Praeger Publishers.

SOROKIN, PITRIM A.

1947 *Society, Culture and Personality*. New York: The Free Press.

SUSSER, MERVYN

1974 "Ethical Components in the Definition of Health." *International Journal of Health Services* 4:539-48.

TÖNNIES, FERDINAND

1957 *Community and Society*. Translated and edited by Charles P. Loomis. East Lansing: The Michigan State University Press.

WEBER, MAX

1947 *Theory of Social and Economic Organization*. Translated by A.M. Henderson and Talcott Parsons. New York: The Free Press.

ZBOROWSKI, MARK

1952 "Cultural Components in Responses to Pain." *Journal of Social Issues* 8:16-30.

EDWARD MONTGOMERY

LIFE HISTORIES OF MEDICAL PRACTITIONERS IN TAMIL NADU: AN APPROACH TO THE STUDY OF VARIATION

ABSTRACT. Perhaps the most striking characteristic of medicine in India today is the great variety of systems which are practiced. This chapter will present an analysis of the biographies of a group of medical doctors (practicing either Ayurveda, Siddha, Yunani, Homoeopathy, or "modern" medicine) as a way of identifying key features of variability in medical practice in a city in Tamil Nadu. Important changes in legislation, growth of public and private hospitals, expansion of pharmaceutical and chemical manufacturers, development of medical practitioners' associations, and changes in disease patterns and population are each reflected in details from these life histories. The overall aim of the chapter is to outline approach for relating the observed variability in medical practice to these factors and for suggesting which have been of greater importance in contributing to the widest ranges of variation.

TWO OF THE GREATEST PROBLEMS FOR THE HUMAN SCIENCES CONTINUE to be adequately describing the organization of human action and analyzing its effects. The many ways in which organization can be described—including ecologically (e.g., Anderson, 1974; Bennett, 1976b),cultural symbolically (e.g., Geertz, 1973), and social structurally (e.g., Barth, 1966; Beteille, 1977; Firth, 1954)—and its consequences detected—upon environment (e.g., Bennett, 1976b), in health (e.g., Audy, 1971; Audy and Dunn, 1974), and as adaptation (e.g., Alland, 1973; Bennett, 1976a)—tend to defy synthetic, integrative formulations (but, see Arensbert, 1972). Many an observer of the human scene has sought to contain the dispersive character of this knowledge through focus upon concentrated realms of activity. Numerous studies may be viewed in this manner, among them many concerned with the culture and practice of medicine.

Excerpts from Life Sequences as an Approach to the Organization of Medicine in India

Several of the recent studies of medicine and health care in South Asia can be interpreted as contributing to our knowledge of the organization of medical action. The works of Beals (1976), Leslie (1973, 1974, 1976), Madan (1969, 1972), Montgomery (1976), and Obeyesekere (1976) can be identified in this regard. However, in these as in most such studies, descriptive attention has been focused on the actions or ideologies of groups or populations of individuals: medical practitioners, institutions, and patients.

There is yet another domain for the description and analysis of cultural and societal organization: the individual human life sequence. Certain prominent studies have illustrated how the study of life histories can illuminate the structuring of social action and culture (e.g., Aberle, 1951; Mandelbaum, 1973). However, the potentials of this approach have been far less than fully realized. Kluckhohn's assessments of some of the opportunities which this approach offers, although they are now over three decades old, continue to retain their full force (Kluckhohn, 1945; Mandelbaum, 1973: 178-179). The sequence of individual life experiences may be examined to learn more about the structuring of culture, of status and role, of change, of variations in meanings, and of idiosyncratic and chance differences (Kluckhohn, 1945: 134-142). To these one might add that the approach offers much scope for study of how sequences of sociol-cultural structure are linked with one another and how they can constitute different phases in the life span. Further, the consequences of the organization of the life span can be studied in the experiences, the responses, the involvements and the detachments of the person who has lived them. Here, perhaps, a more clearly phenomenological outlook (e.g., Kaplan, 1968) may be conjointly pursued with utilitarian concerns. Finally, the approach presents rich prospects for yielding productive cross-cultural, cross-societal comparisons, as, for example of the ways that the phases or stages of life can be structured (see Buhler, 1968: 186; Erikson, 1968: 287; Mandelbaum, 1973: 180-181).

This article seeks to explore very preliminarily the possibilities for further understanding the organization of medicine and health care in India and South Asia through the study of individual life sequences. Here excerpts from transcripts of tape-recorded short biographical interviews with four traditional Indian medical practitioners are presented as a basis for analysis. The biographies were recorded and transcribed during 1968-1969 as part of a broadly focused research project on the practice of medicine and the providing of health care in northern Tamil Nadu, southern India. The study has been discussed elsewhere (Montgomery, 1974/1975, 1976). These four practitioners were part of the group of 76 privately practicing physicians within the municipal limits of the town of Vellore, North Arcot District (Montgomery, 1976), who, in turn, were among just over 100 such private medical practitioners in the greater Vellore area which had approximately 150,000 residents then. These particular practitioners and the several others chosen for the biographical interviews were so selected because they represented the prominent variants of local medical practice (Ayurveda, Yunani, Siddha, Homeopathy), and they were interested and willing to take the time to reflect on and discuss their lives. They were not randomly selected from the local practitioner population and thus their representativeness cannot be based on that statistical sampling procedure. However, their representativeness can be asserted on the basis of their demonstrable comparability with numerous characteristics typical of the whole population of private medical practitioners which I have already described (*Ibid.*). This comparison is illustrated clearly in Table 1. The biographically interviewed physicians probably were typical in one important respect: their more open reflectiveness. Prior to the biographical interview, each completed a lengthy, structured interview questionnaire concerning background, education, training, and medical practice (for details see Montgomery, 1976), and thereafter appointments were arranged for the semi-structured biographical interviews. Most of these short biographies were tape-recorded within two 1- to 3-hour sessions during parts of two days. The procedure for the interviews was designed by me, and the interviews were conducted by a co-researcher on the project, an experienced psychiatric social worker and interviewer, T. Vasanth Kumar. In his transcriptions, he sought to preserve fully the idom of expression for each interviews. In my editing of the transcripts, I have deleted passing remarks on momentary events, lengthy repetitive comments, and the elements of superficial conversation. The materials presented here clearly concentrate on aspects of the practitioners' lives pertinent to their medical careers, and the brevity of these excerpts precludes their being considered as life histories. It

TABLE 1

COMPARISON OF FOUR PRACTITIONERS WITH PATTERNS IN VELLORE PRACTITIONER POPULATION

Characteristics	*1*	*2*	*3*	*4*	*Vellore Pattern* (*N=76*)
Interviewed in	English	Tamil	T&E	Tamil	42% Tamil, 31% English, 27% T&E
Sex	Male	Male	Male	Male	95% Male, 5% Female
Age in years	42	58	60	40	6 is average; 47% are over 45
Married	Yes	Yes	Yes	No	93% are married
Birthplace	Madras	Vellore area	Vellore	Kerala	67% born in Vellore
First language	Urdu	Tamil	Tamil	Malayalam	68% use Tamil, 12% Urdu
Education	SSLC	5th Std.	SSLC	SSLC	63% have SSLC or higher
Medical college	No	No	No	No	78% never attended
Family medical tradition	Yes	Yes	Yes	No	38% have family tradition
Medical assn. memberships	None	None	None	None	37% have none
Clinic location	Separate	Home	Home	Home	71% have in own home
Has assistant	No	Yes	No	Yes	69% have none
Keeps records	Yes	No	Yes	No	64% keep none
Sends referrals	Yes	Yes	Yes	Yes	78% send referrals
Receives referrals	Yes	Yes	Yes	Yes	57% receive referrals
Prepares some medicines	Yes	Yes	Yes	Yes	53% prepare at least some
Gives Cosmopolitan medicines*	Yes	No	Yes	No	59% give at least some
Years practicing in Vellore	9	20	12	8	13 is average
Patients per day	10	5	5—6	5	15 is mode, 42% have 10 or fewer
Medical systems usually Practiced	Y,H,A,S,C	A	H,A	A,H	63% regularly use 2 or more systems; 58% use at least Homoeopathy

*Medical systems: Y (Yunani), H (Homoeopathy), A (Ayurveda), S (Siddha), C (Cosmopolitan, sometimes identified as "Allopathy" or "Western" medicine), T (Tamil) E (English).

should be noted that because assurance was given to the practitioners that their anonymity would be protected in all ensuing reports on the study, their actual names and those of their clinics, any possibly identifiable kin and associates, and affiliation have altered. Some details concerning the practitioners and their practices which were reported during the initial, structured interviews in 1968 are given to introduce each of the cases.

BIOGRAPHICAL EXCERPTS 1: DR. S. M. AHMED

Dr. S.M. Ahmed was born in Madras in 1926. He is a registered Yunani and Homoeopathic practitioner who practices Yunani, Homoeopathic, Ayurvedic, Siddha, and Cosmopolitan ("Allopathic") medicine. He treats an average of 10 patients daily at his Ahmed Clinic and is known locally for his general medical skills. He prepares some of the Yunani medicines that he dispenses, and he uses imported German Homoeopathic medicines sometimes. He belongs to no medical associations and has neither an automobile nor a telephone. In an interview in English of 26 November 1968 he spoke of his life in the following words.

"My parents lived in a small village called Tiruvadi in South Arcot District. It is in Tindivanam Taluk. We had land there. My grandfather was a Yunani Hakim, appointed by the Arcot Nawab. In those days, the Nawab used to give land to his family physicians, and the physicians used these lands for cultivation of food crops and so forth. So my grandfather was also a big landlord. But I was born in Madras. Because my paternal uncle had settled down in Madras City long ago and he and his wife and children were in Madras itself, my mother went and stayed at their house for the delivery. There I was born on the 3 November 1926. Even now I remember the house number, street, and city zone where I was born: no. 29, Moore Street, Madras-1.

"My parents came back to the village soon after my birth. My father was Headmaster of the Sinuvadi Elementary School at that time. He was practicing Yunani in those days. I was brought up well by my parents and studied at the same elementary school. After completing my elementary schooling, I joined the high school in Meenambur which is very near to my village. As ill luck would have it, I fell victim to smallpox. I suffered from smallpox for a long time, with the result that my eyesight got affected. This impaired by education to a great extent. My father took me to a number of eye specialists in Madras City, and at last I was treated by one Dr. Zakharia, a famous opthalmologist. He continued to give treatment for a couple of years. After a long span of time I regained my eyesight, and then only was I allowed to read my books. I was 12 at that time. Throughout these two or three years I had not been able to go to school. But my father never wasted his time or my time, as he started coaching me in our Islamic religious principles and other books. As I was unable to read them myself, he used to read aloud to me. I used to follow those lectures carefully and enthusiastically. As I already knew to read and write in Tamil, English, and Arabic from my elementary school days, I did not find it difficult to follow my father's lectures. I learned the Koran, the holy book of Islam, by heart. At my twelfth year, my father admitted me to the elementary school in Tindivanam. My father shifted the family from Sinuvadi to Tindivanam to help me to get better educational facilities. For a few months I had special tuition at home, and later I was admitted to the elementary school directly. I was given a seat in the fifth standard. I was attending classes regularly. I used to listen to what was being taught by the teacher. At home I would never study those lessons. But then I was shining well in the examinations. I was considered to be a very intelligent fellow. My father's ambition was to educate me to the maximum level. He had plans of sending me to Law College after I finished my general education.

"I used to assist my father in his clinic, and especially during his absence from the clinic I used to give necessary treatment to his regular patients. Thereby I grew in knowledge and wisdom in the medical as well as academic fields. Yunani seemed to be a sort of daily affair at home, and I never felt that it was a profession in those years.

"After I passed my SSLC, I did not want to continue my education as I feared that further studies would affect my eyes once again and that continuation of studies which meant studying hard might strain the eyes to a considerable extent. So I decided to join some polytechnic and study electronics and other subjects in which I was genuinely interested. In 1946 I joined the Indian Institute of Technology and Central Polytechnic at Madras and studied for about two or three years. Unfortunately I did not get through the examinations. But I had confidence in myself to start a business in radio and other electrical goods in Tindivanam. My father was appointed

Khasi, a religious welfare officer, a non-official gazetted rank, by the Government for South Arcot District in 1943. So Tindivanam had become a permanent place to settle down.

"I started my business in radio and electrical goods. Although the business showed some signs of prosperity. I speculated more and more, and then realized that I had been cheated by no worse a partner than my own friend. This resulted in a great financial loss for me, and I had to wind up my business immediately.

"Again I was confronted with problem of settling on a job. I did not know whether I should continue my studies or engage myself in a good professional line. Of course, the choice was mine. During this unsettle period, I evinced a keen interest in the Yunani books collected by my father. I started reading one after the other, as a pastime. Inwardly, that is, in my heart, I felt as though a spirit of confidence and new hope was kindled, and therefore I studied all those books on the Yunani system of practice, and whenever I had any doubts I consulted by father. All these books were in Urdu and Arabic.

"In 1952 I was once again contemplating to start a new business, but this idea did not materialize as I fell ill again. I was taken to specialists in Madras, and they diagnosed my illness as T.B. and advised that I be admitted to the Tambaram T.B. Sanatorium. I was in Tambaram T.B. Sanatorium for about five or six months. God had mercy on me in that I got completely cured of T.B. and was much more healthy at the time of my discharge from the sanatorium.

"During my hospitalization at Tambaram, I found myself interested in the various activities in the hospital performed by the doctors and nurses. This influenced my mind to the extent that I also wished to devote my life to the sacred professional field of medicine.

As soon as I returned to Tindivanam I wanted to become a doctor. I was aware that my educational background and family circumstances would not permit me to become an allopathic doctor. I came across an advertisement in a newspaper by the Kumbakonam Indian Institute of Homoeopathy offering postal tuition and also a diploma at the end of the course. Frankly, I joined the Kumbakonam Institute just to get the diploma and then register my name as a Homoeopathy practitioner, and in short, I wanted that I should be called "doctor." I could not find an easier way to become a doctor, and this was the only way out for my confused state of mind. But I put forth maximum interest and zeal in the homoeopathy course, and I secured the diploma A.M.I.H. in 1952.

Since 1952 I have been practicing homoeopathy and have found the system as one of the best and safest medical systems. Many a drug is very effective in curing illness. So I really appreciate the homoeopathy system.

"I was practicing at Tindivanam from 1952-1958. My father was also giving a lot of guidance in my practice. After I studied homoeopathy and got the diploma, I used homoeopathic drugs as frequently as possible.

"Later on I shifted to Vellore. My father was growing old, I had two grown-up sisters who had completed high school, and in Tindivanam there was no good college for ladies. One of my brothers-in-law was in Vellore, and he advised me to settle down here itself so that I could admit my sisters in the local woman's college. As per his advice I decided to come over here, and at last I found a good house in this locality, which was conducive to setting up my practice. The clinic is separate from the house, on the next street over. I opened my clinic on 1st May 1959. During the initial stages of my practice, it was very dull. Later on I found that my practice was improving day by day.

"I got married in 1961. Now I have four children, three girls and one boy. My wife is also from our own family. Her father is a L.I.M. working at a Government medical center in Madras. My eldest daughter is showing keen interest in the medical field. Sometimes she helps in picking up this and that for me, and if I go out anywhere, she is able to dispense the drugs to the regular patients as per my instructions. She is only 7. Still, she is very bright for her age. I wish that my only son becomes a lawyer. In my family I want my son to do law and become the ablest advocate.

"In Islam we are supposed to pray daily five times. Being a medical practitioner, I do not find time to pray five times a day. So as soon as I get up from my bed I say my morning prayer, and before I go to bed I say my night prayers. In my family we do not go to mosques every week. From my childhood I was brought up with a good religious background by my father. Even now I like the Koran very much because of its applicability to modern life.

"I have a number of successful cases to my credit. I have met with failures too during my practice. Although these failures make me feel awfully bad, I gain much more experience as I consider them as lessons. I will never get discouraged or panic over the unfavorable results. I try my best to help such patients to seek better medical aid from a private doctor or a hospital, and I assist them in getting admission and other things to my level best.

"I once had bed arrangements in my clinic for inpatients. Now I do not provide any such facilities. I have a well-furnished examination room and separate waiting rooms for men and women in my clinic. I have a good stock of medicines: Siddha, Ayurveda, Allopathic, Yunani, and Homoeopathic. Mostly I dispense Yunani, and of secondary importance I use Homoeopathy and Allopathy. I do not have any one to assist me in my dispensary. Two leading lady doctors in the Allopathic field send children's cases to me frequently. No Yunani doctor sends cases to me, nor do I have any relationship with them. Normally for my visits I charge Rs 2 during the day, Rs 3 during the night hours. About 75 to 100 patients are given free medical aid every month.

"You know, I am a family man. So I cannot stick to one particular system of practice. Depending upon the nature of my client, I use various drugs each time. I use Siddha and Ayurveda drugs, and sometimes I use Allopathy drugs. But mostly I am using Yunani and Homoeopathy drugs. For major illnesses which may require immediate relief, I use Allopathic drugs or injections, as the case may be.

"Yunani and Ayurveda systems have many common features between them. In both systems herbal medicines are being used. The most important and fundamental difference between Yunani and Ayurveda is that non-vegetarian extracts are used in the preparation of certain Yunani drugs, whereas in Ayurveda such extracts are never used. Otherwise, in almost every other drug is used a combination of fruits, roots, herbs, leaves, nuts, honey, and similar ingredients.

"Allopathy is a fine system of medicine. The whole world is behind this system. Large funds are spent on the research and development fields in Allopathy.

"If a large amount of money were spent for the development of Yunani, this would surely increase its scope to a great extent also. But for the preparation of Yunani drugs, one should buy the required ingredients in bulk quantities, and this is too costly for the Yunani practitioner. The patient should consume his drugs in large quantities, and the effect of these medicines would be evident after a long time. Hence Yunani is not liked by many. Also, amongst Yunani practitioners (Hakims) a good relationship does not exist as amongst Allopathic practitioners. All the Yunani practitioners maintain a secrecy about certain formulae of Yunani drugs. By nature they are accustomed to develop this sort of behavior pattern.

"The Ayurveda system is also a good one in the sense that if the patient takes Ayurveda drugs regularly for a long time, he will be cured of his ailment. But Siddha is a bit dangerous system in the sense that the preparation of Siddha drugs is a very difficult process. You should be extremely vigilant over the ratio or quantity of the various metals, acids, and arsenic used in this process. The Siddha practitioner should take all these risks involved into consideration before administering Siddha drugs to his patients.

"In Homoeopathy we can be sure that there would not be relapse of the illness. But in Allopathy this is not so. The permanent cure can be derived only from Yunani and Homoeopathy."

Biographical Excerpts 2: Dr. P.K. Nagaswamy

My native place is a village not far from Vellore. I studied up to the fifth standard. My village had one elementary school up to that standard only. I was taught civics, science, history, hygiene, mathematics, and religious subjects. I know Tamil, I learned Telugu, but I do not know English. I am Komutti Chettiar by caste. My father was a merchant. He had a small shop dealing with provisions like salt, chillies. I was assisting my father after school hours. In addition he was practicing medicine. I used to powder tablets, grind medicines in the grinding mill, and assist him in such odd jobs in the preparation of medicines. My father also had a medical store. My mother knew preparation of medicines to a small extent. I was assisting both. My parents were highly religious. I had a tuft for a long time. I removed it only after several years without the knowledge of my parents. I was more attached to my mother. My father used to get angry every now and then. Even then my father would tell me that I should turn out to be a good man. He would give me instructions as to how I should be charitably disposed towards one and all, and all the fundamentals and the techniques of charity. It was for my own welfare and interest that he scolded me. I realized this only after the death of my father.

I was studying in the fifth standard when my father died. He died at the age of 70 due to old age, not due to any sickness. After the death of my father the family responsibility and maintenance fell on my shoulders as my elder brother was very irresponsible. In my 10th year I stopped going to school. In my 14th year I went to Bombay, later to Bangalore where my relatives advised me to open a jewellery shop, and then to Bellary. During the year 1942 I had very good business at Bellary. I greatly improved my financial position. During the year 1944 I established my jewellery shop in the Commissary Bazaar at Vellore. I had a business in rolled gold. In my business I had to utter lies then and there. I did not like the practice of being a liar. I lost everything in the shop and by about 1946 I became poverty stricken. In 1948 after closing the jewellery shop I opened the medical dispensary. For all patients I tried the cases by feeling the pulse, studying the disease, and then giving medicines. Then, God's will . . . My first medicines prepared in Ayurveda were medicines for fighting T.B. germs. Mother was telling me every now and then to concentarte my attention on medical profession and continue the hereditary treatment. She was also telling me of the principles of charity. In my medical profession I was practicing with conscience and with fear.

"In 1959 my mother died of cancer. She was admitted to the hospital for radium therapy, and was bed-ridden there for a long time. She was discharged and after a lapse of 90 days she died. When my mother was laid up and was nearing her end, she called me by her bedside and told me as follows: 'do not abandon the charitable medical profession and if any marriage alliance party comes to you readily offering you a bride for your prospective marriage, do not stand in the way of the marriage celebration.' When she spoke tears were flowing in her eyes. I sobbed and promised her that I would carry out her two wishes. I was penniless, and in our caste a man cannot get a bride unless he is rich. So nobody would give me a daughter in marriage. My wife is not of my caste. It was an intercaste marriage. The girl's mother oftentimes approached me saying that she had a daughter who was not married for want of a suitable bridegroom. My numerous friends collected and donated a sum of nearly Rs 2000 for my marriage expenses. It was a reformed marriage. Several friends attended the wedding. All castes were represented. All things happened due to my late lamented mother. I married only for the sake of fulfilling my promise to my mother.

"I believe in God and do everything according to his decrees and wishes. There is nothing in our action. He protects my entire family. We are preparing medicines. It should be a good manufactured product. If God has no mind our efforts may become waste and turn into cinders.

"I was 38 years old when I entered the medical profession. I studied Ayurvedic medicine further through a postal tuition course from Hyderabad. I got postal tuition in the Telugu language and got a diploma in Ayurveda and a certificate as a Registered Medical Practitioner. Also, my father has written books and I am easily following them. My grandfather has written books and I am following these also. I learned Allopathy from an L.I.M. doctor in Puthur. He has given me a certificate.

"Cases which I can undertake and do successfully, I take. Otherwise I will direct them to attend the hospitals. Some doctors consult me for doubts. I will give them my opinion and clear their doubts. I can give injections. I do not perform operations as I am not efficient at it. I will give English or Allopathic medicines. I spend an average of Rs 500 monthly for preparing medicines and meeting the cost of the dispensary charges. I get herbs and plants, etc., from the hill villagers from the adjoining hill villages in Vellore Taluk. I pay money to the tribals and get the medicinal plants. All the medicinal preparations are named after my father and mother, and they will be distributed at the time of the annual ceremony for my father and mother as these days are considered very auspicious in our family for the distribution of medicines. My father's and mother's names have been adopted for medicines because nails, hair, and rheumatism are connected with my father, and blood, fatness, muscles, vitality, and heart are connected with my mother. Among my preparations, I prepare medicines for asthma and T.B.

"In Siddha, every preparation should be scrupulously clean. If anything is incorrectly mixed or prepared, everything will go wrong and become a waste. Such preparations will cause danger to the patients. There are the best medicines for blood pressure in Siddha. Because I have not adopted Siddha, it should not mean that I have contempt for Siddha medicines. Rather, if anything is unclean, disproportionate or imperfect, loss of life is involved. But in Ayurveda, it is harmless medicine. It is made up of purely herbal leaves and plants.

"My wife will assist me and will give medicines only in emergency cases like snake bite or scorpion stings. She will give green leaves which I have prescribed for such poisonous insects. Other medicines she will not have in stock. I do not give such medicines to her. My mortal fear is that my wife may give wrong medicines in her absent-mindedness and that I may have to worry for the same at a later stage. Even grinding medicines I do not trust to my wife as she may not put medicine in proper ratio and grind the required number of times.

"We should examine the patients visually. We should treat them to the best of our knowledge. If that is impossible, we should ask the patient to get such and such a medicine and to see such and such a doctor for his treatment. As I am an expert in the feeling of pulse, I will give proper medicines to the patients after feeling pulse. I will tell patients to avoid sexual intercourse for some time as the vital power which is important for the killing of germs may be lost. We should not inform the patients the name of the diseases and the nature of the disease they are suffering. It is not our family custom. If we tell the name of the disease and give him that medicine, the patient may get dejected. We may as well cut him into pieces and butcher him with a knife. Never in our lives will we reveal the name of the disease to the patients. By telling them the disease names we are leading the patients to the hands of God Yama.

"A doctor should have patience and cheerfulness. He should not get angry with anybody. If any doctor is bent upon money as his only consideration, he may not prosper. That is my principle. If money comes to me as fees for my professional service, it is God's will. If the patients do not give me money for my professional services, I am not worried. Some patients will say that my family and children should prosper and live happily, and that blessing is enough for me. In respect of fees, I will not compel patients to pay. If anybody willingly gives, I will receive. The practice among people is this: they will spend all their money on big doctors in big hospitals. By this time their diseases are aggravated. By this time they will have no money and then only they will rush to me for treatment.

"If anybody is actually interested to learn how to prepare medicines I will encourage him and give him detailed instructions. I have got three children, one son and two daughters. I am doing this profession as the eighth generation, and my son will also take up the same hereditary profession in the ninth generation. Whatever medicines I give and whatever practice I follow I am writing in a book so that my son may follow. After my generation I will hand over the book of medicines written by me to my son for his observance and guidance."

BIOGRAPHICAL EXCERPTS 3: DR. N. RAMA RAJ

I was born, educated, employed in Vellore and retired here also. I am now aged 60 years. I have got full experience in the medical line. My father, grandfather, and great grandfather, all of them were employed in Siddha and Ayurvedic systems of medicine. They were very successful in their careers and gained mature experience in the medical profession. My father served in the Health Department. Even though he served in the Public Health Department, he had an attachment to the Ayurvedic system of medicine, and my father and my entire family advocated Ayurvedic medicines and were handling this system of medicines and medical practice only. He was not enamored of money, and he did not do any act purely with the intention of getting money or amassing wealth. He did not practice Ayurvedic system expecting income from this, but he had an attachment towards this, and he and his family members were accustomed to this system of medicine only. For the sake of general welfare and ensuring public health and as a daily routine, he practiced Ayurvedic system of medicine in a useful manner as a service to the public. He served as an Assistant Health Officer in municipalities. While serving in Cochin state and Andhra state, he took to the medical profession also, and simultaneously was engaged the medical field along with his job in municipal service. Even in my school days, when I was free at home and at leisure, my father would give instructions to grind certain medicines in the grinding machines, to pick out marked medicines and specified drugs as required by my father for his clients. All these contributed to my selecting the medical profession, and I was very eager to learn medicine and to further pursue my studies for settling in the profession. I began to learn all the various medicinal herbs and to acquire experience. Several Ayurvedic doctors would see my father and would discuss the various aspects of Ayurvedic medicine. I would listen to their talk and would recollect their deliberations in an eager manner. At times they would have differences of opinion with my father in regard to Ayurvedic and Siddha medicines. During their deliberations and discussions and differences of opinion on the two systems, they revealed certain new truths which helped me to understand all the intricacies in the two systems and also the correct methods and truthful results in them. When I became an adult and settled in it permanently, I made up my mind accordingly. There were certain family difficulties which prevented me from joining the Allopathic system of medicine. Hence I did not study Allopathy system and settle down as an Allopathic doctor. Therefore I stopped my education at that end. I joined Government service in 1933. From then onwards, I had my practice at home. My father recorded some entries and professional notes. I assisted my father when he was engaged in the medical profession, and side by side I also learned professional matters. All these helped me in good stead, and I began to prepare certain specified medicines and drugs during my leisure hours at home, and all the time I was usefully employed. I began to give medicines free of charge to the patients coming to my house and also free professional service to them. I would not approach the patients and demand money from them either for services rendered or for the preparation of medicines. I would not compel them to pay money. If anybody came to me and insisted that I should receive money towards the cost of preparation of drugs and the value thereof at least, only in such cases would I receive money. I would attend to my patients with eagerness and meticulous care at all times of the day. Patients could come to me at any time requiring medical care and attention. I would immediately treat such patients with zeal and would render them all medical services and facilities available with me.

"As I was employed under Government service, I was transferred to several places. I served at Tiruvannamalai for a period of 12 years and in the Tirupattur area for a period of seven years. Along with Government duties where I was employed, I had my private medical practice continuously and simultaneously also. The latter was a side profession. I continued my medical practice privately in places like Ranipet and Gudiyattam. In places like Tiruvannamalai and Tirupattur I was leading very good practice and was enjoying my profession in fairly useful and sound manner with the public support. I hung up a notice board in front of my house indicating the location of my dispensary. The well-wishers in Tiruvannamalai and Tirupattur towns advised me to resign from Government service permanently and to set up my private medical practice there. They insisted that I should have permanent medical practice.

"I retired from Government service in July 1968, and since then I have wanted to continue my private practice regularly, and I have determined to set up the same in an efficient manner. Side by side I am running a Madras Homoeopathic Institute. My intention is that I want to admit as many educated people who have got enthusiasm to learn Homoeopathy, to give them six months training in Homoeopathy, and to send them on as doctors. With this object in view, I am running the school for the training of Homoeopathic doctors. I opened the institute in the year 1959 in this town. But I am running the institute in a wholehearted manner ever since my retirement in July 1968. I am now confined to medical profession and concentrate my full energy on this only. I award Diplomas in the name of the Madras Homoeopathic Institute under my own responsibility, and I get the Collector's recognition and assistance for the procedure. I am giving practical training also.

"I am now 60 years old, and engaged in medical profession for the past 30 years. I want to live for another 100 years and render medical service. This is my desire. Any help possible I will render to my friends and officials at any time if they need my help and come to me.

"In my medical practice during the past 30 years there were no cases of failure in the cases undertaken by me. If I feel doubtful of any case, I will direct the patient to go to an adjoining hospital and take treatment. To that end I give them good facilities and make convenient arrangements.

"I have got full belief in Ayurveda and Siddha medicines. Frequently I am doing research work in Ayurvedic practice. My forefathers (father, grandfather, etc.) all have written notes of Ayurvedic and Siddha medicines. I am practicing their notes and adopting procedures as outlined in the notes. I have got further notes written up by Siddhas in manuscripts. Unless there is strong Tamil foundation, we cannot understand the medical notes writteen by various Siddha doctors and put them into practice with ease. Medical men of those days were very good scholars in Tamil literature. Today medical notes written by our old educated veteran Siddhas in Tamil appear very difficut to follow. Today people who sell tablets for purgatives and nothing else pose themselves as doctors who can cure diseases. If this state of affairs continues any further, the growth and popularity of Ayurvedic medicines and also Siddha medicines will disappear in the long run.

"I want to make further researches and advances in medicine and still further improve the medical science considerably. I am now given new and extra strength and energy to go still further and find out the hidden truths. I am very much interested to develop my practice. I have planned to open two dispensaries and run both the same. First of all I am arranging to open a dispensary at Sethuvalai. Some big men of the place are encouraging me and are cooperating with me. I have not located a suitable site in the area. If I could secure a place, I would open the dispensary today and stock it with medicines as I have got a stock of Ayurvedic medicines which will last for about 1½ years. Secondly, I want to open a dispensary in Saidapet at Sankaramatam. The reasons for these ventures are that the people in these areas have no ample medical facilities. Therefore I am determined to open a Free Homoeopathic Dispensary at Sankaramatam. Besides, in this area there was a prominent figure who was living in good popularity, and hence I want to open a Homoeopathic dispensary in his name. I am making arrangements to achieve my long-felt need. The dispensary will be opened very soon. I have planned to accept donations alone. People who are well placed in life can purchase Homoeopathic medicines and keep them in stock as the cost price of the preparations is very cheap.

"In Homoeopathy there are good medications and good procedures and sound diagnosis. Some Homoeopathy institutes give postal tuition after receiving Rs 120 or Rs 150 as a fee and then send the diploma to the trainees after some months. People who have undergone the course have their diplomas duly framed and open a dispensary. They are not capable of diagnosing correctly. It is not possible also. Because their course of training is such. As the chemists and druggists sell Allopathic medicines in their shops to the people for various ailments, so also these so-called doctors do not know anything except prescribing Aspro for headache and Saridon for cough. They do not diagnose, and their practice is in such a fashion. In fact, Homoeopathy, so far as I am concerned, I can advocate and boldly say that the same is the best system of medicine in the world. Several kinds of tablets are prepared. Anybody can take. Cheapest treatment. Easiest treatment. Harmless drugs. No fear of reactions or side-effects. But our state has not recognized Homoeopathy as yet. If the system is recognized, the standard will greatly increase, and the medical profession will show remarkable advance with good possibilities and potentialities in years to come.

"In Ayurveda, medicines effect cure in the long run. Hence Ayurvedic medicines cure chronic cases and such chronic patients need the same. This is one truth gained from my experience. In Allopathy certain medicines control the disease rapidly. Besides in Allopathy daily research is taking place and fresh good drugs and medications are prepared. In Ayurveda there are opportunities for sound research but sufficient facilities do not exist. All Ayurvedic medicines if their potency is increased according to Homoeopathic practice will respond successfully. In Allopathy side-effects are many, but there are no side-effects in Ayurveda or Siddha or Homoeopathy. They are harmless. But slow and steady cure."

BIOGRAPHICAL EXCERPTS 4: DR. T. KRISHNAMURTHY

When I was between 17-18 years old, the resolution to join medical profession was deeply planted in my mind. My mother is responsible for this. I was reading in school. My mother was practicing Ayurveda system, and she was treating poor patients of the locality free of charge. During her menstrual period she would call me and direct me to take medicines and annoy me. She would say "Take that medicine, take this medicine," and in this way she would be constantly worrying me during the menses periods. At times I would become angry, get wild and protest and be disinclined to hear her words, especially when I had to attend daily games and sports in the school playground. I would scold my mother in the following way: "For each and everything why should you summon me?" Due to my young age and hot temper I would get angry at my mother frequently. Even then I would be assisting my mother as I am bound to help my mother. My father died when I was three years old. One day my mother was very angry and scolded me in the following manner: "You, my young child, this medical profession is going to feed you and finance you. When you grow up you are going to become a leading doctor. Then only will you get good prospects, good status, and your daily food." What she said that day out of anger has become true. Her scoldings harvested the desired results. Today I owe my existence on account of my mother, and even today whenever I take my food I think of my mother whom I consider to be my God and then only take my food.

About the age of 21 I had a desire to got out of my homeland and see various foreign places and their people and their activities. I left my house out of anger saying that this medical profession will not help me to get my daily food and did not consider that the medical profession will be my life saver. I started from my native place and reached Tiruneveli. I took refuge in a house in the town. The owner of the house was also a doctor. Only after getting accommodation in the house I came to know of this. I was there for six months. He did not train me in the medical practice. I did not like to learn from him. After six months I left for Tiru-chchirapalli. I took room in a washerman's house at Vannarpet, and for the purpose of earning my daily bread when without any job whatsoever, I began to spend my time in the medical profession as per instructions given by my mother and out of the experience gained by me from my mother. First of all I was diagnosing various diseases of the children who attended my dispensary for medical treatment. I treated several children with success and as a result I got good income and my popularity also spread. As I got good name and good sum in my professional practice, and as I was getting success after success, I wanted to establish my medical practice still further. I wanted to study further all the intricacies and learn the profession and diagnose various ailments. I was ambitious to fulfill my objectives. Such a desire arose from my mind.

"Subsequently, I worked as an assistant under Dr. T.A. Mathuram who was running Guru Vaidya Dispensary at Tiruchi. After working there for a period of one or two years, I came away to Rasipuram town of Salem District. There I roamed about various villages for my medical practice, and I was fully employed in my medical profession there. Then I came to Theerthagiri Hill Forests of Harur Taluk (Dharmapuri District) and settled there for over a period of five years. I was living with the Samiyars in Theerthagiri Hills as they were residing there. I spent my time in Vedanta and divinely powers and enriched my knowledge of these subjects as a result of my close acquaintance with the Samiyars. I would be putting questions, arguing with them on Vedanta, Divine powers, etc. Side by side I enumerated all the medicinal plants and herbs in the hills and began to do research and experiments on their healing powers and peculiar functions and their marvellous action. From there I proceeded to places like Marandahalli, Paparapatti, Palacode, and I stayed in the villages for some time. My life was spent in this way: going to a village, staying there for some time, and then moving to another village. This was in the year 1952. I travelled in villages in Salem District, and I spent several days in almost all villages there. From my young age I was very fond of seeing various places and gaining fresh and varied experiences in such places. My principle was to see one village, then make a journey to some other place. In this way I could acquire different experiences as are observed in the villages. Another thing: I learned medical profession out of my own efforts and not through anybody's training or pushing up. I wanted to improve my knowledge, and I had a desire to experiment with new drugs and new herbs and medicinal plants, to find out various herbs, use them on patients and meet with success in my proposed venture. If I was invited by the relatives of the patients in adjoining villages to come to see them, I decided that I should get appropriate fees for seeing them in their houses or I should have an opportunity to study new experience, fresh truths about the herbs and medicinal plants available in the various villages. Hence my object in touring different villages was not with the idea of increasing my professional income, but with the object of finding out fresh hidden truths in the medical profession. There were special opportunities and ample scope to learn fresh things and gain fresh truths and varied experience.

"I toured in Marandahalli and other villages for a period of three years (1952-1955), and then left for the Javadi Hills situated in North Arcot District. I heard that important medicinal herbs were in those hilly areas. In the hills I toured in the villages Puliyur, Mambatti, Mathiyampatti, Kathiripatti, Kambalaihill villages. I collected medicinal herbs. With the help and guidance of the hill villagers there I toured in the forests for a number of days only by foot. There if you say you are a doctor, several people will rush to you and encircle you. So also it happened in my case. When I said I was a doctor, all people assembled. I practiced there and gave medicines to the patients. I served them. I began to talk about some important herbs. If anybody knew a particular herb and had knowledge of its uses, I began to talk with him to know the place where the herb was growing, and with the assistance of the hill villager I began to collect the same. To achieve my object, I would finance the hill villagers by giving one or two rupees and also give them money for their food and other incidental expenses for their journeys. They would have satisfaction. For myself, I was happy in that I had obtained success in the medical field. In this way I had several opportunities of knowing about several medicinal herbs during my tours in the hill villages.

Subsequently, after journeying in several places and after spending a period of nearly three years in Javadi Hill villages I reached Sathanur. The construction of Sathanur Dam had been taken up in 1952, and the scheme was implemented by then. Nearly 15,000 laborers were working on the dam spot. I was the only doctor there. I worked day and night and earned a lot of money. But that money hoarded by me was only shortlived and did not remain with me. There I spent nearly Rs 4000 in connection with my marriage celebrations. Though I invested such a huge sum, the marriage did not last long. On the fifteenth day after marriage, divorce took place. I incurred a very heavy financial loss. Since I had earned a reputation and name and become popular, I would have settled at Sathanur itself permanently along with my wife. But after my recently wedded wife divorced me, I did not want to live there any longer as my conscience did not permit me. Once again I wished to lead a fresh and new life, and I left Sathanur and reached Vellore. I met K.V. Rajan, owner of a chemist's and druggist's shop. He requested me to settle at Vellore itself, to prepare Ayurveda medicines, and to supply him as and when required by him. Ever since 1960 under his support I have received raw materials from him for the manufacture and preparation of medicines, and with this stock I have prepared various medications to supply K.V.R. and also other medical shops. Each proprietor put his own label on the respective medical bottles and packets, etc., and sold the medicines. Gradually I stopped supplying medicines to the shops, and quite recently I have completely stopped.

"From the beginning of my 26th year up to the beginning of my 31st year I was practicing and undergoing training in Ayurveda under P.S. Varier of Kottakkal. He gave me practical training and taught me as to how the tablets and capsules should be prepared. They should be prepared by a formula. One should not take up their preparation unless you have all the ingredients as specified in the formula. If an ingredient is added in a lesser quantity, that medicine will not be useful and will not give the desired result. Giving such medicine to a patient is a great sin. My learned tutor, Dr. P.S. Varier, advised me to work in an impartial manner. He also advised that in preparing medicines, I should do as prescribed in the formula. I am bearing this in mind even today, and when preparing medicines I abide by his instructions and act according to his sound advice. Several stocks for preparation of medicines are lying idle for want of the required quantity of the component parts. I am always adhering to my revered guru's instructions faithfully.

"In 1948-49 I studied Homoeopathy and Ayurveda in Dr. Murthy's Homoeopathic and Ayurvedic Institute in Kanchipuram. I had undergone training privately by postal tuition from Madras Homoeo Hall for about one year. I read Homoeopathy by getting notes from this institute by post.

"My father served as an Executive Engineer in Government service. My mother was practicing Ayurvedic system of medicine in a successful manner. My mother's father and grandfather were Ayurvedic doctors by profession hereditarily. At present, my mother's brother is having professional practice as a doctor at Trivandrum. My mother died only in the year 1960 all of a sudden. I was a most unlucky person in that I was not by her bedside at the time of her last days and I could not feed and give her drinking water through mouth as was expected of a son for his mother at the time of her death. At the critical hour of learning of my mother's death I was put to another acid test by God. All of a sudden three women came to my dispensary carrying a 10-year-old girl in their arms and they placed the girl on the floor of my dispensary. The girl's mother said "The daughter is suffering from delirium and she is having symptoms of delirium. Please save her life." I was under a shock on hearing the sad news of the death of my mother, and I was sitting with tears in my eyes. Seeing this, the girl's mother asked "Doctor, sir, why are you unhappy? What has happened for your present sadness?" I said, "nothing. Some mental worry." So comforting myself I began to diagnose the patient's disease and concentrated my efforts on giving relief and effecting recovery of the patient from her illness. The temperature of the patient decreased, and the patient was recovering gradually. The mother placed Rs 2 on my office table and said, "All your mental worries will be over and end in good. As you have saved my daughter from the present catastrophe, so also God should save you fully from your present worries." As I had the consolation of the patient's mother at the time of my grief, I obtained some mental relief and once again took my seat on the chair. At this point I was imagining in my mind that it is very easy to utter 'duty' by mouth, but we are now in a state where we do not know where we stand, and in this condition God has employed us in new environments to face new experiences. In this condition whoever approaches us for our assistance and help we should render suitable assistance to them according to our capacity and we should render suitable assistance to them according to our capacity and we should satisfy their requirements. We should not expect any reward or remuneration, but we should revert to our old circumstances and render professional service to the suffering humanity. This is what is called 'sense of duty'. Whenver we perform any duty or action, we should not expect any remuneration or any gain, and we should act on our own accord. Then only it is sense of duty. If we expect what will be the resultant benefits, it is not duty but actual trade or business enterprise. Anticipating anything from our action and then entering upon our duties will not help us even to the extent we expected. Therefore, according to my ideal, whenever we perform any duty or render any service, we should have the sense of duty not expecting any material gain or result, and we should not give room for any feeling in our duty as we do in trade purposes. We are duty bound to do some act, and with that feeling, we must execute the act. The money we get, the fame and good words which we get are all results of our action, but there are all trivial and insignificant ones which lead you to feel happy and be proud for a moment. When these are compared to your duty performed without waiting for the result, this is only dust and rubbish. For the present, I consider my medical professional practice as the first duty. The fees offered by the patients out of their own free will, I consider as my professional income and I discharge my duties accordingly. So far as time permits, I am taking part in the divine and religious functions such as *bhajanas, ratha kalakshepam*, going to temple for worship, etc., for the past six seven years. As the learned Tamil scholar Vallalar has said, my debt is to serve. I am serving my duty accordingly, and I serve the masses as in duty bound.

"I have travelled in many places have a good knowledge of various medical drugs and their preparations and also the various systems of medical profession. I have spent 29 years of service so far in the medical profession. Given my advanced age, I do not want in the future to amass wealth or name or fame. All those desires to earn money and hoard riches have vanished from my mind completely. All these sudden changes are due to my old age. I have got property in my native town, and also landed property and wealth and with these I can lead a life of happiness and luxuriant living. In spite of all these moveable and immoveable properties, I do not want to lead a life of happiness and prosperity. I prefer to live in a hut. Living in a single room gives me mental peace and rest. Just now please look here: if you remove the curtain in my dispensary room, in the back portion there is a room wherein I have stored the utensils and the various provisions required for kitchen purposes and my bedding, easy chair and library books. All these present a house-like appearance. The front portion of the room, I have kept the almirah containing medicines, medicinal bottles, empty bottles, and various medications, and also I have placed a bench, chair, and table. All these for the dispensary, to present a dispensary appearance. I am a single soul here. For myself alone this single room has got all facilities like a dwelling house. All the necessary facilities are available in my dispensary room. I have got several friends, and all of them have helped me a good amount and allowed me to live in this prosperous condition. For spending my time I have got friends, a few gossiping friends, some lazy people who will encircle me and waste my time by their usual pranks, good people, bad people, then people who come to me for medical aid and treatment including males, females, and children. Also people who come to me and consult me beforehand before purchasing a house, lands, gardens, trees, and cattle, and other people who come to me for suitable matches for their daughters and sons. And, those people who come to me for consultations of horoscopes, astrology, palmistry. All the above are my friends, and they have kept me in a happy position.

"In the present happy circumstances I grow in age day by day, and I am spending my life without any laziness or tiresomeness or vexation. I do not want to earn money or fame in my present medical profession. I have learnt a lot in the medical profession, and I have had very many experiences in the above field. If a student who has got interest to learn this with fervor comes forward and enquires of me, I have to teach him a lot about my medical profession and the very many experiences I have tackled. The trainee should be very successful in the profession like myself. He should also conduct himself in the same way as I have towards the poor masses. He should understand the difficulties of the poor, their position, their bodily ailments, and should render them suitable medical aid and deal with them in honest and fair ways. I have got such an ideal to fulfil. Up until now, I have not come across such a student who can fulfil my ideal in my present life.

"What I wish for is that I want to tour in a few places for a few more days to learn of new medicinal herbs, their preparations, and methods of treatment. What all I have learnt in the medical field I should jot them down in writing and record entries in a book form. The method of preparation of various medicines and how to use on patients should also be written up along with my experiences so far gained in the medical profession. All these should be bundled up and put into one gunny bag. I have to select a deserving man from among people who I come across, and to hand over this bag to the most fit man saying, 'take this bag and go through the same, and read the experiences in the medical field, be a medical practitioner and lead a happy life with your family in the medical profession. You should think that your duty in the medical profession is your foremost and first duty and that to which you should be sincerely devoted.' So far as I am concerned, I want only contentment. I have no desire to earn money and hoard riches by saying I am a doctor. I want to be aloof and reserved and discharge my professional duties."

COMMENTS

Some comments on these four life sequences should now be made. However, these few remarks are obviously not exhaustive, and it is my hope they and the practitioners' own accounts will serve to stimulate further analyses by others.

The challenges that these or any documents of life sequences pose are: fitting them to an adequate description of life as a continuous process with stages or phases and satisfactorily explaining it. Looking over these brief excerpts, one can reasonably ask if there are enough pieces available to know what sort of puzzle they might form. In my opinion, these short biographical narratives do provide sufficient evidence to discuss these cases as meaning-rich sides of the lives of four men deeply engaged in the practice of medicine. In other words, these cases illustrate the significance and meaning that medical practice has for these men. The accounts clearly do not provide much information about what meanings medicine, as they practice it, has for their family, their patients, or others. Perhaps most importantly, these excerpts do provide some valuable perspective on the social and cultural structuring of private medical practitioners' lives in this region of India.

These four sets of biographical excerpts persuasively demonstrate that the social and cultural organization of the private practitioner's life is essentially multifaceted. The nature of the practice of medicine in this setting is at once an extremely social, interactional endeavor just as it is also highly individualized and self-maintaining. These practitioners are simultaneously beneficiaries of a formal, ascribed, hereditary role tradition and informal, achieved, self-determined life experiences. Their having taken up medicine seems almost to have been predetermined and yet, just as distinctively, their lives are the products of retrospectively identifiable unpredictable, chance events. In decision terms, their career choices can be traced to parental influences as well as to their own emergent commitments. The skills they manifest partly have been taught to them by others and partly have derived from their own practical clinical experiences. The medications they employ in their practices are both genuinely indigenous and foreign in character. Their actions are partially governed by both ancient Indian concepts of duty and legal provisions regarding medical registration and drugs derivative from the colonial context. Their livelihood is less a profession than an occupation, and neither term is fully apt. Likewise, their work is in some ways a business and perhaps in more, a charity, but it is not simply either one or a combination of both. Their position in life is respectable and at the same time, somewhat uncertain. At points, each of their lives appears traditional, but also, there is no doubt that all are definitely modern. In less complicated ways, certain of these features have been reported for medical practice in other regions of India. T.N. Madan has noted the joint character of career decision-making and the business or trade-like professionalism in Ghaziabad, Uttar Pradesh (Madan, 1972: 88-90, 93-94). Several authors have described the joint use of traditional and cosmopolitan medicines by traditional medical practitioners in different Indian states including Kerala (Neumann *et al.* 1971) Punjab (Neumann *et al.*, 1971; Bhardwaj, 1975), Delhi, Haryana, Madhya Pradesh, Rajasthan, and Uttar Pradesh (Chuttani *et al.*, 1973; Bhatia *et al.*, 1975).

An equally definitive correlative conclusion that these biographies support is that such private medical practitioners are decidedly *not* professionalized in the usual sociological sense of the term. These physicians certainly are not concerned to wield social or political-legal influence to regulate practice or education in medicine. Indeed, by example their lives contribute to an open, informal, exploratory, incorporating sort of medicine which is primarily individually-controlled insofar as it is regulated at all. Notwithstanding this fact that their medicine is so strongly individualized, these men are professionals in a much broader, human sense. All speak in clear terms that reveal their principles of ethical practice. Moreover, their satisfactions and sense of self-esteem gained from their medical activity seem intimately bound up with the principles they impose on themselves. In the rather circumscribed spheres of their living, a remarkable sense of integrity prevails. First, it is noteworthy for its obvious independence from professionalism in the socio-political mode. Much more significantly for understanding their lives, the development of this sense of integrity may figure prominently in marking the transitions in the phases of their lives and in the engagement and growth of experiences which permit fuller articulation of their personal and social worlds.

REFERENCES

ABERLE, DAVID F.
1951 *The Psychosocial Analysis of a Hopi Life-History.* Comparative Psychology Monographs, Vol. 21, No. 1.

ALLAND, ALEXANDER, JR.
1973 *Evolution and Human Behavior.* (Second Edition). Garden City, New York: Doubleday and Company, Inc.

ANDERSON, JAMES N.
1974 "Ecological anthropology and anthropological ecology." In John J. Honigmann (ed.), *Handbook of Social and Cultural Anthropology*, pp. 179-239. Chicago, Illinois: Rand McNally, Inc.

ARENSBERG, CONRAD M.
1972 "Culture and behavior: structure and emergence." *Annual Review of Anthropology* 1: 1-25.

AUDY, J. RALPH
1971 "Measurement and diagnosis of health." In Paul Shepard and Daniel McKinley (eds.), *Environ-Mental*, pp. 140-162. Boston, Massachusetts: Houghton Mifflin Company.

AUDY, J. RALPH and FRED L. DUNN
1974 "Health and disease." In Frederick Sargent II (ed.), *Human Ecology*, pp. 325-343. New York: American Elsevier Publishing Company.

BARTH FREDRIK
1966 "Anthropological models and social reality." *Proceedings of the Royal Society of London* (Series B), 165: 20-34.

BEALS, ALAN R.
1976 "Strategies of resort to curers in South India." In Charles Leslie (ed.),

Asian Medical Systems, pp. 184-200. Berkeley: University of California Press.

BENNETT, JOHN W.

1976a "Anticipation, adaptation, and the concept of culture in anthropology." *Science* 192 (28 May): 847-853.

1976b *The Ecological Transition; Cultural Anthropology and Human Adaptation.* Oxford, England: Pergamon Press.

BETEILLE, ANDRE

1977 *Inequality Among Men.* Oxford, England: Basil Blackwell.

BHARDWAJ, SURINDER M.

1975 "Attitude toward different systems of medicine: a survey of four villages in the Punjab—India." *Social Science and Medicine* 9 (November-December): 603-612.

BHATIA, J.C., DHARAM VIR, A. TIMMAPPAYA, and C.S. CHUTTANI

1975 "Traditional healers and modern medicine." *Social Science and Medicine* 9 (January): 15-21.

BUHLER, CHARLOTTE

1968 "The course of human life as a psychological problem." *Human Development* 11: 184-200.

CHUTTANI, C.S., J.C. BHATIA, DHARAM VIR, and A. TIMMAPPAYA

1973 "A survey of indigenous medical practitioners in rural areas of five different States in India." *Indian Journal of Medical Research* 61 (June): 962-967.

ERIKSON, ERIK HOMBURGER

1968 "Life cycle." In David L. Sills (ed.), *International Encyclopedia of the Social Sciences.* Vol. 9, pp. 286-292. New York: Macmillan.

FIRTH, SIR RAYMOND

1954 "Social organization and social change." *Journal of the Royal Anthropological Institute* 84:1-20.

GEERTZ, CLIFFORD

1973 *The Interpretation of Cultures.* New York: Basic Books.

KAPLAN, BERT

1968 "The method of the study of persons." In Edward Norbeck, Couglass Price-Williams, and William M. McCord (eds.), *The Study of Personality: An Interdisciplinary Approach*, pp. 121-133. New York: Holt, Rinehart, and Winston, Inc.

KLUCKHOHN, CLYDE M.

1945 "The personal document in anthropological science." In Louis Gottschalk, Clyde M. Kluckhohn, and Robert Angell (eds.), *The Use of Personal Documents in History, Anthropology, and Sociology*, pp. 78-173. Social Science Research Council Bulletin No. 53. New York: Social Science Research Council.

LESLIE, CHARLES

1973 "The professionalizing ideology of medical revivalism." In Milton Singer (ed.), *Entrepreneurship and Modernization of Occupational Cultures in South Asia*, pp. 216-242. Durham, North Carolina: Duke University Press.

LESLIE, CHARLES

1974 "The modernization of Asian medical systems." In John Poggie and R. Lynch (eds.), *Rethinking Modernization*, pp. 69-108. Westport, Connecticut: Greenwood Publishing Co.

LESLIE, CHARLES (ED.)

1976 *Asian Medical Systems*. Berkeley: University of California Press.

MADAN, T.N.

1969 "Who chooses modern medicine and why." *Economic and Political Weekly* 4 (37): 1475-1484.

1972 "Doctors in a North Indian city: recruitment, role perception, and role performance." In Satish Saberwal (ed.), *Beyond the Village: Sociological Explorations*, pp. 79-105. Translations No. 15. Simla: Indian Institute of Advanced Study.

MANDELBAUM, DAVID G.

1973 "The study of life history: Gandhi." *Current Anthropology* 14 (June): 177-196.

MONTGOMERY, EDWARD

1974-75 "Trance mediumship therapy in southern India: A transcript of a session." *Ethnomedizin* 3 (1-2): 111-126.

1976 "Systems and the medical practitioners of a Tamil town." In Charles Leslie (ed.), *Asian Medical Systems*, pp. 272-284. Berkeley: University of California Press.

NEUMANN, ALFRED K., J.C. BHATIA, S. ANDREWS, and A.K.S. MURPHY

1971 "Role of the indigenous medical practitioner in two areas of India—report of a study." *Social Science and Medicine* 5: 137-149.

OBEYESEKERE, GANANATH

1976 "The impact of Ayurvedic ideas on the culture and the individual in Sri Lanka." In Charles Leslie (ed.), *Asian Medical Systems*, pp. 201-226. Berkeley: University of California Press.

PART TWO]

PATIENTS, PRACTITIONERS AND HEALTH CARE SETTINGS

T.N. MADAN

*WHO CHOOSES MODERN MEDICINE AND WHY**

ABSTRACT. Medicine is an important field in which displacement of the traditional professional, through elimination or absorption of his knowhow by his modern counterpart, is an essential part of the process of modernization. It is of considerable interest, therefore, to find out who are the people in a developing society who adopt modern medicine and what their reasons are for doing so.

A national policy for offering medical services is determined by various forces. India, due to her checkered history experienced the contributions of allopathy, homoeopathy, Ayurveda, Unani and myriad other small medical systems. It is commonly believed that people's preferences regarding the use of these systems have been colored by a complex set of variables. Revival movements in some of these systems gained popularity after the independence of the nation for various reasons including the system's relationship with the cultural heritage of the people. Therefore, it is of utmost importance for policy and planning to know who prefers a certain or a combination of systems and why and clear up certain assumptions regarding the influence of the age, education and upbringing (whether urban or rural) of a person on his acceptance of modern medicine. Even where a significant association was found, its nature turned out to be different from what had been anticipated.

*This is a slightly revised version of an article that appeared in *Economic and Political Weekly* 4 (September 13) 1969, pp. 1475-1484. The editor is grateful to Dr. Krishna Raj, editor of the *Weekly*, for permitting to reprint this article in this volume.

The author acknowledges with thanks the assistance of R.C. Bhatnagar who administered the interview schedules to the interviewees and P.C. Verma who carried out the statistical analysis of the data collected. The latter also gave help at all stages of the inquiry. He, P.C. Joshi and S. Navlakha read an earlier draft of this paper and gave valuable suggestions. The responsibility for the paper in its present form is, however, wholly that of the author.

This paper reports some of the results of a preliminary inquiry carried out in Ghaziabad town near Delhi.

MODERNIZATION IS A COMPREHENSIVE PROCESS WHICH AFFECTS ALL aspects of a society, but not necessarily in the same measure. Modernization is accompanied by the emergence of new professional services, though not all of them lack counterparts in the traditional society. The co-existence in a society of traditional and modern professional services represents a situation full of interest for sociological inquiry.

Two fairly obvious possibilities may be postulated. Either the two types of a professional service will co-exist or they will come into conflict with each other, leading to displacement of the one by the other. The displacement of a traditional professional service by its modern counterpart may be of crucial importance in certain cases to the process of modernization. It would be, therefore, of considerable interest to identify the acceptors (and the resistors) of the new professional services.

Medicine is an important field in which displacement of the traditional professional, through elimination or absorption of his knowhow by his modern counterpart, is an essential part of the process of modernization. It is not my intention here to engage in an examination of any particular traditional system of medicine so as to show what its strong points or weaknesses are. Nor do I want to deny the important place such systems will occupy in India, particularly in the rural areas. My concern is with the fundamental fact that whereas modern medicine is experimental, and therefore capable of advances in diagnosis and treatment, traditional medicine is a closed system and non-experimental. It is, therefore, incapable of improvement within the traditional framework. Attempts to introduce experimentation and research are broadly confined to the standardization of pharmacopoeia. These attempts are, moreover, themselves a departure from tradition: they are attempts at modernization. What is more, many of the basic principles of the traditional systems of medicine prevalent in India have been shown to be erroneous in the light of the findings of modern medicine. A good example of such errors is a afforded by the ayurvedic (ancient Hindu) theory of the constitution of man as a harmonious mixture of five elements, viz, earth, water, fire, air and ether.

Now, if increasing acceptance of modern (allopathic) medicine, and more importantly of the principles underlying it, is acknowledged as an essential part of the process of modernization, it would be of considerable interest to find out who are the people in a developing society who adopt modern medicine and what are their reasons for the choice that they make. The present paper reports some of the results of a preliminary inquiry carried out in an Indian city with a view to answering the above questions. I will present and discuss here only the data obtained from patients; data obtained from medical practitioners are being published separately.

The Setting

Ghaziabad is situated 20 kilometres east of Delhi on the Grand Trunk Road. It had a total population of 70,438 in 1961. The level of literacy was 47.30 per cent in the total population and 56.95 per cent among men. The total number of persons classified as workers was 19,775 who represent 28.07 per cent of the city's population. Of these, 496 (2.51 per cent) were engaged in agriculture, 6,939 (35.08 per cent in industry) and 12,340 (62.40 per cent) in services.

Ghaziabad is a subdivisional headquarters within the Meerut district. There is one State Government and another Central Government (railway) hospital in the town with 102 and 12 beds, respectively. Besides, there is an Employees' State Insurance Dispensary, a company dispensary and a private nursing home. The Municipality runs a maternity welfare and family planning clinic and provides the usual public health services.

At the time of the inquiry (February-April 1968) there were 37 registered medical practitioners in the town of whom 13 were working in the various hospitals and dispensaries, the rest being engaged in private practice. All but one of the private practitioners provided free consultation at their clinics but charged money for dispensing services. Besides, there were 14 big and small chemists' and druggists' stores for sale of patent drugs, injections, etc. Only 2 of these stores also provided dispensing services. We found that the owners of these shops were often consulted by customers regarding suitable medicines for various ailments and were even addressed as doctors. It was also observed that many grocery shops kept stocks of such popular medicines as Aspro or Vicks cough drops.

It was not possible to find out how many practitioners of traditional systems of medicines were carrying on practice in Ghaziabad. That there was a considerable number of *vaids* (practitioners of Hindu ayurvedic medicine) and *hakims* (practitioners of unani tibbia, or Greek medicine) was beyond doubt. As far as we could find out, all the *vaids* were Hindus and nearly all the *hakims* Muslims. It may be pointed out that unani tibbia came to India with the Muslims and in Arabic and Persian translations of Greek texts.

RESEARCH METHODS

The data for the present study were collected in the following manner. After an interview schedule had been prepared, it was administered to the heads of 50 households. In the light of this experience, a revised interview schedule of 36 structural questions was drawn up and coded. It was then administered to the heads of 500 households who, in the light of sociological studies of the family and household in India, were deemed, for the purpose of this study, as being the principal decision-makers on such issues as the choice of a system of medicine.

These 500 households represent a 3.5 per cent random sample of all the households in Ghaziabad city. In the absence of any reliable household list, a sample could not be drawn up prior to the commencement of the investigation. Every twentieth house was contacted for information and care was taken to cover every ward of the city. The total number of houses in Ghaziabad being 14,440, every twenty-fourth house should have been chosen to obtain a sample of 500. We, however, selected every twentieth house to ensure that information from at least 500 households would be collected and that there would be no shortfall in this number. As the unit of our study was the household, and not the house, not more than one household resident in a house was selected for investigation.

After completion of the sample survey, 50 schedules (i.e., 10 per cent of the sample) were reinvestigated by a second investigator. The responses received by him were very close to those received by the first investigator, the difference being less than 5 per cent.

The questions that were put to those interviewed with regard to the choices they made between four systems of medicine—allopathy, homoeopathy, ayurveda and unani tibbia—focused on the following aspects of the problem:

(1) What type of treatment is preferred and whether the age or sex of the patient makes a difference to choicemaking? It was thought advisable to divide the patients into three categories—viz, children, adult men and adult women—because of the statement of several allopathic doctors in the course of an earlier inquiry, that non-allopathic cures are often preferred by people in the treatment of children's diseases.

Similarly, it seemed highly probable that women prefer to consult allopathic lady doctors for the treatment of the so-called "female disorders" rather than the practitioners of the other systems of medicine who are all men. Moreover, only allopathy offers surgical relief in cases of gynaecological disorders or in complicated obstetric cases.

Each interviewee was asked to answer the question in terms of the choices that were actually made whenever there was illness in the family, rather than in terms of what in his (or her) opinion ought to be done, or would be done if there were no constraints of any kind on choice-making. Answers to these two questions—what is done and what ought to be done— may not be different, but we did not presume this and concentrated on inquiring about choices that are actually made.

(2) Whatever the preference of a household, it was thought significant in the context of modernization to inquire into the single most important reason which leads them to the choice they make. It is reasonable to expect that belief in the efficacy of a particular kind of treatment must be the most important consideration that weighs with a household in its choice of it. Obviously, people want to be cured of disease and to get well. It would be interesting, nonetheless, to find out if the criterion of effectiveness of treatment is sometimes subordinated, at least at the level of verbalization, to a less rational consideration such as the cheapness or free availability of consultation and treatment. Further, do such considerations as a system of medicine being traditional, or the existence of kinship ties with a particular medical practitioner, also assume in some cases enough importance to be stated as the principal determinant of choice? It goes without saying, however, that such an affirmation does not exclude the criterion of efficacy.

(3) Finally, do households employ different systems of medicine for different types of illness, or for the same illness at different times?

If so, how common (or rare) is it to combine different systems instead of exclusively relying upon one of them? Such combinations of systems may be resorted to for the kind of reasons mentioned above including efficaciousness. Nevertheless, they would indicate a lack of commitment to modern medicine. As was pointed out earlier, traditional systems are themselves, however, undergoing modernization these days.

The responses obtained to the above questions were tested for significance of association with the following socio-economic characteristics of the household head or of the household: age, education, occupation, place of birth and upbringing (rural or urban), monthly household income and religion. It was hypothesized that younger, better educated, white-collar workers are more likely to prefer allopathy and to do so for rational considerations. An urban background and relative economic well-being (measured by household income) were also considered factors conductive to the choice of allopathy. It will be seen that these factors are of a mutually-reinforcing character. Thus, generally speaking, a younger person is more likely to be better educated, and therefore in a relatively better paid white-collar job, than an older person. Similarly, a person with an urban background is not only more likely to be better educated but is also more exposed to modern medicine from his early childhood onwards.

Religion was considered an important factor because two traditional systems of medicine, namely ayurveda and unani tibbia, are associated with Hindus and Muslims, respectively. The association between ayurveda and Hindus would seem to be almost completely exclusive. It may be recalled here that the sample contained respondents from four religious groups including Hindus and Muslims.

THE SAMPLE

Attention may now be drawn to some characteristics of the sample of interviewees. Nearly half of the household heads (48.6 per cent) belong to the group of 25-40, and a little over 80 per cent to the combined age-group of 25-55. All but 6 of them are males and all but 24 are married. About half of the number of the household heads (289 or 57.8 per cent) were born and brought up in an urban area. Only 19 of the interviewees were illiterate, which gives us a literacy percentage of 96.2 per cent. What is more, as many as 302

(60.8 per cent) have had education of the level of matriculation (or higher secondary) and above, including 112 (22.4 per cent) who have reached the degree (BA/BSc) or post-degree levels.

In terms of occupation, 147 (29.4 per cent) are clerical and related workers; 96 (19.2 per cent) are sales workers; 73 (14.6 per cent) are professional workers including engineers, doctors, teachers and other professional workers; and 64 (12.8 per cent) occupy administrative, executive and managerial positions. The remaining 120 (24.0 per cent) fall into the residual category of "other" workers consisting of production process workers, services and recreation workers, transportation workers and other laborers.

Besides the above information on household heads, data were also collected on four attributes of households, viz, religion, caste, monthly income and size. The great majority of the households (467 or 93.4 per cent) are Hindu. Sikh households (19 or 3.8 per cent) come next, followed by Muslim (8 or 1.6 per cent), Jain (5 or 1.0 per cent) and Christian (1 or 0.2 per cent) households.

Clean or "twice-born" castes account for 405 (86.7 per cent) of the 467 Hindus in the sample. They are followed by Hindus of the service castes (52 or 11.2 per cent) artisan castes (6 or 1.3 per cent) and peasant castes (4 or 0.8 per cent).

In terms of monthly income, 13 (2.6 per cent) households have a monthly income of less than Rs 100, 364 or 72.8 per cent fall in the income group of Rs 100-500 per month; 72 or 1.44 per cent earn between Rs 500 and Rs 1,000 per month; and 49 (9.8 per cent) earn Rs 1,000 per month or more. (Two interviewees did not answer the question on household income.)

Coming to size, 82 (16.4 per cent) households had up to 3 members; 234 (46.8 per cent) had between 4 and 6; 137 (27.4 per cent) had between 7 and 9; and 47 (9.4 per cent) and 10 or more.

FINDINGS

Let me now present an analysis of four findings with regard to the above questions.

(*a*) Preference for a particular system of medicine (see Table 1): Our inquiry revealed an overwhelming preference for allopathy; around four-fifths of the interviewees indicated that they choose it for treatment of all three categories of patients. Though ayurveda is the next most preferred system of medicine, only 11 per cent of the

TABLE 1
PREFERENCE FOR SYSTEMS OF MEDICINE

(*Percentage Distribution*)

Social and Economic Factors	Type of Treatment Preferred: Children — Allop	Homoeo	Ayur	Unan	Men — Allop	Homoeo	Ayur	Unan	Women — Allop	Homoeo	Ayur	Unan
Age (Years)												
Below 25	90.9	9.1	—	—	86.9	—	8.7	4.4	95.5	—	—	4.5
25-40	80.9	6.0	10.2	2.9	82.7	3.3	9.5	4.5	82.4	4.2	9.6	3.8
40-55	78.7	5.8	11.6	3.9	80.1	4.8	12.1	3.0	78.1	6.1	12.2	3.6
55 Plus	62.7	11.9	15.3	10.1	72.0	4.4	11.8	11.8	71.6	6.0	13.4	9.0
Total	77.9	6.8	11.2	4.1	80.6	3.8	10.6	5.0	80.1	4.9	10.5	4.5
Education												
Illiterate	93.3	—	6.7	—	94.7	—	—	5.3	94.4	—	5.6	—
Literate	80.8	—	11.5	7.7	86.7	3.3	3.3	6.7	82.8	—	10.3	6.9
Primary or Jr Basic	75.5	4.4	11.9	8.2	77.1	2.7	10.1	10.1	72.6	3.4	11.6	8.8
Matriculation or Hr Sec	76.8	8.9	11.3	3.0	79.5	4.7	12.1	3.7	79.3	6.4	11.2	3.1
Degree or Post-grad Degree	80.2	9.4	10.4	—	83.0	4.5	12.5	—	83.8	6.3	9.0	0.9
Total	77.9	6.8	11.2	4.1	80.6	3.8	10.6	5.0	80.1	4.9	10.5	4.5

RESULTS OF TESTS FOR SIGNIFICANCE OF ASSOCIATION

	Children	Men	Women
Age	Chi-sq= 9.63, d.f.=2*	Chi-sq= 4.37, d.f.=2	Chi-sq= 5.30, d.f.=2
Education	Chi-sq= 2.16, d.f.=3	Chi-sq= 4.45, d.f.=3	Chi-sq= 3.93, d.f.=3

NOTE: Values marked *are significant at 1 per cent level.

interviewees mentioned it as their first preference. Its second place, after allopathy, may have been expected in view of the preponderance of Hindus in the city population. Homoeopathy and unani tibbia follow ayurveda, in that order, and are obviously not much used.

The association between the choice of allopathy and the various socio-economic characteristics of household heads and households, listed above is as follows:

(1) Age: The association between the decision-maker's age and preference for allopathy is significant in the case of children only: the younger the decision-maker the greater seems to be the likelihood of his choosing allopathy for the treatment of children (For the results of the tests of significance of association, see Table 1).

(2) Occupation: There are significant differences between the different occupational groups with regard to the choice of allopathy, but in the treatment of men only. The highest preference for allopathy, but in the treatment of men only. The highest preference for allopathy is shown by the category of "other" workers, followed by clerical workers, administrators, professional workers and sales workers (see Table 2).

(3) Religion: The data show that for all three categories of patients, Hindus show a lower preference for allopathy than non-Hindus. The difference is, however, significant only in the case of children and adult men.

The rural or urban origin and upbringing of the household head, and his education, are not significantly associated with the choice of allopathy. The same is true of household also. With regard to these three factors no association was found at the 5 per cent level of significance. Also noteworthy is the fact that none of the 6 characteristics of the decision-maker, or of the household, seems to be significantly associated with the choice of a system of medicine for women (see Table 3).

(b) Reasons for preference for a system of medicine (see Table 4): A little over four-fifths (80.4 per cent) of the interviewees gave effectiveness as the principal reason for their choice of a system of medicine. Age, and the rural or urban upbringing of the decision-maker, do not seem to be significantly related to choice-making on the rational ground of effectiveness. The other factors are, however, so related.

TABLE 2

PREFERENCE FOR SYSTEMS OF MEDICINE

(*Percentage Distribution*)

Social and Economic Factors	*Type of Treatment Preferred*											
	Children				*Men*				*Women*			
	Allop	*Homoeo*	*Ayur*	*Unan*	*Allop*	*Homoeo*	*Ayur*	*Unan*	*Allop*	*Homoeo*	*Ayur*	*Unan*
Occupation												
Professionals	72.8	10.2	17.0	—	75.4	1.4	20.5	2.7	81.7	2.8	14.1	1.4
Administrators, Executive Officers and Managerial (Including Directors) Workers	75.9	15.5	6.9	1.7	78.1	12.5	7.8	1.6	75.0	15.6	7.8	1.6
Clerical and Related Workers Including Other White-Collar Workers	76.2	5.4	13.8	4.6	83.0	2.7	10.9	3.4	77.6	4.2	13.3	4.9
Sales Workers	74.7	6.9	11.5	6.9	70.3	5.2	11.5	12.5	75.8	3.2	11.6	9.4
Other Workers	86.8	1.9	6.6	4.7	90.0	0.8	5.0	4.2	88.3	2.6	5.8	3.4
Total	77.9	6.8	11.2	4.1	80.6	3.8	10.6	5.0	80.1	4.9	10.5	4.5
Income Below 250	76.9	3.2	12.8	7.1	82.4	2.2	8.2	7.2	77.8	2.3	12.5	7.4
250-500	74.8	9.7	13.2	2.3	76.4	4.6	15.4	3.6	78.5	6.7	12.3	2.5
500-750	78.9	3.8	11.5	5.8	84.2	—	10.5	5.3	85.7	1.8	8.9	3.6
750-1000	84.6	15.4	—	—	86.7	13.3	—	—	86.7	13.3	—	—
1000 and above	90.7	9.3	—	—	85.7	6.1	4.1	4.1	87.8	6.1	2.0	4.1
NR	100.0	—	—	—	50.0	50.0	—	—	50.0	50.0	—	—
Total	77.9	6.8	1.2	4.1	80.6	3.8	10.6	5.0	80.1	4.9	10.5	4.5

RESULTS OF TESTS FOR SIGNIFICANCE OF ASSOCIATION

	Children	*Men*	*Women*
Occupation	Chi-sq = 6.63, d.f. = 4**	Chi-sq = 15.02, d.f. = 4	Chi-sq = 7.89, d.f. = 4
Income	Chi-sq = 5.88, d.f. = 3	Chi-sq = 4.29, d.f. = 3	Chi-sq = 4.19, d.f. = 3

Table 3

PREFERENCE FOR SYSTEMS OF MEDICINE

(*Percentage Distribution*)

Social and Economic Factors	*Type of Treatment Preferred*											
	Children				*Men*				*Women*			
	Allop	*Homoeo*	*Ayur*	*Unan*	*Allop*	*Homoeo*	*Ayur*	*Unan*	*Allop*	*Homoeo*	*Ayur*	*Unan*
Rural/Urban												
Rural	75.6	6.5	14.1	3.8	76.8	3.3	13.7	6.2	77.8	4.3	13.6	4.3
Urban	79.7	7.1	8.9	4.3	83.4	4.2	8.2	4.2	81.8	5.3	8.4	4.5
Total	77.9	6.8	11.2	4.1	80.6	3.8	10.6	5.0	80.1	4.9	10.5	4.5
Religion												
Hindu	76.8	7.0	11.8	4.4	79.7	3.3	11.4	5.1	79.3	5.0	11.1	4.6
Sikh	93.3	6.7	—	—	94.7	5.3		—	94.7	5.3	—	—
Jain	100.0	—	—	—	100.0	—	—	—	80.0	—	20.0	—
Muslim	100.0	—	—	—	87.5	—	—	12.5	87.5	—	—	12.5
Christian	—	—	—	—	100.0	—	—	—	100.0	—	—	—
Others	—	—	—	—	—	—	—	—	—	—	—	—
Total	77.9	6.8	11.2	4.1	80.6	3.8	10.6	5.0	80.1	4.9	10.5	4.5

	Children	Men	Women
Rural/Urban	Chi-sq = 1.06, d.f. = 1	Chi-sq = 3.51, d.f. = 1	Chi-sq = 1.23, d.f. = 1
Religion	Normal Variate = 2.38**	Normal Variate = 2.00*	Normal Variate = 1.71

Note: Values marked * are significant at 5 per cent level and those marked ** are significant at 1 per cent level.

TABLE 4

REASONS FOR PREFERENCE OF SYSTEMS OF MEDICINE

(*Percentage Distribution*)

Social and Economic Factors	*Effective-ness*	*Cheap-ness*	*Free Avail-ability*	*Tradition*	*Kinship*
Age (Years)					
Below 25	82.6	4.3	8.7	4.3	—
25-40	81.9	2.1	8.6	6.6	0.8
40-50	76.5	1.2	13.3	7.8	1.2
55 Plus	83.8	1.5	2.9	11.8	—
Total	80.4	1.8	9.4	7.6	0.8
Education					
Illiterate	84.2	—	15.8	—	—
Literate	76.6	—	20.0	3.3	—
Primary or Jr Basic	71.8	3.4	14.8	10.0	—
Matriculation or Hr Sec	80.5	1.6	6.8	9.0	2.1
Degree or Post-grade Degree	91.9	0.9	2.7	4.5	—
Total	80.4	1.8	9.4	7.6	0.8
Rural/Urban					
Rural	78.7	2.4	10.9	8.0	—
Urban	81.6	1.4	8.3	7.3	1.4
Total	80.4	1.8	9.4	7.6	0.8
Occupation					
Professionals	91.8	1.4	1.4	5.4	—
Administrators Executive Officers and Managerial (including Directors) Workers	92.1	1.6	—	6.3	—
Clerical and Related Workers including Other White-Collar Workers	72.1	1.4	17.0	8.8	0.7
Sales Workers	82.3	4.2	1.0	9.4	3.1
Other Workers	75.8	0.8	16.7	6.7	—
Total	80.4	1.8	9.4	7.6	0.8
Income					
Below 250	72.5	3.3	17.1	6.6	0.5
250-500	80.5	1.0	7.7	10.8	—
500-750	94.7	—	—	5.3	—
750-1000	100.0	—	—	—	—
1000 and above	85.7	2.1	2.0	4.1	6.1
NR	100.0	—	—	—	—
Total	80.4	1.8	9.4	7.6	0.8

Religion					
Hindu	79.5	1.7	9.8	8.1	0.9
Sikh	94.7	—	5.3	—	—
Jain	80.0	20.0	—	—	—
Muslim	100.0	—	—	—	—
Christian	100.0	—	—	—	—
Others	—	—	—	—	—
Total	80.4	1.8	9.4	7.6	0.8

RESULTS OF TESTS FOR SIGNIFICANCE OF ASSOCIATION

Age	Chi-sq=0.74, d.f.=2
Education	Chi-sq=2.54, d.f.=3**
Rural/Urban	Chi-sq=16.51, d.f.=1
Occupation	Chi-sq= 19.58, d.f.=4**
Income	Chi-sq= 17.41, d.f.=3**
Religion	Normal Variate=2.14*

NOTE: Values marked * are significant at 5 per cent level and those marked** are significant at 1 per cent level.

(1) Education: If we combine illiterate respondents with those whose educational level is upto primary, then the preference for effectiveness as the principal criterion for choice is found to increase as we move toward higher levels of educational qualifications. The preference percentages reaches 92 per cent in the case of the most highly educated decision-makers.

(2) Occupation: Effectiveness as the basis for choice between the systems of medicine, seems to be most favored as a criterion by professional workers and administrators who, at the same time, place the least emphasis upon tradition. Clerical workers are by comparison the occupational category which places the least emphasis upon this criterion, though they themselves highly prefer it as compared to the other criteria.

(3) Income: As monthly household income increases, the tendency to choose on the ground of the effectiveness of treatment also seems to rise. This significant association holds good for all income groups except the highest (Rs 1,000 and above). Since 6 per cent of the respondents in this income group have mentioned kinship ties with particular doctors as the main determinant of their choice of treatment, it is likely that though they did not mention effectiveness as the principal basis of choice, they did not mean to deny it.

(4) Religion: The data show that the choice of a system of medicine

among non-Hindus is more governed by the criterion of effectiveness than among Hindus. Hindus also give effectiveness as the most important single criterion; they are, however, the only respondents who mentioned tradition as a basis for choice.

(c) Combination of systems of medicine (see Table 5): It was assumed from the very beginning of the inquiry that the co-existence of several systems of medicine is likely to be reflected in their combination by some patients, even when there is a clear preference for one particular system. It would be worthwhile to find the percentage of households who resort to such combinations (as we have defined the term).

TABLE 5

COMBINATION OF SYSTEMS OF MEDICINE

(*Percentage Distribution*)

Social and Economic Factors	*Combines Treatment*	
	Yes	*No*
Age (Years)		
Below 25	39.1	60.9
25-40	65.4	34.6
40-55	65.1	34.9
55 Plus	70.6	29.4
Total	64.8	35.2
Education		
Illiterate	63.2	36.8
Literate	63.3	36.7
Primary or Jr Basic	61.1	38.9
Matriculation or Hr Sec	65.8	34.2
Degree or Post-grad Degree	68.8	31.2
Total	64.8	35.2
Rural/Urban		
Rural	68.7	31.3
Urban	61.9	38.1
Total	64.8	35.2

Social and Economic Factors	*Combines Treatment*	
	Yes	*No*
Occupation		
Professionals	74.0	26.0
Administrators, Executive Officers and Managerial (including Directors) Workers	62.5	37.5
Clerical and Related Workers Including Other White-Collar Workers	68.0	32.0
Sales Workers	67.7	32.3
Others	54.2	45.8
Total	64.8	35.2
Income		
Below 250	61.5	38.5
250-500	72.3	27.7
500-750	68.4	31.6
750-1000	46.7	53.3
1000 and above	46.9	53.1
NR	100.0	—
Total	64.8	35.2

Religion		
Hindu	64.7	35.3
Sikh	63.2	36.8
Jain	80.0	20.0
Muslim	62.5	37.5
Christian	100.0	—
Others	—	—
Total	64.8	35.2

RESULTS OF TESTS FOR SIGINIFICANCE OF ASSOCIATION

Age	Chi-sq=	7.73,	d.f.=3
Education	Chi-sq=	1.81,	d.f.=4
Rural/Urban	Chi-sq=	2.47,	d.f.=1
Occupation	Chi-sq=	9.84,	d.f.=4*
Income	Chi-sq=	15.08,	d.f.=4**
Religion	Chi-sq=	0.06,	d.f.=1

NOTE: Values marked *are significant at 5 per cent level and those marked ** are significant at 1 per cent level.

A majority of the households (64.8 per cent) were found to combine different systems of medicine, and the reason given in every such case of combination was that some diseases are more readily controlled or eradicated by treatment according to a particular system. The decision to combine different systems of medicine was found to be significantly associated with occupation and income.

(1) Occupation: The highest tendency to combine systems seem to be characteristic of professional workers. They are followed by clerical and sales workers, administrators, and "other" workers in that order.

(2) Income: If households with a monthly income of less than Rs 500 are compared with those having higher incomes, the percentage for combinations declines from 67.1 per cent to 57.0 per cent.

SUMMARY AND CONCLUSIONS

(1) The first noteworthy conclusion of the inquiry is that a four-fifths majority of the interviewees have a first preference for allopathy. There is thus hardly much evidence of resistance to the growth of modern medicine because of allegiance to traditional systems. About two-thirds of the household heads said, however, that they make use of more than one system of medicine. The most common reason

(76.6 per cent) for whatever choices or combinations are made is the belief that the chosen course of treatment is going to be efficacious.

(2) The assumptions that a particular system, the main reason for the preference, and the combination of systems on the one hand, and the characteristics of household heads and households on the other, the following conclusions may be noted:

(3:1) It is clear that the rural-urban dichotomy of the birth and upbringing of the decision-maker is not significantly associated with the choices or combinations he makes between the various types of treatment, nor with the reasons that underlie his choices. In other words, the rural migrants tend to behave like the indigenous urban population in the choice of medical treatment. The assumption that rural migrants in urban areas are more likely to choose a traditional system of medicine than those born and brought up in such areas has not been borne out by the inquiry.

(3:2) The age of the decision-maker also does not seem to be an important determinant of behavior within the area of inquiry. Education enters only in influencing the stated reason for a choice: the better educated a person the more his tendency to maintain that principal reason for his choice of a particular type of treatment is effectiveness.

(3:3) The assumption about the association between Hinduism and ayurveda is confirmed by the data. In fact, Hindus seem to choose all three non-allopathic systems more frequently than non-Hindus, though their own preference for allopathy is also very high (76.8 per cent). Also noteworthy is the relatively greater importance the Hindus attach to tradition as a criterion of choice-making. Religion thus emerges as a significant factor in the Indian situation with regard to the choice of treatment, though certainly not so important as to be regarded as an obstacle to the growth of modern medicine.

(3:4) The most significant determinants of choice-making that emerge from our analysis are occupation and income. Thus, we find the category of "other" worker at the top of the list of those who favor allopathy. They are the last but one group with regard to effectiveness being recognized as the most important reason for choice-making. And they are at the bottom of the list with regard to the combination of systems, i.e., they tend to rely generally and almost exclusively on allopathy. They obviously depend upon the free consultation and treatment available in Government hospitals and dispensaries, though they tend to stress effectiveness as a criterion for choice-making much more than free availability of consultation and treatment. There is, of course, no contradiction involved in what they say and what they do.

Professional workers represent the other pole, as it were. Compared to other groups, except sales workers, they show the lowest preference for allopathy; they, along with administrators and executive officers, attach more importance than the other groups to the choice of treatment on the ground of effectiveness; and they combine various types of treatment more than the others. The behavior patterns of "other" workers, as well as professional workers, are internally consistent.

Regarding clerical workers and administrators, it may be noted that those of them who are in Government service or employees of certain firms are entitled either to free treatment or to the reimbursement of medical expenses. Either facility is, however, applicable to allopathic treatment only.

(3:5) Income levels are, of course, connected with the ability of a household to pay for the preferred type of treatment. In view of the above observations about occupation and free medical facilities, it is understandable, at least partly, as to why no significant association was found to exist between household income and the preference for a particular system of medicine. It is, however, noteworthy that such an association was found between the reasons for preference for a system of medicine, and the willingness or unwillingness to combine different types of treatment on the one hand, and income levels on the other. Higher income seems to go both with a greater concern for effectiveness as well as with a greater reliance on a single system of medicine.

In conclusion, it may be pointed out that the interest and usefulness of the present exploratory inquiry lies in its having led to the questioning or refutation of certain assumptions regarding the influence of the age, education and rural or urban upbringing of a person on his acceptance of modern medicine for himself and for his family. Even where a significant association was found—as in the case of occuption and income—its nature turned out to be somewhat different from what was anticipated. It may be added that the assumptions were formulated in the light of contemporary literature on the modernization of developing societies.

The above conclusions are, however, limited by the fact that they are based upon data drawn from a single north Indian city. No claims are, therefore, made about the general applicability of these conclusions. What would seem to be called for are more studies of the kind reported in this paper, based upon more rigorously drawn samples.

JOANNA KIRKPATRICK

THE DELIVERY OF HOSPITAL SERVICE IN NORTH INDIA : A CLIENT-INSTITUTION INTERACTION MODEL[1]

ABSTRACT. The article presents data and analysis from a case study of the gynecology ward of an Indian mission hospital in Punjab. Pertinent literature on client-institution interactions in delivery hospital services to people in non-Western non-industrialized societies is briefly discussed, and the model broached. The microsituation is typified by confrontation between clientele and hospital as institutions, a situation that varies cross nationally more with social structure than with culture. Microsituations involving patients and hospital staff, and their social interactions in terms of role expectations and unofficial behavior, are analyzed from the perspective of symbolic interactionism and the definition of the situation. The microsituations include reference to: illness definitions; concepts of the hospital; diet and its complications; ritual and secular status in the ward; pollution; blood as limited resource; escorts in the ward; the patient or sick role; and instrumental vs. expressive aspects of the nursing role in relation to the social structure of the clientele. In conclusion; a model is delineated which represents and predicts client-institution interaction in societies where the social structure of secondary institutions varies with that of primary groups and institutions. The model's analytical power is explored in terms of both the case study findings and the relevant sociological literature.

[1]This article is based on ten months of field work, six of which were spent in interviewing and observing in the gynecology and obstetrics wards of Brown Memorial Hospital of Christian Medical College, Ludhiana, Punjab, India, 1965-66. I wish to acknowledge the gracious assistance and cooperation of its administration, staff members and patients. The field research was prepared partly under the assistance of an N.I.H. Traineeship at the Department of Anthropology, University of California, Berkeley. I also wish to thank mentors and colleagues who have read and commented on the paper, in particular Dr. Gerald D. Berreman, Dr. Ruth Bunzel, and Dr. Luis Kemnitzer. I alone am responsible, however, for any faults of fact or interpretation.

ACCOUNTS OF HOSPITALIZATION IN PRE-INDUSTRIAL SOCIETIES, WHETHER they refer to European peasants or to tribal and peasant peoples on other continents, generally recognize the reluctance of families to permit a member to be separated from their control, care, observation, and concern in order to receive treatment as in-patients (see, for example, Leighton and Leighton, 1944; Caudill, 1951; Friedl, 1962; Blum and Blum, 1965; and Bell, 1969). The specific reasons for such reluctance may vary cross-culturally, but analytically the phenomenon can be stated as a case of the nonconvergence of secondary institutions (bureaucracies, like hospitals) with social systems organized on the basis of primary relations and institutions (such as kinship and other primary networks.) As Gluckman (1962:344ff.) noted, people in primary-type societies cannot easily segregate the events of daily life from the persons associated with them to the extent possible in highly industrialized societies. Dangerous events thus have wider consequences for a greater number of significant others and significant relationships than is the case in societies like that of the United States or industrialized Europe, where social roles are more segregated and the range of significant others tends to be narrow.

Clients of bureaucracies in pre-industrial societies, therefore, do not approach dealings with bureaucratic organizations as autonomous individuals if at all possible. Instead, they prefer to face these organizations as members of a primary unit. This confrontation is mediated either through their attendance with one or more kinsmen or personal friends, or through favors (referred to in Punjab as *sifaarish,* or *lihaaz*) done by their "contacts"—their acquaintance through primary affiliations with one or more persons employed in the bureaucracy (cf. Khare, 1972; Morrison, 1972). Such affiliations may be based on kinship, residence as co-villagers or neighbors, or patronage institution. In a country like India, where over 80 per cent of the population still live in villages, bureaucratic universal norms, which are nontraditional and alien, are either unknown or are mistrusted as a basis for providing services (Wyon and Gordon, 1971:94).

The client does not consider himself as one among many individually entitled to those services, but on the contrary he tends to see himself as individually helpless against the machinations of bureaucracy unless his claim is bolstered by the presence of people from within his own primary network. He expects that the claims of other clients will be similarly managed, and that the organization dispenses its services in particular ways. That this notion of the situation is realistic would not be disputed by most Indians nor by the foreigners who have lived in India.

Any account of the delivery of hospital services to patients in India, therefore, must consider the discrepancies or conflicts between modern, or "Western" cultural definitions of those services and the Indian definitions of themselves as clients of the hospital. In this report I will show how women patients in the gynecology ward and the staff members responsible for their care mutually deal with such discrepancies; that these problems are not unique to the Indian situation is evident in other surveys of the social settings of hospital care cross-culturally (see Glaser, 1970). The aim of this account is to demonstrate not only that conflict in the delivery of modern health services has a cultural basis—for that has been amply elaborated by now—but to suggest a social structural statement of the confrontation of clients and bureaucracies in situations where clients' social lives are still embedded in the primary institutions of kinship and the rural or "urban village" (Gans, 1962).

I propose that in such cases there will be found an inverse relation between custodialism (or authority to control) in the client group and custodialism in the bureaucracy. What this means for the inpatients in such circumstances is that if authority and control over persons within their families is high, the ability of the hospital to isolate these patients from kin and to control their definition of the situation and their behavior as inpatients will be low. I suspect that this inverse relation between clients and bureaucracies could be stated for all societies, or social settings, where we find that the clients' lives are still organized wholly or mainly on the basis of primary relationships, roles, and social situations.

I shall return to this model in the final section of the paper but first I should present in some detail data on conflicting definitions of the situation in the gynecology ward to show the ways in which the hospital organization's staff were unable to impose their definitions on the patients. An important mechanism for such an imposition is the isolation of the patient in the sick role in order to socialize him or her to ward norms, definitions of self and situation (cf. Coser, 1962:39-41). To the extent that patients cannot be isolated from kin, the hospital staff cannot subject the patient to their uniform efficiency requirements, with all of their attendant psychosocial discomforts.[2]

The potential clients of modern health services, or of some variations of these, constitute most of the world today. They are the populations of the economically undeveloped countries, where poverty and scarcity, as well as crucial reliance on primary membership, groups, dominate their access to effective health resources.

That a female ward and its services forms the basis for this study could be considered a limitation on the generality of my conclusions. It should be noted, however, that in India as in many other preindustrial nations (cf. Glaser, 1970: 90-91) women are less likely than men to be inpatients. It is reasonable to infer, therefore, that the resistance to utilizing inpatient services can be examined even better with female than with male clients. It was noted at the mission hospital in Ludhiana, however, that male patients, too, had kin or friend escorts.

THE RECRUITMENT OF GYNECOLOGY PATIENTS TO BROWN MEMORIAL HOSPITAL

Patients came from all over northern India to this hospital, located in Ludhiana town in the primarily agricultural state of Punjab. In 1965-66 the town population was approximately 400,000, and there were three other hospitals besides Brown Memorial: The Government Civil Hospital, a private Maternity Hospital and Dayanand Hospital, the last one founded and operated by the Arya Samaj—a neo-Hindu reformist sect. The Christian hospital and medical college, founded in 1894 by Dame Edith Brown (Reynolds, 1968) originally for the treatment and medical education of women in Punjab, has for a long time occupied an important place in the Indian community of medical institutions. The mission operates a large, 500-bed hospital, and its plan for 1972, example, projected the training of 300 medical students, 200 nurses, 50 paramedical students, an expected clientele of 180,000 for its outpatient clinics, and some 15,000 as inpatients (Here in Ludhiana, 1972). Operating on a non-profit basis, the hospital's main support is through medical

[2]A classic statement on expectations or components of the sick role in the United States was given by Parsons and Fox (1972). Also see a discussion of generalized extension of modernizing hospital services in a cross-cultural perspective in Glazer (1970).

service and medical education fees, with the deficit assumed by its union board of Protestant missions.

The staff members on the gynecology ward, besides ward *ayahs*, lady health visitors, and sweepers, consisted of Indian junior and senior physicians, Indian nurses, two foreign missionary women senior physicians, and one foreign male physician. In short, most of the staff were Indian. About half the nurses were Christian, and the others were either Hindu or Sikh. Since they were well trained and only the best were hired at the hospital, their point of view *vis-á-vis* the patients tended to reflect the modernization of their consciousness consequent to their education.

Patients' families characteristically dealt with female illnesses first by trying home remedies, after which the help of folk practitioners (*hakims* or *vaids*) would be sought. Local nurses in dispensaries might be consulted, and it was they who often referred patients to a hospital. Staff members at Brown Memorial and many patients said that families refused to treat women as early in their illness as men, partly because of their presumed indispensability for domestic duties and childcare, and partly because of potential exposure to strange males. In order of importance, the reasons patients gave me for their reluctance to seek treatment in hospitals were (1) the expense; (2) removal from home and family; (3) fear of exposure to male doctors; and (4) fear of painful procedures. Only one patient, a Brahmin, mentioned the ritual impurity of the ward as a motive in avoiding a hospital.

A large number of patients were interviewed within and outside the gynecology ward during the course of research, and among them, data were systematically recorded for a sample of 105. Occupational data were obtained for 99 patients. Most of them were directly supported by husbands, and indirectly by the families with whom they lived. Only two were self-supporting, poor widows who worked as daily wage labor. As shown in Table 1, the profile of occupational categories indicates that the majority in this group constituted what might be termed the economic middle range on a scale of financial resources.[3]

[3]It was not possible to obtain precise information on family income from patients. Such data are considered secret, and some patients seemed to fear that, should they tell me anything, I would disclose it to hospital staff members. The ability of a woman's kin to pay for her treatment, therefore, had to be inferred from their occupation and verbal cues.

TABLE 1
OCCUPATION OF BREADWINNER

Business	36
Family Farm	30
Salaried Service	20
Wages	13
Total	99

Since the business category included such occupations as shop owner, grain dealer, timber merchant, small factory owner, accountant—with shops predominating—it is reasonable to infer that, in this mainly agricultural state, these occupations formed part of the urban middle-class of the region. The family farm grouping was dominated by owners, with only two families cultivating land on shares. In salaried service, civil service jobs prevailed. These too are mainly middle-class socio-economically. The wage labor group, on the other hand, contained a segment of employment which partially represents the poverty classes of India: factory labor, odd jobs, piece work at home and household service.

If we remember that the joint-family ideology still predominates in north India, especially among business and farming groups, then it is legitimate to assume that the majority of patients in the sample, and probably in the ward, were members of families with financial resources. Other evidence on this point is also available. Both doctors and nurses, for example, reported that most of the patients paid the fees assessed. Shop owners usually have access to ready cash, and landowners to credit. Patients who were willing to discuss finances said that, once the family decided on hospitalization for a patient, the cash for fees would be found somehow. Finally, since the hospital charges fees as a significant measure of its budget, it would attract fewer people as inpatients than would the local civil hospital. The Brown Memorial also operates numerous free outpatient and travelling clinics. The physicians were alert to the poverty of some of their patients, and would arrange in those cases for the reduction or waiving of fees.[4] But practically all the patients said that medical care should be cheap, if not free.

[4]Many of the poor patients whom I interviewed in the ward were also receiving free meals and medications. Some patients made critical comparisons of Brown's fees to those of civil hospitals they had previously attended, but it was clear from their accounts that their stays in other hospitals had been longer than at

Related to the matter of costs is another factor, residential proximity to services, which is structurally important in more than a commonsense way. Convenience of physical access is, of course, basic in decisions about where to go for treatment. However, because of the traditional biases in favor of home care and the protection of women from strange men, the proximity of *kin* to the health resource was also important. Within my sample of patients almost half lived in Ludhiana District, and of these 70 per cent lived right in the town. The residences of the others were scattered all over the northern region of India, with the largest concentration from one town being only five. Data on the place of accommodation of their escorts support the statements of several patients, that proximity of the hospital to nearby kinsmen was significant in their recruitment. Table 2 shows the distribution:

TABLE 2
ACCOMMODATION OF ESCORTS OF OUT OF TOWN PATIENTS

Friends in Ludhiana		2
Relatives in Ludhiana		25
Relatives in nearby villages		4
	Total	31
Hostel or rented room		25
(N=105)	Total	56

Slightly over half of the patients came from other districts and states, and over half of these were staying with kin (two with friends, in the town).

NORTH INDIAN FAMILISM AND RECRUITMENT

What the patients did not necessarily speak of because they took it for granted, but what was abundantly clear from their behavior, was that they could not consider themselves as lone individuals confronting the necessity of hospitalization. They arrived attended by one or more relatives, some of whom remained as escorts for the duration of their stay. The reasons for this prevalence of relatives

Brown, and moreover that they had obtained no relief from their symptoms. It was at this point that some patients came to Brown Memorial. If they had gone there in the first place, of course, their total expense would have been less. But they had no way of knowing this, except to learn from experience.

and their necessity to the security system of the patients can be found in the structure of north Indian families, both Hindu and Sikh, and in varying degree in any primary-type society which emphasizes familistic values. In such societies, the worth of the individual is more a function of familial worth and status than of his or her own individual efforts. In this respect, obviously, people and families in India are vastly different from their counterparts in industrialized societies.

Authority in the north Indian family is exercised by elders, with separate but interdependent role systems for the two sexes. Ideally, all able members work together for the economic welfare and social status of the unit, and although partition of the joint property between brothers is a common result of centrifugal stresses within the family, joint ownership and management remain the ideal. Within this unit, despite tendencies toward feminine modernity in such outward forms as clothing styles, or the discarding of purdah between a woman and her elder male in-laws, women continue to be sheltered and socialized by their kinfolk. The family unit is the reference group for female self-identity (see Mandelbaum, 1971). As such, the presence of its representatives is therefore necessary to support the self image, the emotional security, and the public image of women patients in the ward.

ILLNESS DEFINITIONS

Illness itself was differentially viewed by staff and patients, although they both held views on its moral etiology. Patients' beliefs included a rather diffuse variety of causes, from accidents to witchcraft, while staff notions were more specific. Some patients expressed theories about improper diet, excessive worry, familial neglect, but they all eventually resorted to the concept of fate, saying that whatever happens is "already written on one's forehead." This notion was related to the theory of *karma,* the cosmic system of reward and punishment attributed to acts in a previous life. Moral peccability could thus be construed as a cause of illness, but with reference to their past lives, not the present one.

Ward sisters and staff nurses I interviewed also attributed moral etiologies to patients' illnesses, but not in terms of *karma.* Although they were Indian, as were the patients, they would refer to the ill-treatment of a patient by a husband or other relative, or their refusal to bring a woman to the hospital in time for early diagnosis and treatment. To these nurses, such behavior was morally wrong, a sign of laziness, neglect, indifference or selfishness on the part of those responsible for a woman's welfare. This response certainly appears to reflect the professional reference of the nurses' attitudes; and, moreover, nurses and other staff would often express an indignation about the condition of patients brought to them that the patients themselves appeared not to feel. Nurses also explained patients' frequent failures to follow up with post-hospital prescriptions as a result of laziness or neglect, and it was in this respect that they and the physicians justified keeping patients longer in the ward than would otherwise be necessary to make sure of their recovery before discharging them.

Although both staff and patients shared notions of the moral etiology of illness, staff views stressed personal and individual responsibility, while patients tended to emphasize cosmic justice. If considered in the light of cognitive dissonance theory, the fate explanation is readily understandable among people who do not, indeed, know much about the causes of gynecological disease, and who have little control over the decisions made about their lives.

Concepts of the Hospital

Patient and staff views of the hospital coincided in one major respect: the superiority of the mission hospital in cleanliness, service, and cures. However, the patients attributed this superiority to the mission's access to foreign funds and technicians, whereas the staff members, while granting the benefits of mission support, believed above all that Brown Memorial's superiority was based on its religious Christian ethic.

However, the patients I observed for six months in and around the obstetrics and gynecology services did not appreciate the missionary evangelism provided during their stay there. Reactions ranged from just ignoring the Bible evangelist as she made the round, to listening silently until she went away, or continuing conversations with other patients and refusing to be interrupted. Several women told me, as we sat outside the ward in the garden, that nothing would ever persuade them to change *their* religion. On the other hand, while patients did not hold the hospital's ethical philosophy to be relevant to their lives, they sometimes chose to invoke it in response to nurses' attempts at social control. One nurse told me that if she, justifiably (to herself), lost her temper while admonishing a patient, the latter might retort by asking, "Is this your Christian *dharma*?," meaning the behavior appropriate to her job and religion. The nurse complained that, "Because we are Christians, we are expected to be twice as good as anyone else!"

There was at least one instance during my stay there, however, when the religious creed of the hospital was central to a person's admission to Brown Memorial. He was a prominent politician of the district, who had been wounded in ambush in a village by his opponents. He insisted on going to the mission hospital because, as he put it, "Nobody there can be paid to poison me." He heard of politicians dying under mysterious circumstances in other hospitals.

There was no real conflict between patients and staff over their definitions of the hospital *per se*, only a kind of disappointment on the part of evangelistic staff members, and resentment among the more militantly Sikh patients, that their religious points of view were at odds.

Diet and its Complications

Diet in the gynecology ward was occasionally a source of controversy, or at least dissonance, between staff and patients. Since the obstetrics/gynecology services were located in the old original hospital building, about half a mile from the new buildings which also housed the kitchens, the dietician was gratified that few of the ob/gyn patients elected to take their meals from the hospital. Those who did so complained that the food arrived cold and tasteless. Food, as well as medication, was considered to have strength-giving properties, yet nutrition was complicated by religious or ritual considerations as well as medical requirements.

For example, the traditionally vegetarian diet of most of the women there, both Sikhs and Hindus, was a source of concern to physicians. The chief physician said that total vegetarians—refusing eggs as well as meat—were poor surgical risks as their wounds did not heal rapidly. The taboo on meat or eggs was also a problem with the high protein diets required by some diabetics, whom anxious relatives would sometimes trick into eating fish or chicken disguised as fried patties or snacks. People on low protein diets, on the other hand, could not understand why foods considered to eminently health giving, like milk and its products, were eliminated from their diets. These and other discrepancies between their cultural food values and the requisite diets of scientific medicine caused the patients no end of worry, and the staff members no end of questions and complaints. Other notions could also be briefly mentioned, such as their views of the hot or cold qualities of medical and food substances. A patient would decide that penicillin was too "hot" for her digestion, or that orange juice was too "cold," causing cough and throat discomfort.

Ritual and Secular Status in the Ward

The Christian ethic of the mission hospital did not permit the allocation of resources according to Hindu ritual criteria of caste status (cf. Bell 1969:40). Beds were assigned as they became available or according to medical criteria, with the most seriously ill patients located closest to the nursing desk. Patients rarely asked to be moved to another bed from the one they occupied, unless they happened to be next to a smelly patient, a very ill or groaning person, or a noisy one. Since all patients received the same nursing care (in accord with ward routine and other instrumental requirements), any of the social liabilities mentioned above would stem from the patient's illness, not from her caste position. One ward sister said that some patients did not want to wear hospital gowns (required only for surgery) for fear they had been worn by a diseased person. When I inquired whether "diseased person" might not be a euphemism for a low caste person, she explained that on the contrary they especially feared contact with clothing worn by lepers.[5] For these reasons, as well as for comfort of the patients in general, ward rules permitted them to wear their own clothing, if clean. It was difficult to detect to what extent rules of touchability operated in patient social interactions. The patients themselves did not like to talk about it, also because of their roughly similar socio-economic stratification, such issues were probably irrelevant most of the time. Three Brahmin women who were interviewed received no special treatment from anyone, nor did they ask for it. A Chamar and two other low caste women did not report ill

[5]In India, as in other parts of the world, leprosy is still fearfully avoided as magically contagious (see, e.g., Bell, 1969 : 247-248).

treatment while in the ward, although one elderly Chamar complained that Jats staying in the *serai* beyond the hospital wall refused her a sleeping place because she was of a lower caste. Caste position seemed to be irrelevant within the ward, although it might become salient beyond the hospital's purview. Also, in taking histories upon admission, nurses do not record *jati* names, but instead religious identification is requested (in keeping, perhaps, with the sectarian basis of the hospital).

That patients adopted the egalitarian ethic of the hospital was apparent in their reactions to suspected favoring of some patients over others. Hindus and Sikhs, for example, both commented resentfully on a presumed reduction in fees for Christians, a practice which had been discontinued for many years (as I was bitterly informed by one Christian elder of the town). This suspicion may well have been fostered, in part, by the policy of identifying patients by religion as well as name.

A common idea was that the rich were treated faster and received better care than the poor, a genuine reality in many civil hospitals, where nurses and orderlies dispense service only for gratuities, and whose physicians sometime will see only the patients who have cash for high fees, as reported to me by numerous Indian patients and Indian and foreign physicians (see Bell, 1960:40). Nursing staff in the Mission Hospital were strictly forbidden to accept such payments, a proscription reinforced by the hospital ethic and image.

Suspicions of favoritism in the ward were related to the relative education of the patients. Educated persons could appear to be receiving better care, since they were less confused and more articulate in their dealings with staff members. Since education in India presupposes relative wealth, the less educated people would indeed be susceptible to suspicions of better treatment for the "rich." But the really rich, belonging to the economic and social elite of the area, would not be found in a public ward. They preferred private nursing homes. From the nurse' point of view, contrary to the patients' suspicions, the favorite patients were the "innocent ones," the gentle, submissive village women, who were less apt to complain or demand services of various sorts.

POLLUTION MANAGEMENT

Staff and patient views of things considered polluting coincided empirically but not morally. Staff views were organized on the scientific category distinction of sepsis-antisepsis, whereas some patients had to contend with traditional ritual purity-pollution distinctions. For example, many thought of the hospital as a ritually impure place, "where sweepers come and go," as one Brahmin put it. For a Sikh woman, a medical procedure of shaving body hair required her to go to a temple after she left the hospital for purification, since the Sikh religion proscribes the cutting of hair. On the other hand, patients appreciated the cleanliness of the ward and of the staff members' uniforms for the same reasons that the hospital maintained them that way, although the habit of some patients—throwing orange peels and paper on the floor—often caused trouble with the nurses and ward *ayahs*.

While patients tended to think of the hospital as ritually impure, Christian staff members viewed their service as a source of moral purification and uplift in their ministry toward Christian goals (cf. Glaser, 1970:41). That some patients were not disposed to accord ethical credit to the hospital on this score was partly a function of their differing definitions of purity, partly a reflection of the strength of their attachment to their own religions. Awareness of the implicit criticism of the evangelistic motive also, perhaps, intensified their resistance to Christian definitions of the situation.

Blood as a Limited Resource

Staff and patients often experienced considerable dissonance about the provision of whole blood for transfusions. Patients shared the belief noted elsewhere in northern India (Carstairs, 1967:83 for Rajasthan; Wyon and Gordon, 1971:66 for Punjab) that blood exists in limited supply in the body, so that its loss for any reason causes debility. Nurses said that patients were always asking for "strength-giving" medications or injections (*takaat ki dawaai*), as these and certain foods were thought to improve the blood. Donations of blood for the sick, however, were considered potentially damaging to one's health. Conflicts arose on this point. One patient told me that two of her brothers had once donated blood, and although one continued in good health, the other had never fully recovered from this experience. If a woman relative were asked to donate blood, she would say that women are "too weak" to give it, but if a man were asked to donate the response would often be the same. On one occasion, I heard a house physician shout at the male escorts attending an emergency patient, "Are you still here? If you don't go immediately and give blood, I cannot be responsible for your patient's life!" Her threat was, of course, rhetorical, and usually relatives could be persuaded to purchase blood from the blood bank if they felt unable to donate it themselves. In any case, staff members were always a reliable source for emergencies.

The blood bank, however, was an additional cause of confusion for patients. Some knew that professional donors were paid by the hospital, yet they were expected to donate it free of charge. Why should they not be paid as well? Of course, it was the reluctance of most persons to donate blood which made the payment of professional donors necessary.[6]

Escorts in The Ward

Hospital rules permitted escorts to visit their patients four times per day, at the three meal times and at afternoon tea. Otherwise, they were to wait outside the wards. However, if they were on occasion permitted to linger, the nurses would rely on them for help in holding bedpans, fetching water, rolling bandages, or giving information about the patient. Escorts also comforted patients physically by fanning or massaging them, and thus their availability for conversation or just their presence provided social and emotional satisfactions for the patients. At such times they were virtually nursing aides.

Most of the staff members I consulted thought that the presence of kin was necessary to keep the patients happy. Only one nurse on gynecology ward duty was of the opinion that relatives were "a terrible nuisance," they got in the way, were always clamoring for something, made the patients feel worse instead of better. Her most telling point, however, was that she thought their presence made the nurses lazy, so that they "did not check up on the patients as often as they should." There was constant pressure on staff members, in

[6]The paid donors were commonly rickshaw drivers. Their health was carefully checked by the blood bank staff and their need for cash encouraged them to donate regularly. Since poverty was their lot, they presumably found it possible to relinquish their adherence to traditional notions about blood. I could not ascertain whether patients had any objections to receiving blood from unknown donors.

this ward and even in the new hospital, from relatives who would try to sneak into the wards through back doors, stair wells, and so forth, in order to unobtrusively take up their bedside posts. Occasionally, escorts would assist a patient in leaving the hospital before formal discharge and payment of the bills. When asked by the nurses how these persons had managed to escape, the other patients feigned surprise or ignorance of the episodes. The ward at times took on the appearance of a genteel combat zone in this conflict between familial claims and organizational routines.

The Patient's Role

Patients are generally required, in hospitals organized on the basis of scientific medicine, to adopt a hospital definition of the situation—the sick role or the patient role—and to behave accordingly. Coser (1962), in her classic study of interpersonal relations in an American hospital ward, wrote that:

> Because the patients have suffered a partial loss of ego identity, they seek reassurance and recognition through self-expressive behavior. The primary relationships established on the ward, like those that characterize family life, may come to be considered ends in themselves...(1962: 99).

Since those patients had to be separated from their kin, as well as from their non-patient roles at home and on the job, they turned naturally to the staff members for self-validation (Coser, 1962:42). Their views of the "good nurse" reflected this orientation to primary need gratification, as 39 out of 51 patients thought that the nurses' "supportive qualities" were most important and only two thought that "professional qualities" mattered most in the nursing role (Coser, 1962:75). Adoption of the sick role in the ward, thus, forced most of the American patients into non-autonomous, need dependent relationships with staff members.

The Indian patients in the mission hospital ward, on the other hand, cared minimally if at all whether or not they were personally liked by staff members. They thought that nurses should be "polite," "they should talk sweetly to us," and also "keep busy and not just stand around talking and gossiping." If a patient complained that she was not receiving "proper care," what she meant by this was that the nurses were not doing their job "properly" by being prompt in response to patient needs for bedpans, medications,discussion about treatment plans, discharge from the ward, and so forth. I did not record data on, or encounter, one single patient who expressed or intimated, hurt feelings as a result of a nurse's presumed attitude toward her. Thus, with respect to a major component of the sick role, removal from ordinary role obligations and normal role situations, (see Parsons and Fox, 1952 for the original attempt to analyze the sick role), the Indian patients did not find themselves helplessly dependent on staff members, as a result of the intervening presence of their relatives as escorts.

Another component of the sick role as proposed by Parsons and Fox (1952) is the presumed obligation of the patient to strive for his or her own recovery. Since patients were usually as passive with staff members as they were with their own kin, their indifference often frustrated the expectations of nurses and physicians in this regard. One day, for example, the ward sister (head nurse) decided that a patient ought to get up and walk a bit, in order to hasten her recovery from surgery. She helped the patient out of bed and started her off down the aisle, admonishing her not to hold on to the other bed railings. The patient reluctantly limped down the aisle, holding on all the way. On another occasion when a patient asked the ward sister for information on reducing fat, the sister tried to show her some exercises. The patient watched politely, but did not try to imitate her. In general, the patients expressed the attitude (exasperating to the nurses), often with folded palms, that "It is all in your hands." In short, socialization of patients to the sick role in this ward took place effectively at the level of *reciprocal performance of instrumental roles.*

INSTRUMENTAL ROLES

Expressive need satisfactions were provided by kin. Since, as Coser has pointed out (1962:70-74), there exists a conflict in the modern hospital's organization of the nursing role between the "loving care" component and the professional orientation, "The extent of 'loving care' that the patient will get will depend on the relative emphasis nurses place on these two role components" (Coser, 1962:71). Such a conflict in the nurse's role was neither potential nor real, most of the time, for the staff members in the mission hospital ward.

The loving care was supplied by patients' escorts, and the nurses were free to concentrate on the instrumental aspects of their role, their actual nursing duties. The only time that nurses experienced stress in this regard was when a patient had no one in attendance. Such patients would withdraw into feigned sleep, would weep a good deal, moan, and in other obvious ways express their anxiety and discomfort. The nurses felt that it was virtually impossible to comfort them. Patients deserted in this fashion took much longer to recover from their illnesses; and, indeed, it seemed that in the absence of kin escorts, hospital treatment on the whole could not have been very successful, nor would there have been many patients willing to be admitted.

Analysis and Conclusions

The establishment of modern scientific hospital facilities in pre-industrial or developing countries and their subsequent, often dramatic success with medical and surgical treatment has resulted in increased demand for these services.[7]

The cross-cultural surveys of Glaser and Bell coincide with my own research results in affirming the importance of primary group escorts to the subjective and objective well-being of inpatients and of hospital accommodations of their policies to this need. Since the typical unit of socialization and adult social interaction of clientele in primary type societies is still kinship, amplified by other primary units such as the village, the neighborhood, or using Hanks's term (1968) patronage *entourage*, it is proposed that the relationship between such clientele and the secondary institutions, or bureaucracies, they encounter can be formulated in terms of one characteristic common to them both: *custodialism,* or the authority to control life space and the access to resources within the unit.[8]

For cross-cultural comparative purposes, it seems reasonable to

[7]Takulia and others (1967 : 7, 43) commented that due to high success rate client demands increased substantially, so did the general hospital use in several developing countries (Bell, 1969). Mechanic (1973) reported a patient overflow in South African non-European wards due to similar results.

[8]This term has been contrasted by Stein and Oetting (1954) with *humanism,* which refers to non-authoritarian aspects of patient management in a mental institution. I have not employed the term in this article, as its many connotations could be confusing.

assert the primacy of familial custodialism *vis-á-vis* individual members for a majority of hospital clientele in primary-type societies, or in societies where industrialization has transformed the social system of only a small segment of the total population, as in many Mediterranean and most African and Asian nations, for example. By contrast, in European or American industrialized societies, Japan being probably an intermediate example, custodialism in the family is comparatively less, while in the bureaucracies it is relatively high. The most general analytical statement, therefore,of the relationship between clienteles and bureaucracies—i.e., between primary and secondary groups—could be expressed in the following way:

> Custodialism in the primary group is inversely related to custodialism in the secondary group.

For hospitals and their primary society clientele, as a particular instance, the model would state that:

> Custodialism in client families is inversely related to custodialism in hospital wards.

In those primary-type societies in which custodialism of family authorities is differentially exerted over men and women, with greater control over the latter, then the articulation between female clients and the secondary institution would, of course, show a stronger inverse relation than for male clients. In practice, this would mean that women patients would have a greater need than men patients for constant attendance, and their families would likewise assume this greater need and behave accordingly. The case of child patients could, possibly, show the strongest inverse relationship as it did in the mission hospital pediatrics ward, where the mothers or female escorts were permitted to stay in the ward at all times, and to sleep there at night with their charges.

Since familistic values are particular, and bureaucratic norms are supposed to be universal in their application, the statement of this inverse relation between the two institutions applies most aptly where the family and other primary affiliations of people are structurally and ideologically opposed to secondary affiliations and norms, as in India, and in many other nations where secondary institutions have been imposed by foreign rule. It is in these nations that one discovers the extremes of nepotic corruption characteristic of some governments, or of civil society, in South and Southeast Asia, which could well be described as the invasion or erosion of civil society by the family. In any case, Goffman (1961:12) has noted the basic incompatibility between primary and secondary institutions in his famous study of a mental hospital, *Asylums* (1961), and this same incompatibility is fundamental to Max Weber's theory of bureaucracy as a social form.

Although the interaction model, as I have formulated it, may appear to be truistic, this appearance is more deceptive than real, as its social significance continues to be ignored in much of the literature on the delivery of modern health care to primary society-type clientele (Glaser, 1970). With this model, any observer, whether inside or outside the relevant institutional setting, could predict areas of client-institution conflict, or could plan organizational innovations of benefit to both. In any event, the model economically expresses the fundamental socio-structural crux of a variety of problems which can appear in the confrontation between familistic clienteles and bureaucratic institutions, problems which might be handled piecemeal, and therefore ineffectively.

Probably the issue most apt to create difficulties is the isolation of the patient in the sick role, i.e., his or her isolation from relatives and or friends during hospitalization. Isolation of the patient from kin is the core idea of the classic statement by Parsons and Fox (1952) on the sick role among modern urban Americans.[9] They formulated this role concept with respect to a particular culture at a particular time in history, yet their analysis continues to appear like an old refrain in the literature on health delivery systems. The possibility that this concept is ethnocentric is not considered, for example, by Glaser (1970:147-148), whose chapter on economics and urbanism in the cross-cultural context of hospital services treats it as an unattained goal. He writes,

Most developing countries have lacked the mass media, the net-

[9]The sick role as they conceive it entails four role components, two rights and two obligations: the rights to removal from ordinary life roles and to expect treatment; the obligations to accept treatment and to strive for recovery. Since this statement is so inclusive, I see no utility for the purposes of this article in distinguishing between sick role and patient role. I use the terms interchangeably.

works of grassroots organizers, and the determination of the government necessary to educate the entire population in the *proper methods of playing the role of patient*. The Soviet Union may be the only developing country that has succeededi n a short time, *to the great benefit of the country's hospitals* (Glaser, 1970:62).[10]

Implied here, of course, is that there is only one proper method, the patient role as understood in technologically developed (and centrally dictatorial, to judge by his example) societies. Elsewhere, Glaser acknowledges the function of kin in providng "...the patient with his customary diet, personal services, and emotional support" (1970:89) but he considers the inclusion of the family in patient ward service as an inconvenient stage in the evolution of hospital services:

> Family institutions are among the last to change when a social system modernizes, and therefore the inpatient's dependence on the family may continue long after other aspects of the hospital have adopted the most *modern forms of organization under the authority of doctors and nurses.* Most modern countries restrict the family to the role of guests during fixed hours, and all nursing and catering are performed by the hospital's own staff. But in a few countries, *kinship ties remain strong and cause an 'uneven' development in hospital structures* (Glazer, 1970:89).[11]

As these citations show, his projection of the optimum modernization of hospitals follows the prevalent authoritarian and custodial model of the modern European or American urban hospital. That this conceptualization of the patient and of the organization of necessary services may not function well in societies different from his own is not considered by Glazer. A more sophisticated approach is evident in Charles Leslie's recent article on the modernization of Asian medical systems, where he suggests that

> . . . we should not assume, as laymen and physicians in the United States usually do, that the ideal of a uniform medical

[10]Emphasis added.
[11]Emphasis added.

> system controlled by physicians is intrinsically superior to other forms and should be the goal of all societies (1974:91).

The foregoing description of life in the Indian ward and my proposed interaction model, relations between familistic clienteles and bureaucratic institutions, emphasizes a viewpoint that we have all but lost in our own society, the legitimacy of primary social relations and groups. Recent work besides my own supports this position (see Bell, 1969; Roth, 1972). In Bell's final chapter on future possibilities for the family in the hospital, he notes that our culture and social system enhance the isolation of the patient from kin. He sees the future inclusion of the family in hospital care as a result of deliberate policy decisions stressing the social importance of strengthening the family (Bell, 1969:273-275).

More recently, Roth (1972) has argued that even in our own society the patient should be accompanied by an escort, whom Roth calls his "agent," (i.e., a person, not necessarily a family member, who is selected by the patient), in order to give the patient greater control over what happens to him in the hospital. Roth predicates this proposal by demonstrating that, (*a*) hospitals are dangerous places; (*b*) most patients find hospitals very unpleasant, entirely aside from the effects of their illness or the diagnostic and treatment procedures; (*c*) hospital treatment is an extremely costly way to treat most ailments (1972:426-431). He suggests that giving the patient or his agent some of the control hitherto reserved for staff members should make hospitals more tolerable and less costly (1972:444-446). Roth argues well the case for and against his proposal, and concludes that

> My effort in this paper has been to conceive of the hospital, not as a physical repository of patients undergoing treatment under the control of experts who make all the decisions, but rather to see hospitals as a cluster of services available to the public on the advice of medical authorities—services which may be drawn upon by patients when needed without relinquishing their civil liberties or relinquishing control over decisions which affect them (1972:446).

I have presented two essentially opposed points of view on the basic conflict between clientele and hospitals, a conflict centered on the custodial, or control aspects of the inpatient role Glaser's position is basically ethnocentric, while that of Bell and Roth should be considered humanistic in its emphasis on the legitimacy of primary affiliations.

In my own research I found that, although cultural definitions and structural situations might conflict there were accommodations between staff and patients such that inpatient treatment was possible among people whose social structure is certainly different from that of the hospital. Despite the extreme reluctance of North Indian families to place the medical treatment of their women in the hands of strangers, beds in the gynecology ward at the mission hospital were usually fully occupied.

Hospitalization for acute illness in our country does not need public legitimation, as our medical institutions and health culture have converged in the general dominance of the scientific ethos. Yet, as Roth reminds us, hospitals are unpleasant and dangerous. Changes will come about, however, only after some necessary demystification of the transcendent authority of secondary institutions and their personnel takes place. The world schedule, if I may call it that, of this process is a long one, involving greater emphasis on public participation in decisions about the delivery of health services as well as the opening up of rigid organizational norms within the nexus of scientific medicine.

Rather than attempt a, perhaps, futile prediction of directions of changes cross-culturally, one notes that Bell's impressions (1969:256) of modernization of hospitals in India are that they may be moving in the direction of "increased responsiveness. . . to international knowledge, standards, communication and consultation, with reduced responsiveness to local demands." He found the Indian government committed to Euro-American standards of teaching, research and training in their more prestigious medical centers, a commitment which would tend toward the exclusion of kin and the isolation of the patient in the sick role. In view of the felt legitimacy of primary relations to clienteles all over the world, it is to be hoped that planners in India and elsewhere, who follow so-called "Western," scientific models of health delivery, will experiment with flexible, open systems of hospital service. This is already happening in the United States in the form of alternative health delivery services, like Women's Health Centers, travelling clinics (particularly important in parts of Appalachia), street clinics among the drug addicts in ghettoes, mothers permitted to stay with their children in some pediatrics wards, and so on.

If for no other reason, the increasing cost of delivering health care in hospitals may bring about a modified return to home nursing of all but the most acutely ill patients. Certainly, the shortage of trained nurses in the developing countries makes it imperative that kinsmen be accepted as part of the health care "team." But whatever the degree of their involvement, policies which do not isolate the patient from his or her relatives or primary contacts need not result in nepotic forms of corruption, as is amply illustrated by the example of successful recruitment and treatment of patients in the Indian Mission Hospital described in this paper.

REFERENCES

BELL, JOHN ELDERKIN
1969 *The Family in the Hospital: Lessons From Developing Countries.* National Institute of Mental Health. Washington, D.C.: U.S. Government Printing Office.

BLUM, RICHARD and EVA BLUM
1965 *Health and Healing in Rural Greece.* Stanford: Stanford University Press.

CARSTAIRS, G. MORRIS
1967 *The Twice-Born,* Bloomington: Indiana University Press.

CAUDILL, WILLIAM
1951 "Around-the Clock Patient Care in Japanese Psychiatric Hospitals: The Role of the Tsukisoi." *American Sociological Review* 26: 204-214.

COSER, ROSE LAUB
1962 *Life in the Ward.* East Lansing, Michigan: Michigan State University Press.

FRIEDL, ERNESTINE
1958 "Hospital Care in Provincial Greece." *Human Organization* 16: 24-27.

GANS, HERBERT J.
1962 *The Urban Villagers: Group and Class in the Life of Italian-Americans.* New York: The Free Press.

GLASER, WILLIAM A.
1970 *Social Settings and Medical Organization; A Cross-National Study of the Hospital.* New York: Atherton Press.

GLUCKMAN, MAX (ed.)
1962 *Essays on the Ritual of Social Relations.* Manchester, England: Manchester University Press.

GOFFMAN, ERVING
1961 *Asylums. Essays on the Social Situation of Mental Patients and Other Inmates.* New York: Anchor Books.

HANKS, LUCIAN M.
1968 "Entourage and Circle in Burma." *Bennington Review* 2: 32-36.

"Here in Ludhiana"
1972 (Unsigned article). Official Publication of Christian Medical College, No. 67:6. Ludhiana, Punjab, India.

KHARE, R.S.
1972 "Indigenous Culture and Lawyer's Law in India." *Comparative Studies in Society and History* 14: 71-96.

KIRKPATRICK, JOANNA
1970 The Open Ward in a Closed Society: Social Interaction in a North Indian Hospital. Unpublished Ph.D. dissertation, Berkeley: University of California.

LEIGHTON, ALEXANDER H. and DOROTHEA C. LEIGHTON
1944 *The Navajo Door.* Cambridge, Massachusetts: Harvard University Press.

LESLIE, CHARLES
1974 "The Modernization of Asian Medical Systems." In John J. Poggie, and R.N. Lynch, (eds.), *Rethinking Modernization: Anthropological Perspectives.* Greenwood Press.

MANDELBAUM, DAVID G.
1971 *Society in India: Continuity and Change*, volume 1. Berkeley: University of California Press.

MECHANIC, DAVID
1973 "Apartheid Medicine." *Trans-action: Social Science and Modern Society* 10:36-44.

MORRISON, CHARLES
1972 "Kinship in Professional Relations: A Study of North Indian District Lawyers." *Comparative Studies in Society and History* 14:100-125.

PARSONS, TALCOTT and RENEE FOX
1952 "Illness, Therapy, and the Modern Urban American Family." *Journal of Social Issues* 7:31-44.

ROTH, JULIUS A.
1972 "The Necessity and Control of Hospitalization." *Social Science and Medicine* 6:425-446 .

STEIN, WILLIAM W. and E.R. OETTING
1964 "Humanism and Custodialism in a Peruvian Mental Hospital." *Human Organization* 23:218-282.

TAKULIA, HARBANS S., *et al.*
1967 *The Health Center Doctor in India.* The Johns Hopkins Monographs on International Health. Baltimore: Johns Hopkins University Press.

WYON, JOHN B. and JOHN E. GORDON
1971 *The Khanna Study: Population Problems in the Rural Punjab.* Cambridge, Massachusetts: Harvard University Press.

PROSHANTA K. NANDI

CULTURAL CONSTRAINTS ON PROFESSIONALIZATION: A CASE OF NURSING IN INDIA[1]

ABSTRACT. This paper examines the proposition that a large degree of occupational independence from the cultural-ethical contexts is important to the development and maintenance of rationalism so that the occupation or profession may retain a free hand to carry on toward its goals. Under scrutiny is the occupation/profession of nursing in a non-Western country viz., India since much of what nurses do there traditionally and currently is constrained by taboos for both sexes. After a brief historical overview of traditional health services, and an appraisal of the current status of nursing vis-á-vis the professional model, some specific advancements as well as some barriers are noted. The relative absence of a secular tradition in the occupational context and the prevailing detrimental attitudinal attributes are seen in nexus and are judged to be major force against the attainment of fully professionalized nursing in India.

ONE OF THE MAJOR TRENDS IN THE CONTEMPORARY INDUSTRIALIZED world is the development and proliferation of professions.[2] While professions in the Western societies have been subjected to much scrutiny, those in the developing societies have not. In a recent study

[1]The article was originally offered to this volume, however it also appears in the *International Journal of Nursing Studies* 14:125-135. The editor is grateful to Dr Kathleen J.W. Wilson, editor of the journal for permission to reprint this article.

[2]We have followed Vollmer and Mills in our use of the concepts "profession," "professionalism," and "professionalization." Seen in this light, the concept of "profession" will refer only to an abstract model of occupational organization whereas "professionalism" will refer to an ideology and associated activities that can be found in many and diverse occupational groups where members aspire to professional status. The concept of "professionalization" will refer to the dynamic process whereby many occupations can be observed to change certain crucial characteristics in the direction of a "profession" (Vollmer and Mills, 1966: vii-viii).

of one profession in a non-Western society, Nandi and Loomis (1974) analyzed professionalization as a socio-cultural process, and identified some of the attributes of the culture as they influenced professionalization.

Important to the development and maintenance of a rational structure in an organization is its success in insulating itself from or relating itself to its social context so as to retain a more or less free hand to carry on toward its goals (see Weber, 1947: 334-5; Scott, 1964: 500-1 and 1966: 266-7). Studies of non-industrial societies indicate that societies characterized by intimate association between bureaucratic organizations and other cultural and institutional complexes have fewer rational characteristics than those enjoying greater independence from their environment (cf. Berger, 1957: 135-145; Abegglen, 1958; Udy, 1962). Assuming that professionalization follows rational principles, this proposition can be extended to include the field of "professions," and it can be argued that a large degree of organizational independence from cultural contexts is related to the growth of professionalism in any area of specialized activity. Although professions are never completely culture-free, generally professions in the modern industrial societies appear to be more independent in this respect than those in the traditional societies. The present paper focuses on the occupation of nursing in India and attempts to analyze the interplay between occupational and cultural contexts and the development of attitudinal as well as organizational constraints against the attainment of fully professionalized nursing in India.

The intimate relationship between occupations and their complex social and cultural systems has long been seen by scholars to be characteristic of South Asian countries (e.g., Bendix, 1967; Mandelbaum, 1970; Srinivas, 1966). As Singer (1973: 1) notes:

> Occupations in these countries are more than just jobs: they are ways of life or, as we shall say, 'occupational cultures,' that is distinctive sets of values, beliefs and social institutions that have become associated with the practice of a particular occupation.[3]

[3]On the question of modernization, Singer, however, observes an ethnocentric bias on the part of Western scholars in their "telling people of South Asian countries who have just gained their independence from colonial rule through active struggles that their societies are too stable and traditional to change" and

Nursing in India in 1946, a year prior to the attainment of independence from England, was characterized by "a lack of professional status" according to the Report of the Health Survey and Development Committee.[4] The conditions in the seventies are not much superior to those described in that report. Despite some structural achievements which will be noted later, socio-cultural constraints still weigh against the growth of full professionalization. For an understanding of these constraints, it is necessary to turn to the cultural-historical context of health services in India.

Traditional Health Service in India

One of the major goals set by planners for health services in India is to professionalize all the roles of the health services. Any serious efforts to attain this objective must overcome two major obstacles. First, trained medical personnel are in exceedingly short supply—one doctor to 4,366 people, one dentist to 67,845, and one nurse to 6,500 (see the Statesman Weekly, April 28, 1973). Second, 75 per cent of those trained in these professions are in the cities and their services are not available to the rural villagers who constitute about 80 per cent of India's population. These villagers are served, instead, by traditional health practitioners.

Among the many thousands of traditional health practitioners in rural India are the *vaids* whose practice is based upon knowledge found in ancient texts of Hindu literature (cf. Lewis, 1958: 265; Swasth Hind, 1960: 138); the *Hakims* who practice a form of medicine that was brought in with the Muslims and Persian scripts (see Marriot, 1955: 258); sellers of magic charms which ward off sickness; the snake-bite curer who usually comes from the lower castes; and, the exorcist who is the Eastern counterpart of the faith-healer in the West.

The rationale of each of these practices varies according to the philosophy or faith in which each is founded. The approach of the religious exorcist, for example, is based upon his devotion to the

---

a growing realization on the part of the Western scholars "that the classical dichotomy of traditional and modern societies was largely a definition of ideal-type concepts and not a description of empirical realities. . ." (Singer, 1973: 2).

[4]Report of the Health Survey and Development Committee (1946, Vol. 2: 335), Chairman: Sir Joseph Bhore. Hereafter this Report is called the "Bhore Report" (1946).

god or goddess who is believed to cause the disease. The exorcist may throw fits and or go into trances and involve the family or even the caste of the patient in the cure. The religious exorcists are usually not from the higher castes and may even be Harijans (called Untouchable before Mahatma Gandhi's time).

Most of the traditional practitioners serve in a web of reciprocal relationships, receiving and rendering rewards as specified by custom. Their activities often involve many more people than the patient as the healing act is performed. Although the efficacy of the systems of traditional medicine is often underestimated by Western health specialists, even such supporters of the ancient secular systems of Indian medicine as the *Ayurvedic, Unani* and *Siddha* must admit that much of the folk medicine which villagers think is helpful is not actually so. One investigator, for instance, in discussing the prevalence of blindness in India (which afflicts millions) states the "eye cougars and quacks [are responsible for] contributing to the high rate of blindness" (Gupta, 1962: 143-6). A noted scholar of Indian demography, S. Chandrasekhar points out that the allopathic doctors dismiss the traditional Indian medicine for it stopped developing after the tenth century when the country lost her political stability as a result of a succession of foreign invasions (Chandrasekhar, 1972: 277). Nevertheless, the traditional systems of medicine are not only widely prevalent but are also popular because of their ancient roots in the cultural ethos of the society. Western medicine which came in with the British is relatively new, often suspect, and expensive, with too few practitioners available in the villages. In reality, traditionalism, fatalism, an overwhelming illiteracy (about 70 per cent), crushing poverty, and a lack of alternatives guarantee the predominate reliance of the people in the practice of traditional medicine in India (cf. Minturn and Hitchcock, 1963: 203-361).

Recognizing the enormous importance of the traditional systems of medicine and the concomitant health hazards to the patients because of nonscientific and nonformalized training of the traditional practitioners, a Central Council of Indian Medicine was set up in 1971 by the Government of India to evolve minimum standards of education. The 72-member Council maintains a national register of qualified practitioners of the traditional Indian systems. The Council has developed uniform syllabi for undergraduate education in *Ayurveda, Siddha* and *Unani.* At the time of writing, there are 92 *Ayurvedic,* 10 *Unani* and one *Siddha* undergraduate colleges, and 20 graduate departments (16 of *Ayurveda,* and 2 each of *Unani* and *Siddha*) which offer education in the Indian systems of medicine (India—A Reference Annual, 1975: 82). All these institutions receive financial assistance from the government. In addition, there are 74 institutions which provide training in Homoeopathy, 6 of which are run by the government. The Central (i.e., Federal) Government, through its Nature Cure Advisory Committee in the Union Ministry of Health and Family Planning, gives grants to research and educational institutes for the development of nature cure. Finally, the Central Council of Research in Indian Medicine and Homoeopathy was set up in 1969-1970. The Council is responsible for initiating and coordinating scientific research in the different aspects—fundamental and applied—of *Ayurveda, Siddha,* Homoeopathy and *Unani* systems of medicine, Nature Cure and Yoga. Boards have been set up in all the states in India for the regulation of practice in their traditional systems of medicine (India—A Reference Annual, 1975: 81-83).

These measures suggest that there is a growing awareness of the issues involved in traditional practices, at least at the government level. Unfortunately, however, the problem is far from solved because, again, most of these schools of medicine are located in the urban areas, and a trained practitioner seldom wishes to go back to the village to practice. The village is unattractive to a trained person of the city because it offers fewer means of physical and emotional comfort—e.g., running water, electricity, transportation, communication, and educational, recreational, and cultural facilities. This problem, however, is not unique to India but exists in advanced industrial societies where rural urban differences are not so acute.

The Dai or Midwife: A Traditional Occupation Antecedent to Nursing

Since about 80 per cent of all Indians live in villages where trained nurses and doctors are not commonly available, the *dai* or midwife is the one who delivers the child. The importance of the *dai's* services can be estimated from the fact that about 21 million babies are born each year. In his study of Punjabi villages in India, Kakar (1972: 14, 26) found that every village had one or two midwives and nearly 100 per cent of the deliveries were conducted by them (cf. Zachariah, 1971: 251-2, 271).

The *dai* operates on the basis of age-old traditions and customs. She inherits her caste occupation as most people do in rural India, and generally comes from the lowest caste so that she is not socially welcome in the higher caste homes where she delivers a child except when a prospective mother goes into labor. Her work of delivering a child is considered low because during and immediately after the delivery the mother and newborn are considered to be in a state of pollution and defilement, the period of which varies from region to region in rural India according to regional or local custom (cf. Lewis, 1958: 47-8). She lacks training in health and hygiene in the modern sense of the terms. One tragic effect of her lack of knowledge combined with general ignorance of the rural population, has been an enormously high rate of infant mortality. The national infant mortality rate, which was as high as 250 for both rural and urban areas per thousand births in the early parts of the twentieth century (India—A Reference Annual, 1973: 8), declined to 108 (rural) and 67 (urban) in 1966 according to the 20th round of the National Sample Survey (Chandrasekhar, 1972: 142). However, it is still high when compared to other countries which have modern health care facilities. The 1965 infant mortality rates per thousand births, for example, were: 12 in Sweden; 14 in Holland; 19 in each of the countries of Australia, England and Wales, and Japan; 20 in New Zealand; and 25 in the U.S.A. (Chandrasekhar, 1972: 105).

The attributes of autonomy and self-direction are not the only attributes called for on the part of the incumbents of a status-role.[5] Specialized knowledge and skills of the occupation are also important, so much so that entrance to it must be through achievement rather than ascription. The *dai* does *not* achieve her position; she is born to it. Her status-role has been developed by tradition and is diffuse, as opposed to specific as in the case of the trained nurse. Modern physicians, for example, are not required to and often resist making medical judgments for relatives or very close friends; they separate their human from their professional functions. Although the nurse's status-role combines a "mother-surrogate" as well as a "healer" component (see Schulman, 1958: 528-37), making her

[5]The concept of status-role may be defined as that which is expected of an individual because he or she is in a given status or position and acting out the role that belongs with this status or position (see Loomis, 1960: 19).

orientation more diffuse than that of some specialized professionals, she must be able to take a detached non-emotional view of her patient's needs. She must be able and free to act rationally in the patient's interest, sometimes against his or her professed wants. The untrained *dai* ordinarily fails to achieve this nonemotional objectivity because of the massive influence of the ancestral tradition (see Bhore Report, Vol. 2, 1946: 397).

The status-role of the *dai* functions in an atmosphere which of course does not promote professionalization. Nonetheless, aspects which could be thought of as promoting professionalization are detailed in the following statement from a well-known village study in India: "The [position] of the....[*dais*] degrades them, if further degradation is possible. Everything to do with a birth is unclean, and these women who touch the new baby and mother are thereby rendered unclean. At the same time their work makes them freer and more sophisticated than their menfolk, because it gives them an entree in homes of high as well as low castes. They carry their freedom with a cool boldness that makes their position enviable among women limited to single courtyards" [as is the case for most village women] (Wiser, 1963: 44-5).

Inadequate Autonomy

One of the principle objectives of professional socialization is the development of autonomy. One of the most difficult problems in socializing Indian women to various professional roles is developing independence, freeing them from subservience to the family and other similar groups where they hold status-roles which were inherited, not achieved. What are the features of Indian society which lead to devaluation of selfhood and autonomy?

Of the three social realms in the life of a rural Indian, family and kinship, village and caste, and the government and the market place, as Marriott (1955: 249) notes, the kinship or family group and the hierarchical links arranged across such groupings seem to be the most important in determining the nature of the self-concept. In the rural communities of the society, it is only within the network of the families related by blood and marriage ties that people rely on one another. The individual feels that people beyond this circle are completely indifferent to his welfare. Thus, a peasant will scarcely dare to venture out of his home village unless he knows where he will find bed and food among relatives. Marriott (1955: 250-1) maintains that the larger family does for the rural dweller what in Western society would be accomplished respectively by "receptionist, lawyer, nurse, orderly, secretary, and bondsman."

The absorption of the Indian individual into the family and hierarchical structure may well account for the failure of the self to develop and become autonomous, and this is more pronounced in the case of women. In an effort to interpret this, Margaret Cormack resorts to Piaget's well-known stages of child development. From her study of Indian women, she concludes that the Hindu girl remains submissive to her parents, accepting them without question because she accepts the family without question. She is not motivated to search for values of her own. Thus in terms of Piaget's stages, she moves rapidly from the first stage, autism, into the next stage, absolutism, where most norms are accepted without question. According to Cormack (1953: 203), however, most Hindu women remain in this stage of absolutism and never move to the final stage in which reciprocity between one's self and others is recognized in such a manner as to require different perspectives in different relationships, and that the individual make his/her own moral judgments.

Students of women's status-role in India vis-à-vis occupation and profession may well argue that these Indian women generally could do with more of that "boldness" mentioned by Wiser (1963). Those who speak thus would agree with Margaret Cormack (1953: 199) that "Hindu women are submissive and that they do not fulfil their potentialities or fully develop their personalities. . .[although] they are relatively secure psychologically." A bold woman is out of place. As one of Cormack's informants observes: "It is a common proverb that 'women's wits are only in their feet.' Women always give in. . . ."[6] The effect of this training on a young female acting out the role of a nurse, making autonomous decisions, exercising authority, and carrying out professional activities independently is obvious. The disadvantages of the female sex-role as compared with that of the male in India have been corroborated by a number of studies (e.g., Das, 1932; Cormack, 1953 and 1960;

[6]In a later study, however, Cormack observed a change among female students in colleges and universities in that they were learning to say "no" (Cormack, 1960: 101).

Weber, 1958; Carstairs, 1958; Bendix, 1960: 144-5; Nandi and Loomis, 1974:43-59).

THE PROFESSIONAL MODEL AND THE INDIAN CONTEXT

In recent work (Wilenski, 1964: 137-158); (Caplow, 1954: 139-140); (Kornhauser, 1963: 1), the professional model has been conceptualized using two sets of specific attributes; namely, structural and attitudinal.[7] Briefly, the structural attributes refer to formalized role-relationships in work including training and socialization. Specifically, they refer to the occupation's becoming a full time vocation, establishing training schools, forming professional associations, and developing a code of ethics. The attitudinal attributes refer to attitudes of practitioners toward their work, and consist of: belief in self-regulation, a sense of calling to the field, use of professional organization as a reference group, belief in service to the public, and a feeling of autonomy (cf. Kornhauser, 1963: Goode, 1957: 194-200; Gross 1958: 77-82; and Greenwood, 1957: 44-55). In addition, Caplow (1954: 139-140) and Wilenski (1964: 137-158) have developed formulations about steps involved in professionalization.

An occupation, in the sense of the ideal-type, may attain the character of a profession through the internalization of certain attitudinal attributes by its practitioners, and by its passage through the structural steps of professionalization. One of the major findings in recent studies is that the structural and attitudinal attributes do not necessarily develop together (Hall, 1968). A profession, may, at a given point, satisfy these conditions in different measures because of its unique history and processes in the work situation. Often, the attitudinal and structural elements do not complement each other.

Conceptually, then, an occupation may be high or low on the professionalization continuum, depending upon how successfully the occupation has obtained command over the two sets of attributes.

Given this framework, let us review briefly the structural advancements made by the occupation of nursing in India (cf. Wilkinson, 1958: Sundaram, 1970; Nandi and Loomis, 1974), and also some

[7]For a summary of these attributes, see Hall (1968: 92-104) especially 92-94.

of the lingering constraints. The earliest hospital in India was started in 1707 at Fort William, Calcutta by the British colonizers. The first training school for midwives was set up in Madras in 1797, although the training was admittedly substandard. It was not until 1809 that a hospital where Indians could go for Western medical care was opened.

The first training school for nurses was started in Madras in 1871 followed by one in Delhi in 1872. In 1882 nursing and midwifery training centers were opened in Calcutta. The Lady Harding Medical College, which was the first medical school for women in India, started a school for training nurses in 1915.

The training programs for nurses and midwives in these schools, however, were diverse and unstandardized. The need for standardization was strongly felt, and expressed in efforts that were initially regional. In 1909 the North India United Board of Examiners for Missions Hospitals was founded to regularize and standardize nurses' training in the Christian Missionary Hospitals in northern India. The idea of standardization of nurses' training was soon recognized as important and several government hospitals joined the Board. The establishment of military hospitals during the First World War helped the process of standardization.

The year 1909 saw a major breakthrough for the occupation when the *Nursing Journal of India,* the first professional monthly journal, began publication. Although there were several regional associations for nurses, a national association had not yet been founded. In 1922 two of the major regional associations merged together to form the Trained Nurses Association of India (hereafter referred to as TNAI), which was the first national organization of trained nurses. TNAI soon became the voice of the profession. This body has been influential in bringing about some significant changes—from government legislation to public opinion.

In 1946 two colleges of nursing in India started Bachelor's programs. Soon after India's independence in 1947, legislation was enacted to form the Indian Nursing Council whose primary function was to oversee the training of nurses. The first Master's program in nursing was instituted at the College of Nursing in Delhi in 1959. At the time of this writing there are 601 nursing and health schools and colleges for the training of nurses, auxiliary nurses/ midwives, and health visitors, and two universities which offer

Master of Nursing programs. In 1973 the number of students in these institutions was 19, 121, 12, 077, and 1,642 for nurses, auxiliary nurses/midwives, and health visitors respectively (see India—A Reference Annual, 1975: 84). Though encouraging, the number of these schools is not sufficient to prepare an adequate number of clinical specialists, researchers, teachers, and administrators.

Development of formal university curricula for nursing, however, encouraging, does not yet have the impact needed because the vast majority of nurses are not trained in these schools. The education of the vast majority is conducted as on-the-job training in the hospitals in total isolation from the system of higher education in the country, and is not recognized by any institution of higher learning. According to Sulochana Krishnan, Principal of the College of Nursing, New Delhi, the primary reason for this nonrecognition is that hospitals recruit students as employees who are included in the staffing pattern as hospital service personnel. The training is dominated by an employer-employee relationship and not by the mentor-student relationship which prevails in academic institutions of higher learning where students have achieved independent status. "In no other program of professional education have the students been so exploited by the management as in nursing" (Krishnan, 1971: 3). Unless this training program is conducted in an atmosphere of learning, scholarship, and professor-student relationship, the occupation will not be able to attract bright students from diverse socio-economic backgrounds. The absence of general education in the present 3½ to 4 years of on-the-job training following a High School diploma for nurses, and the 2½ years of training for auxiliary nurse-midwife in the Auxiliary Nurse-Midwife School following a seventh grade education hardly prepare the "trained" nurse or midwife to a professional level. In order to achieve what has been recommended by the Bhore and Mudaliar Committees[8] it is imperative that hospitals which offer nursing education start independent colleges of nursing affiliated with universities to ensure standards.

Despite these structural achievements, nursing in India faces formidable attitudinal constraints which deter its attainment of full professionalism; these constraints stem largely from the low

[8]Report of the Health Survey and Planning Commission, Chairman: A. Lakshmanaswami Mudaliar, August 1959-October 1960.

status granted the occupation. Unlike the structural developments described above which are relatively free of such constraints, the attitudes towards nursing are intricately linked with the general attitudes of the rest of the society. The low status of the occupation has to be understood in terms of traditional Indian notions of pollution and defilement which are frequently focused on body functions, e.g., menstruation, sexual relations, body emissions (see Bendix, 1960: 145n). Since a nurse's job may involve handling bed pans, blood, faeces and other body emissions, her work is often considered "socially unacceptable" and "indecent" (Cormack, 1953: 170).

An implicit but important element in the attitudinal attributes of professionalism is the emotional growth and maturity of the practitioner. A strong sense of calling implies feelings of worth and self-respect on the part of the practitioner in regard to the occupation. An occupational self-concept depends largely on what others think of the profession and practice. This is where cultural attitudes come into play in a most involved way. If the cultural attitude toward the occupation is negative, it is, at best, difficult for the practitioner to have a positive attitude of worth and self-respect. Lack of self-worth and self-respect cannot but adversely influence the attitudinal attributes of professionalism (cf. Cooley, 1922: 183-5 for the concept of the "looking-glass self").

For anyone who has spent some time recuperating in a hospital in India, it is not difficult to perceive that nurses are popular scapegoats; they are blamed for whatever goes wrong in the hospital by all—the patients, their relatives, doctors, and the administration. Even the student physicians, reportedly, are informally advised by their seniors not to socialize too much with the nurses because the latter do not belong to their station and may take undue advantage.[9] Stratification is almost absolute. Doctor-nurse marriages, common in many countries, hardly ever take place in India. The doctors are not the only ones so disposed. The lowest class of supportive employees, orderlies, wardboys and sweepers take a nonchalant approach when nurses need their assistance and cooperation. Haté (1969: 205-6) reports the comment of one nurse: "Nowa-

[9]This statement is based on conversations which the author had with his sister when she was a student physician in India.

days these fourth class people hardly care to obey us. The patient suffers and doctors are angry with us."

The attitudes of the government and public and private agencies toward nursing in India are reflected in the working and living conditions of nurses, which are not as bleak as before but still are far from satisfactory. One study (see Haté, 1969: 205-6) reports that nursing is characterized by overwork and helplessness.

> The first thing they (nurses) pointed out was that the number of patients is more than the provision of beds in the wards and they said they cannot refuse patients. They have to attend them. So they usually have to continue for a couple of hours longer than the scheduled time....They have to be on their feet all the eight or more hours of their duty. They have to be kind to the patients and attentive to the doctors. If they pull on patiently, as they usually do and in addition have to work for a longer time, one can imagine how exhausted they must be.

Another area of distress and concern to the nurses is the living accommodations provided by most hospitals. The typical dwellings allotted to the nurses are shabby and inadequate, and are not the best places to go for rest after an exhausting day at the hospital. Although the nurses do not have to live in these quarters, most of them, in fact, have no other alternative. They cannot commute from any distance because of severly inadequate public and private means of transportation. In an editorial comment the *Times of India* wrote on 15 April 1968: "The general failure on the part of hospital administration all over the country to provide their nursing staff with accommodations no better than that reserved for the lowest-paid employees is a cause of serious concern" (see Haté, 1969: 205-6). In general, two of the major deterrents to women's employment in India are restricted mobility and non-availability of proper housing facilities.

Employees, especially those in white collar roles in public organizations in India, usually develop strategies to cope with such problems. Strategies may involve anything from delaying the return of files to restricting output to what the informal group norms consider a day's work. Because of strong unionism among employees, bureaucratic bosses generally go along with their employees and overlook minor violations of the rules as long as they are not blatantly conspicuous. These strategies, however, are unavailable to nurses because of their nature of work. Laxity or default may be traced easily to the defaulting nurse. A neglected patient may agonize in pain or a disease may turn worse if medication or help is not given at the porper time. Unionism and collective bargaining have been declared illegal for nurses according to the recent decision of the Supreme Court of India (see Veerappa, 1970: 149, 169).[10] Political agitation, as Caplow notes (1954: 139), is one of the definite and explicit sequential steps involved in professionalization of any occupation, and by this court decision is not available.

In Western society it often happens that occupations involving work which is considered disagreeable have lower rank than others. However, any occupation as important as that the nurse or *dai* in India would in the West rise in the ranking system. Disagreeable features of the work might somehow be offset by its importance to the community and society. In developed societies important work having disagreeable qualities sometimes bring high rewards. The case of the undertaker in the West may be cited as an example of this. His income is relatively high compared with others having comparable training.

INEFFECTIVE ORGANIZATIONAL CONTEXT

Apart from the low cultural evaluation of nursing, the failure on the part of the trained nurses to promote the cause of their occupation adequately has to be noted. This inadequacy, however, is not limited to the nurses' organization alone, but is common to almost all organizations in India. There seems to be a wide gap between planning and execution, setting of goals and developing realistic procedures to attain those goals.

Historically, capacity for organization along secular lines has not been a strong point in Indian cultural development. The ancient texts of the Hindus are entirely silent about this aspect of

[10]When nurses in Delhi did go on strike in 1973, the official journal of *The Trained Nurses Association of India*, through a lead article, condemned the strike as well as the nurses' conduct during it as deplorable. "By unruly behavior and neglect of patients the nurses defeat their own ends because they forfeit the sympathy and respect of the general public and their employers." (see Adrenvala 1973: 357-58).

social life. These texts have no framework for an organization which is secular and universalistic in principle and application. Not that there were no sound organizations in India up until the recent past, but most such organizations were developed along parochial interests, especially religion and caste. There are thousands of castes and subcastes with distinctive characteristics and elaborate social organization. In a study in the north Indian city about a decade ago, Nandi (1965: 84-99) found that every caste from the Brahmins to the Sudras had developed organizations to further its own interests.

The industry, artistry, and finesse for which the Hindu artisan was noted (see Weber, 1958: 113) were based on solo efforts rather than on group efforts involving diverse resources and manpower characterized by specialization and division of labor. Such extreme industry on the part of one person or family is in large measure due to *dharma* (i.e., dedication to one's caste norms and values) which induces them to work so hard. Organizations involving culturally diverse constituents which cut across parochial rootings are rather recent phenomena in India.

With the independence of the country from Britain in 1947 and adoption of her secular constitution in 1950, it would seem that parochial forces would be gradually replaced by those ideologically more secular and national. However, the evidence does not indicate this change. The caste system has not disappeared in independent India. It has been revitalized, and today its influence is evident in almost all walks of life—in politics, in business enterprises, in educational institution, to name a few (cf. Srinivas, 1964; Lewis, 1964).

In sum, organizations in India have yet to develop a secular tradition which will be relatively free from ascriptive cleavages. With constituents influenced by diverse traditions along lines of caste, community, region, religion, and language, allegiance to secular goals is likely to be rather low. It is more than likely that organizations characterized by such cleavages will lose in terms of efficiency, effectiveness and rationalism. It is the obvious result of the lack of independence of the organization from its cultural context.

CONCLUSION

The argument is not that Indians underrate conservation of life, alleviation of suffering, and promotion of health—the three basic tenets of nursing ethics. It is that those who are trained for and charged with these responsibilities are at the same time denied a decent working and living condition, and that their work is looked down upon as unseemly. The nurse's lack of professional status, her low and unattractive salary, indequate recognition of her services by the community, little incentive for quality performance, hardship of rural assignment without satisfactory compensation, insufficient and inadequate university programs for training are the result of the lack of independence of the occupation from the cultural context. The usual lip service of the Indian health administrators and policy makers to the nobility and humaneness of the profession without corresponding moves toward providing its practitioners with a noble and humane environment has deterred the growth of professionalism in nursing in India to the detriment of the occupation and to the society as a whole.

REFERENCES

ABEGGLEN, J. C.

1958 *The Japanese Factory*. Glencoe, Ill.: The Free Press.

ADRENVALA, T.K.

1973 "Professional Behaviour—Some Aspects of Nursing Practice." *Nursing Journal of India* 64 (October): 357-8.

BENDIX, REINHARD

1960 *Max Weber—An Intellectual Portrait*. Garden City, N.Y.: Doubleday and Co.

1967 "Tradition and Modernity Reconsidered." *Comparative Studies in Society and History* 9 (April): 292-346.

BERGER, M.

1957 *Bureaucracy and Society in Modern Egypt*. Princeton, N.J.: Princeton University Press.

BHORE REPORT

1946 *Report of the Health Survey and Development Committee*. (Vol. 1 and 2, Chairman: Sir Joseph Bhore). Delhi: Government of India Press.

CAPLOW, THEODORE

1954 *The Sociology of Work*. Minneapolis: University of Minnesota Press.

CHANDRASEKHAR, S.

1972 *Infant Mortality, Population Growth and Family Planning in India*. London: George Allen & Unwin Ltd.

CARSTAIRS, G. MORRIS

1958 *The Twice Born*. Bloomington: Indiana University Press.

CORMACK, MARGARET

1953 *The Hindu Woman*. New York: Bureau of Publications, Teacher's College, Columbia University.

1960 *She Who Rides a Peacock*. Bombay: Asia Publishing House.

COOLEY, CHARLES H.

1922 *Human Nature and the Social Order*. New York: Scribner's.

DAS, FRIEDA M.

1932 *Purdah, The Status of Hindu Women*. New York: Vangard Press Inc.

GOODE, WILLIAM J.

1957 "Community Within a Community: The Professions." *American Sociological Review* 22 (April): 194-200.

GREENWOOD, ERNEST

1957 "Attributes of a Profession." *Social Work* 3 (July): 44-55.

GROSS, EDWARD

1958 *Work and Society*. New York: Thomas Y. Crowell Co.

GUPTA, U.C.

1962 "Thousands Can Be Saved From Going Blind." *Population Review* 6: 143-6.

HALL, RICHARD H.

1968 "Professionalization and Bureaucratization,." *American Sociological Review* 33 (February): 92-104.

HATE, CHANDRAKALA A.

1969 *Changing Status of Women in Post Independence India*. Bomby: Allied Publishers.

India—A Reference Annual.

1973 New Delhi: Government of India.

India—A Reference Annual.

1975 New Delhi: Government of India.

KAKAR, D.N.

1972 "Role of Indigenous Midwife in Family Planning Programme."*Nursing Journal of India* 1 (January): 14, 26.

KRISHNAN, SULOCHANA

1971 "Status of Women in Nursing Profession." Working paper presented to the Committee on the Status of Women in India (unpublished).

KORNHAUSER, WILLIAM

1963 *Scientists in Industry*. Berkeley: University of California Press.

LEWIS, JOHN P.

1964 *Quiet Crisis in India*. New York: Doubleday Anchor.

LEWIS, OSCAR

1958 *Village Life in Northern India*. Urbana: University of Illinois Press.

LOOMIS, CHARLES P.

1960 *Social Systems—Essays on Their Persistence and Change*. Princeton, N.J.: D. Van Nostrand.

MANDLEBAUM, DAVID G.

1970 *Society in India*. (Volume 1 and 2). Berkeley: University of California Press (2 Vols).

MARRIOTT, MCKIM
1955 "Western Medicine in a Village of Northern India." In Benjamin D. Paul (ed.), *Health, Culture and Community*, pp. 239-68. New York: Russell Sage Foundation.

MINTURN, LEIGH and JOHN T. HITCHCOCK
1963 "The Rajputs of Khalapur, India." In Beatrice B. Whiting (ed.), *Six Cultures—Studies in Child Rearing*, pp. 201-361. New York: John Wiley and Sons.

NANDI, PROSHANTA K.
1965 "A Study of Caste Organizations in Kanpur." *Man in India* 45 (January-March): 84-99.

NANDI, PROSHANTA K. and CHARLES P. LOOMIS
1974 "Professionalization of Nursing in India: Deterring and Facilitating Aspects of the Culture." *Journal of Asian and African Studies* 9 (January-April): 43-59.

REPORT OF THE HEALTH SURVEY AND PLANNING COMMISSION
1960 Chairman: A. Lakshmanaswami (August 1959-October 1960), Ministry of Health, Government of India. Madras: Jupiter Press.

SCHULMAN, SAM
1958 "Basic Functional Roles in Nursing: Mother Surrogate and Healer." In E. Gartly Jaco (ed.), *Patients, Physicians, and Illness—Behavioral Sciences and Medicines*, pp. 528-37. Glencoe, Ill.: The Free Press.

SCOTT, W. RICHARD
1964 "Theory of Organizations." In Robert E.L. Faris, (ed.), *Handbook of Modern Sociology*, pp. 485-529. Chicago: Rand McNally and Co.
1966 "Professionals in Bureaucracies—Areas of Conflict." In Vollmer and Mills (eds.), *Professionalization*, pp. 265-75. New Jersey: Prentice Hall.

SINGER, MILTON B.
1973 "Modernization of Occupational Cultures in South Asia." In Milton B. Singer, (ed.), *Entrepreneurship and Modernization of Occupational Cultures in South Asia*, pp. 1-15. Durham, N.C.: Monograph and Occasional Papers Series, Monograph No. 12, Program in Comparative Studies on Southern Asia, Duke University.

SRINIVAS, M.N.
1964 *Caste in Modern India and Other Essays*. Bombay: Asia Publishing House.
1968 *Social Change in Modern India*. Berkeley: University of California Press.

THE STATESMAN WEEKLY.
1973 *The Statesman* (April 28). Calcutta. The Statesman Press.

SUNDARAM, S.
1970 "Growth of Nursing in India." *The Nursing Journal of India* 11 (November): 353-54, 381-82.

SWASTH HIND
1960 Delhi: Central Health Education Bureau, (Government of India) 4 (April): 138.

UDY, S.H. JR.
1962 "Administrative Rationality, Social Setting, and Organizational Development." *American Journal of Sociology* 68: 299-308.

VEERAPPA, M.
1970 "Supreme Court Verdict Adverse to Trade Unions." *Nursing Journal of India* 5 (May): 149-169.

VOLLMER, HOWARD M., and DONALD MILLS (eds.)
1966 *Professionalization.* New Jersey: Prentice Hall.

WEBER, MAX
1947 *The Theory of Social and Economic Organization* (Translated into English by A.M. Henderson and Talcott Parsons). Glencoe, Ill.: The Free Press.
1958 *The Religion of India* (English Translation by Hans Gerth and Don Martindale). Glencoe, Ill.: The Free Press.

WILENSKI, HAROLD L.
1964 "The Professionalization of Everyone?" *American Journal of Sociology* 70 (September): 137-58.

WILKINSON, A.
1958 *A Brief History of Nursing in India and Pakistan.* Madras: The Trained Nurses Association of India.

WISER, WILLIAM and CHARLOTTE
1963 *Behind Mud Walls* 1930-1960. Berkeley: University of California Press.

ZACHARIAH, S.
1971 "Midwifery Service in Rural West Bengal." *Nursing Journal of India* 8 (August): 251-71.

KLAAS W. VAN DER VEEN

*SOCIO-CULTURAL ASPECTS OF MEDICAL CARE IN VALSAD DISTRICT, GUJARAT STATE**

ABSTRACT. As in the rest of India there is a vast discrepancy between the medical facilities of private practitioners in the urban centers and the state-paid rural Primary Health Center in Valsad District. Though the majority of the rural population and the tribal communities are dependent on the services of the PHCs, the State Health Centers are still under-utilized. Structural factors can explain the ill-functioning of the PHCs yet there is reason to take into account socio-cultural factors. The efforts to introduce modern (Western) medicine have too often neglected the fact that the average Indian villager interprets the relationship with a doctor in terms of a diffused many stranded and mutually obligatory relationship. The people tend to believe that they "invest in people" and status accentuation is the main mechanism to control their relationships. Through some cases it has been illustrated that these socio-cultural aspects influence the effectivity of medical care.

IT IS NOW GENERALLY ACCEPTED THAT SOCIO-CULTURAL FACTORS play an important role in the effective use of modern medical care. Failures to realize real improvement of the health situation indicate that effective community medicine demands a proper understanding of the social milieu. This holds true for the Western world but more so for the so-called developing nations. The introduction of technical medical concepts as well as an organization mainly based on Western ideals and practices were often found to be in

*Data for this paper were collected in January 1976, during which a field trip to the Valsad region was supported by a research grant from Amsterdam University. I wish to thank my colleague and friend Ismail A. Lambet for his hospitality. I also am indebted to Dr. Sjaak van der Geest for his critical comments on the first draft of this paper.

clash with the structure of traditional society. This in many cases is caused due to financial and structural limitations. Lack of funds makes it difficult to realize the goals in health care but this is only a part of the story. In this paper, an attempt has been made to analyze aspects which are related to the general character of social relationships in a highly stratified society where the socio-cultural elements determine the actions of the people (see Wolf, 1966: 60-95).

The efforts to introduce modern medicine and a new health organization have often shown a certain disregard for the fact that the majority of Indians in the village-setting interpret health, sickness and their relationship with doctors in terms of their general view of the world. This means that they give excessive importance to the maintenance of primordial attachments. These can be defined as relationships based on the explicit assumption of a personal bond between the partners. Such relationships can be between status-equals as well as between partners with widely different status. Essential is the many-stranded character of such relationships, which means that it is built upon the inter-weaving of many ties which implicate one another: economic exchange implies kinship or friendship, neighborliness or a patron client relationship and these in turn are reinforced and represented by social symbols and rules of behavior that are socially sanctioned and sustained by the members of the group as a whole (Wolf, 1966: 80).

The paper has been divided in four parts. The first part presents general information about health care in the district. Section 2 deals with some possible reasons for the under-utilization of state medical facilities and Section 3 relates to the problem to the context of socio-cultural factors in the village setting.

Valsad is the southernmost district of Gujarat State on the west coast of India. The Valsad (or Bulsar) district was established in 1962 after the division of the former Surat district into a northern (Surat) and a southern (Valsad) part. According to 1971 census, the total population of the Valsad district was nearly 1.5 million of which 82 per cent live in rural areas. The density of population is 273 per kilometer (for Gujarat state this amounts to 136 per kilometer).

During the period 1961-1971 the population growth in Valsad was about 25.57 (for Gujarat as a whole it was about 29.39). Literacy (in the sense that people are able to read and write) amounts to 46 per cent for men and 29 per cent for women (an average of 37.5 per cent). Over half 54.5 per cent of the population belongs to the so-called tribal castes (Dhodiya, Naika and Dubla). The Dubla are landless while the Naika and Dhodiya are small landowners. Generally speaking these tribal castes belong to the poorest category of the population. The general literacy is far less among this category of the population and still lesser among women which is about 10 per cent.

The former untouchable castes in this region represent about 3 per cent of the total population and as a group they are, contrary to many other parts of India, not the poorest.

The estimated distribution of caste groups in South Gujarat is as follows:

High castes (Brahmans, Kshatriya and Vaisya)	10 per cent
Middle castes (Shudra and Artisan-castes)	20 per cent
Muslim, Parsi, Christians and others	10 per cent
Tribal and low castes	60 per cent

STATE HEALTH CENTERS AND PRIVATE PRACTITIONERS

It is estimated that the State Health Centers serve at least 60 per cent of the population. It is a prominent feature of the Indian health organization that private practitioners exist side by side with the State facilities. The State centers provide treatment and medicine at no cost to the patient while the private practitioners charge fees depending on their status and prestige ranging from Re 1 to Rs 40. Medications are charged in addition to consultations.

Apart from the division between the State medical facilities and the private doctors there is another important difference between doctors of the Western system of allopathic medicine, and practitioners of other (indigenous) medical systems including homoeopathy, Unani and Ayurvedic, the latter two relate to formal training in the ancient Muhammedan and Hindu medical traditions. Nowadays such a training takes about four years in addition to basic knowledge of allopathy.

There are also registered medical practitioners who do not have any formal training. They mostly are trained as assistants to allopathic doctors. Some experienced hands were allowed to appear in an examination to become registered medical practitioners in villages where no officially recognized doctor is available. Though such a diploma to practice is not available now in Gujarat State, however, there are many RMP's working in remote villages. The official recognition of these para-professionals with practical knowledge of Western medicine but limited formal education was part of the efforts to provide immediate health services to the rural areas. The Ayurvedic and Unani practitioners are also officially registered as RMPs. There is still another category of *un-official* "medical men"—the male "Bhagat" and the female "Bhagtani" who wish their clairvoyant trance performances to play an important role in curing, healing and treating a variety of diseases.

The health manpower strategy in India during the three last decades was characterized by a preference for the concentration of limited resources on the expansion of high-level medical education and a consequent concentration of health personnel in urban areas, an unwillingness to recognize indigenous medical practitioners and also an opposition to the delegation of the primary curative functions to paramedical personnel (Maru, 1976: 1263, see Doyal and Pennell, 1976 for a critical comment on this strategy).

This policy is in contrast to the Chinese solution (at least after 1965). In China the accent has been more on redistribution of medical manpower and physical facilities in favor of rural and poor sections of society.

This required an increase in admission to medical colleges, a shortening of the duration of the medical curriculum and especially placing greater emphasis on the use of para-professionals and indigenous medical practitioners in regular health organizations (Maru, 1976: 1264-1265).

Through the centralization of power in the hands of the leadership and proclamation of a socialist planned economy, the development of a private sector in health care was impossible in China.

In India, the concern was to increase the stock of medical manpower, which has been achieved through the expansion of medical colleges and paramedical institutions where formal full-time education has remained the most important method of training. Since 1960 the number of medical colleges has increased from 57 to 102. The enrollment more than doubled and the number of doctors increased by 97 per cent reaching a record high of 137, 930, while the number of nurses and Auxiliary Midwives nearly trippled to 107,900 in the same period (Maru, 1976: 1259). This increase, however, was especially important for the creation of a group of well trained "specialists," entering private practice (hospitals and clinics) in urban centers. This general picture also holds true for the Valsad district.

STATE HEALTH CENTERS IN THE VALSAD DISTRICT

According to the 1971 census, there were 18 Primary Health Centers headed by at least one allopathic Western trained doctor, one or more nurses and/or auxiliary nurses, midwives, specially trained personnel for family planning, sanitation, TB and Leprosy care. Besides these, 46 Mother and Child Health Centers handled educational and preventive tasks of childbirth. There were 12 Dispensaries or Health Sub-centers, which were smaller and less well equipped than the Primary Health Centers offering basic medical services.

The civil hospital serves the population in Bulsar, the District Headquarters, which carries 50 beds and 40 in Navsari where the civil hospital is also the headquarters for the district TB care.

During 1961-1971 the number of PHC's increased by 29 per cent (from 14 to 18), while the facilities of Mother and Child Health Centers, Dispensaries and Health Sub-centers increased from 7 to to 46.

The all-India target was to have a PHC to serve a population of about 60,000 to 80,000 which has not been yet achieved, the ratio is 1 PHC to about 83,000 people (see Maru, 1976 : 1259). Though the overall government policy regarding indigenous medical facilities has not been very encouraging the Valsad district has witnessed a great increase in the activities of government Ayurvedic medical care. Until 1966 there were no state facilities in this field. However in 1971, one Ayurvedic hospital and three dispensaries were established with a total number of 20 beds. These offered services to 420 indoor patients and 8,387 outpatients.

PRIVATE MEDICAL FACILITIES IN THE DISTRICT

The dispensaries run by private practitioners are generally in the larger villages, and there are 19 private hospitals, nursing and maternity homes, mainly in the cities of Bulsar, Billimore and Navsari, which are run by one or more private practitioners (mostly Western trained allopathic doctors). There are also a few hospitals and nursing homes run by charitable associations such as the hospitals in the interior *talukas* (subdistricts) of Bansda and Dharampur, respectively with 50 and 21 beds. The latter are meant primarily for the poor, while the former are intended only for the upper classes. It is financially impossible for the poor to afford *regular* treatment by private practitioners.

The total number of beds available in the district in 1971 was 510. It can be estimated that at least 60 per cent of these will only be used for the upper-middle and upper class (less than 10 per cent of the total population). According to the District Health Department in Bulsar, in autumn 1971 there were 286 medical practitioners in the district: 123, or 43 per cent of them practiced in the cities of Bulsar, Billimora and Navsari, which shares only 12.5 per cent of the district.

The Primary Health Center at Aligam

Aligam (a fictitious name) is a village of about 4000 inhabitants of whom 50 per cent belong to the tribal, and other lower castes including a large number of Muslims. Aligam is situated near the National Highway connecting Surat city with Bombay. The choice of Aligam PHC was mainly guided by possibilities for additional background-information. Though Aligam is not typical, the only definite distinction it has from other villages is that it is a "Muslim-village" (Muslims being the leading landowning group) who form about 7 per cent of the total district population.

The Aligam PHC is composed of two doctors (a couple), an auxiliary nurse, midwife and other para-medical personnel such as a laboratory assistant. Presence of this technician is certainly not common at all PHC's or subcenters. The salary for fully trained laboratory technicians, who after secondary training had an additional training of several years, is not satisfactory. Moreover the minimal equipment of the PHC's makes laboratory work unsophisticated and much less interesting than work in private laboratories in the cities. This lack of opportunities to the laboratory technicians in the rural areas is again a structural disadvantage of considerable importance.

In addition, there is a dispenser of medicines who also keeps records of medicines and their distribution. Then there are specially trained para-medical officials for Family Planning, a Sanitary Inspector and Supervisor, a Vaccination Supervisor as well as the so-called Leprosy and TB workers. Two Auxiliary Nurses Midwives are posted in nearby villages, but they are attached to the PHC. The TB, Leprosy, Vaccination and Family Planning workers tour the nearby villages and report to the Aligam Center once or twice a week.

Next to the para-medical personnel there is a staff which includes a clerk, a driver, several peons and sweepers working at the PHC. The center has a jeep, but it can only be used for special purposes like vaccination drives, family planning campaigns among others. The Center is open for consultation from 9:00 A.M. to 12:00 P.M. In the afternoon the doctors, nurses and others are expected to make housecalls in nearby villages.

In principle all medical care is free of charge. In most cases, the doctor is supposed to administer simple and cheap medicines. Generally speaking there are no injectable medicines available. The purchase of medicines is done by the District Medical Officer at the District Headquarters and since the pharmaceutical industry in India is only partly government-controlled there is opportunity for the customary promotion mechanism to influence sales of specific medicines (see Doyal and Pennel, 1976: and Djurfeldt and Lindberg, 1975: 24, for a critique on this structural obstacle to an optimal use of resources).

Each year there is a 10 per cent increase in the number of male patients while the number of female patients remains constant. The male-female ratio in the subdistrict shows 1.5 per cent more females. Table 1 indicates that there was a sharp decline in the

TABLE 1
NUMBER OF PATIENTS VISITING THE ALIGAM PHC 1971-1975

Year	*Total*	*% old*	*% new*
1971	12,305	48	52
1972	8,718	60	40
1973	10,836	44	56
1974	11,937	31	69
1975	12,253	41	59

number of patients in 1972. This decline may have been due to a very active Family Planning Department campaign which took place in 1971-1972. A strongly negative opinion prevails among the people against the Family Planning Department due to a fear that patients at the PHC are obliged or forced to have themselves sterilized by means of tubectomy or vasectomy. It may also have caused opinions due to the arrival of a new doctor. In May, 1972 a new lady doctor joined the staff and in December her husband also entered the service at the PHC as a doctor. There is a strong tendency to regard the relationship with a doctor at a more or less personal level and patients are initially somewhat reserved when a new doctor arrives. People have a great mistrust for the unknown. Since the private practitioners business depends upon their popularity, it is believed they pay more attention to their visiting patients. It is not uncommon for the poor patients as well, to consult other medical doctors, quacks or "bhagats" in addition to the doctor at the PHC. Djurfeldt and Lindberg (1975: 109-112) reported a similar situation in South India. A sharp decline in the number of patients was noticed due to "change of policy . . . mostly as a result of change in staff," the number of monthly attendants at the clinic dropped from an average of 1500 to 1000 a month. Hassan (1967: 166-184), who did an intensive research on a PHC in North India, found a considerable decline in the number of patients after the replacement of the doctor incharge, an average monthly attendance of about 1400 dropped to about 900 when a much less liked doctor started working there. The data of Djurfeldt and Lindberg confirm this picture. So there is every reason to believe that *under-utilization* is a concurrent aspect, not only at the Aligam PHC but at many other communities as well. Bhatia (1975: 19) states on the basis of a thorough study of several PHC's (in different Indian States) that enormously increasing needs for medical care services are responsible for the creation of a very large number of the socalled Registered Medical Practitioners (RMPs) or ("quacks" especially in the countryside).

Another indication for the availability of other medical facilities is the distance from which the patients come to visit the Aligam PHC. I took a random sample of 300 patients during the winter, summer and monsoon season. About 57 per cent came from the village Aligam itself, and about 75 per cent came from the adjacent communities within a radius of 3 kms. King (1966: 27) states about

Afri a that "the average number of outpatient's attendance per person per year will be seen to halve itself about every two miles for the hospital and dispensary and every mile for an aid post; while attendance halves every half mile. This may be an indication that people can consider the use of other medical facilities if they are available.

The dependency on a nearby doctor is, however, very pressing, especially for the poor. They earn daily wages and will loose an indispensable part of their income if they have to go a long way to visit a doctor. Famous specialists (allopathic or indigenous doctors as well as "bhagats") get patients from considerable distances, but this only concerns cases in which no satisfactory treatment could be found nearby.

The problem of under-utilization of the free state-organized medical facilities is crucial. This holds true also for TB treatment. A study of the TB treatment center in Valsad district suggests that the existing facilities are not at all used optimally. Djurfeldt and Lindberg (1975) did a one year research in a Tamil village, in order to furnish information to the "Swalows," a Scandinavian charitable organization running an aid-project and a Western medical clinic in the village of Thaiyur. They stress that structural factors are responsible for the under-utilization of the medical facilities: the obvious weakness of the system itself, i.e., the irrational use of resources; the emphasis on cure rather than prevention; the general structure of the society in which the modern allopathic medical system is supposed to function. Also, because it can do little to alleviate the results of object poverty, malnutrition and deficiencies in hygiene and sanitation. Consequently "the relative inefficiency of the allopathic system is the basic reason for the relative efficiency of the indigenous system" according to Djurfeldt & Lindberg (1975: 112).

However, the importance of these structural factors should not be overemphasized. It is also necessary to take into account other aspects as well. Since the arguments of Djurfeldt and Lindberg are relevant to the extent that they represent a typical Western approach to the problem, some further discussion is needed.

REASONS FOR THE UNDER-UTILIZATION OF ALLOPATHIC MEDICAL FACILITIES

It is important to know that Djurfeldt and Lindberg studied the introduction of Western medicine at a charitable clinic, financed by a Scandinavian organization and run by two foreign volunteers, a nurse and a midwife, while the Indian doctor of a nearby PHC visited the clinic once a week. The structural drawbacks of many Indian PHCs, a pernicious lack of funds as well as a certain reluctance towards the main task of PHC doctors, a "service spirit" and orientation towards work for the rural poor (Takulia, 1967: 46-68) did not hold true for this clinic.

The Scandinavian clinic could spend Rs 2000 a month on medicine (to serve only about 5000 people) while the budget for medicine at an average PHC (like the one in Aligam) is between Rs 1500-3000 a year to serve a population of several thousands. Apart from this relatively abundant financial facilities the clinic gave other substantive aid. "In severe cases the clinic staff took the patient directly to the hospital in their landrover. In other cases, they gave money to cover costs for hospital visits. They also made recommendations for the patients for securing easy hospital admission and better treatment (see, Djurfeldt and Lindberg, 1975: 110). All services which seldom can be given by other PHC personnel.

Yet, only 10 per cent of the patients from the village go for treatment at this clinic. All in all, only one third of all possible patients visited the clinic, mostly obtaining services of other allopathic or indigenous medical practitioners and magico-religious healers. While 25 per cent of the patients received treatment at other allopathic centers (mostly private), the other 25 per cent were treated by indigenous healers and 16 per cent combined allopathic and indigenous treatment outside the Swalow-clinic. In order to account for the remarkable result (or rather lack of result) the authors have tried to measure the effectivity of the different systems of medicine; at least in the opinion of the villagers about the efficiency of the different systems.

According to Djurfeldt and Lindberg (1975: 170-171) "there is no statistically significant difference in the number of patients cured. Only the religious therapy (exorcists, God dancers and priests) seem to be more efficient in treating their patients." The latter rightly believed that people with certain types of psychosomatic complaints go to religious specialists. It is for Djurfeldt and Lindberg, however, important to note that "with the existing distribution of patients between the systems, they manage about equally well in treating their patients," and they presume that the villagers are aware of this. Therefore, they say, "the people of Thaiyur remain

TABLE 2

NUMBER OF PATIENTS WHO REPORT THEY HAVE BEEN CURED BY DIFFERENT TYPES OF TREATMENT (THAIYUR VILLAGE)

Type of Treatment	*Number of Patients*			
	Cured	*Not Cured*	*Total*	*Ratio of cured to total*
1. Swalow-clinic	7	7	14	0.5
2. Other allopathic treatment	22	13	35	0.6
3. Indigenous, religious treatment	12	1	13	0.9
4. Indigenous, secular treatment	12	7	19	C.6
5. Combinations of treatment	23	21	44	0.5
6. Subtotal	76	49	125	0.6
7. No treatment, non-codable			15	

doubtful at the mere oral testimonies of the 'believers' in allopathic methods. They continue to rely to a large extent on their 'own' doctors." And because the villagers "function as any intelligent human beings," a "scientific experiment need to be conducted before their eyes to convince them that the allopathic system is superior" (Djurfeldt and Lindberg, 1975 : 170). These arguments of the authors are colored by typical Western rationality. And it is especially this type of rationality which prevents many Westerners, as well as Westernized Indians, from understanding people's viewpoint. Indian villagers must after all use their intelligence and rationality in a social setting that is totally different from the Western industrialized, urban and affluent society. I trust the rationality and intelligence of the Indian (villager). I am surprised that Djurfeldt and Lindberg (who give ample data about the poverty of the vast majority of the village population) do not explain why the excessive richness of the Swalow-clinic and their Western charitable background do not attract the poor villagers.

Possible Remedies for the Under-Utilization of Allopathic Facilities

I fully agree with Djurfeldt and Lindberg (1975: 214) when they criticize the "shortsightedness of a health policy which spends its meagre resources on one medical system which provides only part of the medical services, while the other systems, which are equally important or even more important than the allopathic one, are left unsupervised, undirected, and unfinanced so that they slowly degenerate and decay." Their most basic remedy against the ill-efficiency of the Indian medical system is in my opinion, however, somewhat hypothetical. They conclude that "only a radical transformation of the economic structure can produce the really forceful weapon to wage the battle against diseases and population growth." Now, there is no doubt that such a radical change will have striking effects for the efficiency of medical care in general and for the health prospects of the poorer sections of the population in particular. It is obvious that medical care can be much more directed and supervised when there would be only state-controlled health centers, as is the case in China. And it is also clear that the effectivity of medical care can be greatly enhanced when medical personnel of different background (allopathic and indigenous) and training ("barefoot doctors" as well as highly educated specialists) would be integrated in a system that is neatly interrelated with existing authority structures at the village level, as is the case in China. That very structure, however, is the result of a revolutionary development. And few people will disagree that the realization of the Chinese revolution(s) was favored by many factors (see especially, Wolf, 1969: 101-155). Such a radical transformation of economic structure does not seem likely in India within a short time, (see Wertheim, 1974: 227-295). It is certainly hoped by Djurfeldt and Lindberg that a revolution will soon be realized in India. And they are also entitled to propagate this with all possible means. But given the fact that a radical transformation has not yet been realized, I prefer to analyze the socio-cultural factors that influence the introduction of Western allopathic medical knowledge in the Indian village.

That sort of socio-cultural information will be of importance even in case a radical change in the Indian socio-economic structure will be realized within short time.

The disadvantage of our present knowledge of the Chinese

experiment is, after all, that we know comparatively little about the type of social control needed to force a good and effective system of medical care on a rural population. It will be clear that the traditional characteristics of a closed peasant society were until recently also present in China, though we still lack information about negative reactions on the modernizing trends in present Chinese society. Let us now turn to a discussion of some general aspects of social structure in Indian villages and their relationship with the medical care system.

SOCIAL AND STRUCTURAL FACTORS INFLUENCING MEDICAL CARE IN RURAL SOUTH GUJARAT

General Aspects of Soical Structure in India

In the Indian village setting primordial relationships are still of great importance in the day-to-day actions of people. Belonging to a group (a joint family as well as the local caste group) determines human behavior to a great extent (see Van der Veen, 1976, and Cohn, 1971: 112). Ascribed status is of over-whelming importance for the regulation of social relationships. The caste system and the consequent sharp distinction between the different socio-economic layers in the village community also create a strong tendency to evaluate every form of groupbound distinction in terms of higher and lower social status. The general structure of "peasant societies," on the other hand, is characterized by a social organization in which the notions of reciprocity and necessary mutual dependency are heavily stressed. One is bound to other people through innumerable mutual obligations and one has to maintain these types of relations (see Foster, 1961). There is consequently a keen recognition of the idea that human beings must necessarily influence each other's behavior and that every act must be viewed against its social background. This does *not* mean that people let the maintainance of social relationships take precedence over their individual personal interests. The result of individual behavior is, however, measured in terms of its effect on the network of social relationships. In other words, safeguarding one's personal interests depends on the maintainance of the soical network. And, therefore, Indian villagers "invest in people" to use the words of Srinivas (1969: 30).

In order to make investment in people useful it is necessary to make relationships as many-stranded as possible. The multiplicity of a relationship makes it possible to oblige a person in many ways in order to press a claim on him or her at any later moment. Relations between people with different status are also characterized by such considerations. The most typical institution in this respect is the patron-client relationship (see Breman, 1974). When such a relationship is sanctioned by the community, mutual obligation is an essential part of it. In a relationship between status-unequals there is definitely a marked difference in the way both partners are expected to express their mutual claims. The person with higher status can do so openly and at any moment. The person of lower status on the other hand, can only express claims by means of an appeal and subject to the goodwill of the person in a "higher" position. This and every other socially-sanctioned relationship is in theory characterized by feelings of responsibility and mutual dependency. It stands in contrast to a common mode of behavior in the West. There single-stranded relationships are much more common. Which means that a relationship is characterized by the predominance of one pertinent single interest that does not commit the participants to involvement with one another in any other situation of life. The full development of a market-economy as well as a capitalistic, individual-centered society is, of course, an important factor contributing to the predominance of single-stranded over many-stranded relationships.

In Western society a conscious distinction is made between the "common" single-stranded relationships and (ideal as well as idealized) many-stranded relationships. The latter must be intimate, "personal" and therefore many-stranded. Ideally such relationships should be devoid of any incentive for personal gain. They should be "intrinsically rewarding," as Blau (1967: 15-16) puts it. And in this respect also, there is of course a vast difference between the ideal and the actual situation. While for an Indian villager any socially sanctioned relationship implies many-strandedness, from a Western perspective every newly established relationship is initially single-stranded and may evolve into a many-stranded relationship. The Western perspective of human relationships induces a sense of task-orientation. In the West the relationship between a grocer and a housewife, a dentist and a patient or an insurance agent and a client, generally speaking, will be single-stranded relationships, and the one specific aspect for which the partners keep in touch is obvious.

In the case of many-stranded relationships there is in the West, however, also a tendency to define the relationships in a task-oriented way. The very fact that a relationship is allowed to develop into a many-stranded one, reflects its task-orientation. The partners, ideally, have chosen each other for a closer bond and the intimate content of their relationships is, so to say, the reason of it.

The difference in appreciation of relationships is vividly illustrated by Parekh (1974: 60-69), who says about the Indian immigrant to Britain, "lacking the English and, for that matter, Western ability to sustain different degrees of intimacy in different types of relationships, he swings between the two extremes of deep involvement and total withdrawal." Moreover, "even if he can interpret signals right, the Indian often finds the slow development of relationships most trying and frustrating." It is in the Western society where it is possible to a very great extent to rely on single-stranded relationships. A widespread social security system, a rather well organized and controlled bureaucracy, makes it possible to invest in money and goods and to obtain special services. When one, however, has to or is accustomed to invest in people, specification and task-orientation are much less effective.

The many-stranded relationships should possess certain qualities in order to make them "useful" for the partners. The tendency to view every social relationship in terms of many-strandedness makes it necessary to maintain diffuse relationships, which means that people differentiate as little as possible between the different aspects a many-stranded relationship comprises (affection, economic interest, intellectual fascination, political interests, to name a few). People are not unaware of these different aspects but by (consciously) mixing and manipulating them they want to make the relationship as enveloping as possible, because every aspect creates an opportunity to put claims forward. In that sense the Indian interpretation of human relationships is definitely goal-oriented. Both partners may profit from the relationship at one time or another. A definite delimitation of the special reason why one needs the partner's help at any given moment must. however, be evaded. Therefore relationships are not interpreted in trems of task-orientation which implies that one or more aspects are specifically taken into account, to define the quality of the relationship.

Another crucial consequence of the Indian as distinct from the Western interpretation concerns the possibility of withdrawal. Since single-stranded relationships in the West are explicitly accepted, it is also acceptable to withdraw from a many-stranded relationship. That means either not developing a single-stranded relationship into an idealized many-stranded one, or, in case such a relationship exists, its gradual minimization to the point of a factual breach in the relationship.

In the Indian setting withdrawal from a socially accepted relationship is extremely difficult. Even when, by Western standards, a relationship lacks the qualities that would make it worthwhile to continue, there is a strong tendency to uphold the outward appearance of its existence.

In the Indian interpretation of relationships *status* is *the* main *means to control* relationships which because of their ideal many-strandedness are meant to imply claims and counter-claims. Accentuation and articulation of status is absolutely essential to gain some control over others. This, of course, is true for those with high status. But for the lower-status person, too, there is a possibility to advance claims by accentuating difference in status. In practice this means a subordination on the part of the "lower." By stressing how poor, inexperienced and stupid one is, it is possible to appeal for the support of the "higher." This is most marked in relationships between unequals with widely different social positions, but it is certainly not restricted to this type of relationship only. Therefore, accentuation of status has an instrumental quality, while the same holds true for the maintainance of diffuse and mutually obligatory relationships, and the refrainment of specificity and task-orientation in social relationships.

Medical Facilities at the PHC and Status Considerations

As noted before, the services of the PHC are meant for the poor. This makes it in itself status-lowering to ask for help at a PHC. When people from middle or higher castes visit the PHC, "it proves that they are misers," as one PHC doctor said. The availability of other medical practitioners (of all kinds and qualifications) therefore constitutes a tremendous obstacle for the effectivity of the PHC service. Practically all RMP's and indigenous medical practitioners administer modern drugs and especially injections (see Bhatia, 1975: 15-16). The traditional as well as the Western-treained medical practitioners charge a fee per consultation but many of them only charge for medicines which makes the administration of drugs their main source of income. It is very common at the PHC that practically every patient asks for an injection. The PHC doctors, however, have only few injectable drugs, since they are only supplied with cheaper, though not necessarily less effective, oral drugs. At the Aligam PHC no special practitioners were mentioned but patients were advised to buy an injection in a nearby town. This doubtlessly strengthens the impression that the PHC gives low-quality services. Going to the PHC is mostly second choice, as Djurfeldt and Lindberg (1975: 110-111) also found for the Swalow-clinic where status was "underrated." Only when one takes into account the crucial importance of status manipulation as a rational device to promote one's own interests in a closed society it is possible to understand this. Otherwise it would seem irrational that people prefer to go to someone whom they will have to pay.

Poor laborers go to the local village IMP or RMP for a reason that is very much related to status-considerations and the obligation aspect. In most cases the local "doctors" form a part of the total pattern of social relationships in the village, which means that the IMP/RMP will have relations with the local elite. By reimbursing the fee of his laborer (client) the patron can oblige two persons: his client and the local private medical practitioner. To all parties it is quite clear that only through the help of the patron the sick man can ask for treatment from a private practitioner.

There is also a structural reason why the majority of patients come from the immediate neighborhood. People who work on daily wages can only visit a nearby doctor in case they do not want to lose a day's income. And though treatment at the PHC is free, it is obvious that the landowning patrons can exert great influence on the decision of their poor employees to visit a medical practitioner who is important to them within the local network. This leads us to another point which is very relevant in this respect. Most of the new PHC's are build at some distance from the congested villages. From the (Western) rational considerations about hygiene and accessibility this is of course sensible. But the spatial isolation of the PHC adds, however, to its social isolation. This social isolation is due also to the official government policy. In order to prevent corrupt practices most PHC doctors are transferred every three years.

Generally speaking fresh graduates join the PHC as a stepping-stone to acquire more clinical experience before starting a private practice and the majority of PHC doctors see their work there as a transitional phase. They are often transferred in order to prevent them from starting an illegal backdoor private practice. From a Western universalistic and bureaucratic point of view this may seem a very wise policy. In terms of effectivity it is not, given the fact that private and state health care exist side by side.

People tend to make a choice and the PHC is mostly at the disadvantage, even when the actual medical service rendered will uot be less effective than that of RMPs and indigenous "healers" who have very limited knowledge.

As Djurfeldt and Lindberg (1975: 162) say, the folk medical practitioners are insiders to the community: "they are diffusely related to their patients, as friends, kinsmen, employers, or colleagues since most of them are part-time practitioners." All this makes for close relations between them and their patients. Their bedside manners make a deep impression and "being insiders these healers are also within the reach of local and particularistic social control." Therefore, for the poor the limited integration of the PHC doctor in the local system is (considered by them as) a real disadvantage. The principle that a person in a social structure which is based upon patron-client relationships has a claim on his superior is hampered in a situation where the PHC doctor is no part of the social network. The indirect influence a person may have on a medical practitioner, because their boss is known to him, does not affect the relation with a PHC doctor.

Also, there is a general belief that doctors working at PHCs are those who are either carefree or inexperienced. It is widely believed that when private practice is much more lucrative no good doctor would join government service. Only exceptionally motivated doctors who are highly dedicated and committed can overcome this bad image as well as the drawbacks of social isolation. And such personalities are apparently rare. The generally advised incentives to overcome the obstacles to recruitment—higher pay and better living conditions for the PHC doctors in the village—will not be of much help when private practice remains a better alternative (see Takulia, 1967: 47-51). The same holds true for a possible compulsory service for doctors in rural areas. This is definitely a means to integrate service in rural state health centers into the total system of medical care. In order to give good results the period of compulsory service should, however, extend over several years. But such a procedure is not a guarantee for the motivation of the PHC doctors. Other measures will be necessary.

MEDICAL FACILITIES, STATUS CONSIDERATIONS AND EFFECTIVITY

Banerji (1974: 18-19) relating the under-utilization and inefficiency of the PHC, says that: (1) the ideal of the primary health center exists only in name....The team leader of the PHC, who is the pivot of the institution not only lacks the qualities needed to provide leadership but he is also a most reluctant worker having interests which are often diametrically opposed to the interest of the PHC; (2) the medical colleges have conspicuously failed in giving the needed orientation to the graduates. The departments of preventive and social medicine have not only failed to bring about the expected social orientation of medical education, but in the bargain, they have also lost their grasp over the practical community health issues; (3) there is a very unfavorable impact of the family planning program on the rural health services; and (4) there is a palpable lack of political will to develop health services for the rural population ... because... the political leadership is much more inclined to develop institutions in urban areas ... for more prestigeous super facilities.

Banerji's conclusions are in line with the points I mentioned before and like Djurfeldt and Lindberg he asks implicitly for fundamental changes. Apart from the political unwillingness of the ruling elite to develop health services for the masses, Banerji's comment is concerned with the possiblities of better training and orientation of the PHC personnel. Though I agree with the necessity of such a reorientation, I still feel that there is a discrepancy between what he wants to be realized and what can be realized.

The most crucial point is that the PHC doctor is a reluctant worker having interests that are often diametrically opposed to those of the PHC. It is therefore essential to bring together these divergent interests. To integrate and supervise the indigenous medical practitioners into the official system, but also to integrate private medical practitioners into the state health organization, on the basis of a fixed renumeration for every non-paying patient treated.

The dangers of such a mixed system (corruption and a notable difference in treatment of private and state-paid patients) are of course known from the experience in most Western countries during the first decennia of the twentieth century. It is therefore understandable that the most modern, i.e., a socialized system of medical care, was taken as an example for the state health system in India after independence. The failure of this system within the Indian social structure is however obvious.

It should be taken into account that in Western Europe the development towards this type of medical care also was a gradual one. In the Netherlands for instance numerous private sick-funds (associations organized by trade unions, industrial concerns, medical practitioners and private persons) maintained a vast network of particularistic relations between medical practitioners and patients, until 1940, when a certain degree of unification was realized (Gezondheidszorg: 110-189). And up to this time doctors simultaneously treated private as well as state-insured patients. "The professionalization of medical care and the medicalization of life," to quote Illich (1975) is in the West only gradually loosened from its particularistic roots. Justified fear for the dangers of particularism and maintainance of a status-quo in the traditional hierarchy, cannot nullify the fact that these aspects are still prominent features of the existing Indian social order. If you do not alter that order fundamentally it is wise to analyze the ways in which the medical care is related to investment in people, instead of "rational" goals.

Diffusion and Obligation in the Doctor-Patient Relationship

The notion of mutual obligation is a central aspect of the interpretation of human relationships in the traditional village-setting. To what extent this applies to the PHC activities can be illustrated by the following examples. At the Aligam PHC a patient came suffering from a rather advanced stage of leprosy. He had been diagnosed at the center some years ago, but after that he never returned, as he said he feared that he "would be obliged" to be sterilized, in return for the free medical help given to him. The PHC is most negatively identified with Family Planning activities, which features prominently in the State Health programs (see Banerji, 1974: 7-8). It is commonly believed that the PHC officials are interested in sterilization because people are paid up to Rs 72 for a vasectomy during Family Planning drives. As pointed out by other scholars (see

Mamdani, 1972) children are believed to be an investment for the poor who lack any form of social security. Thus limiting the number of children is considered irrational. It is important to note, as Mamdani (1972: 23-24) states, that many people told him that "they had accpeted contraceptives (but generally not used them) because they wanted to help the Family Planning Worker who did his best. This shows the extent to which medical care is placed in a wider context than a single-stranded relationship with a person or an institution.

The negative results of this particular view of the relationship between the individual patient and what should ideally be a neutral, service-rendering institution or official, is shown in the way PHC personnel use coercion and other kinds of pressure tactics and offer bribes to entice people to accept vasectomy or tubectomy (Banerji, 1974: 8). The whole gamut of particularistic, diffuse and many-stranded relationship manipulation is used to get "cases." In this case it is in the interest of the PHC worker who should deliver results.

Furthermore, a very common complaint about the work of the PHC personnel is that they are not at all active in their approach to patients when it concerns other forms of treatment. A striking result is the disastrous defaulters' problem in TB treatment. The data of the TB center in Valsad district indicates that in 1974, 1593 housecalls were made by the 9 TB workers in the district for a number of 3326 recognized defaulters. Roughly speaking this could mean that only one in every two defaulters was approached to resume treatment. The number of housecalls would indicate about one visit per TB worker every two days. This is definitely not much if we take into account that the TB workers are supposed to devote much of their time to detection of new cases and making housecalls on defaulters. One may be inclined to relate this lack of activity on the part of the TB workers only to their slackness and ill-motivation. Such an accusation is not wholly unwarranted, because PHC workers use all possible means of persuasion when their own interests are at stake. There is, however, another side to this matter. It can be expected that TB workers visit the defaulters with whom they have a more general relationship, while it is not "possible" for them to go and visit people with whom they only have a single-stranded relationship. When there is only a TB worker-TB patient relationship, it is task-oriented and does not involve any further commitment from the partners.

In a Western setting it is quite normal for any official like a TB worker to go and urge the defaulters to resume their treatment. Both parties accept and know that it is his job to do so, and both parties understand that this single aspect is a sufficient reason for the actions of the TB worker. In the Indian village setting it is different. It is extremely difficult to compartmentalize a relationship because doing so would rob the relationship of its many-stranded and diffuse, mutually obliging character. From the patient's side as well as from the side of the TB worker only a relationship that is many-stranded is an excuse as well as a reason for directly intervening in the other's life. This explanation may seem exaggerated. It is, however, in line with many other observations concerning the work of PHC officials as well as private doctors and healers (see also Djurfeldt and Lindberg, 1975: 162-165; Marriott, 1955).

In 1974, the first thing that struck me was the great amount of time devoted by the PHC personnel in visiting with "important people." The important men were not necessarily high-caste people, but they were at least influential in their wards. These were just social calls and from a Western task-oriented view, such visits were a sheer waste of time. In the village setting they were a necessary part of the utilization of networks. These visits also marked a tendency to keep a distance from the village people as a whole, as Banerji remarks. Banerji (1975: 16) says that PHC officials "take advantage of the village power structure and confine themselves, as far as possible, to satisfying the privileged gentry of the village. In doing so they: (*a*) win approbation and rewards from the so-called community political leaders; (*b*) appease the least disagreeable segment of the community; and (*c*) get a free hand to 'tackle' the rest of the community. It is, however, not solely motivated by an act of self-interest or a shrewd way of serving their own ends." It is also a way of doing what is normal because it is difficult to imagine any other way of "tackling" a community.

In the Indian setting knowing the right people, getting their support and through them influencing the other members of the community in a diffuse and non-specific way is a most common thing to do. Of course, one can have strong objection against such behavior which implies confirmation of the already existing social structure of inequality. In order to prevent this one cannot reproach PHC workers for selfishness when they themselves think that their patronizing approach to the community is the best one. Nor can one accuse them of laziness when they themselves feel that they do much by approaching only the people whom they can "oblige." And everyone with experience of social life in an Indian village will know how subtle a procedure that is. Let us look at another aspect.

The Aligam PHC had diagnosed two persons suffering from leprosy more than a year ago, but they had not revisited the PHC since. One of them had received some treatment from a private practitioner, but the other had not received any treatment. Since the symptoms of their illness had grown worse they decided to revisit the center. When these men were present at the office, an official from a nearby village came and began talking with the leprosy worker. He said that he was very interested in his work and being now at the office he wanted to learn more about it. What he wanted turned out to be a detailed report about which people from his native village were under treatment. This conversation took place in the presence of the two men who had had so much difficulty in coming back for treatment. To them it was quite clear that their privacy will never be guarded by the leprosy worker. The intricate twist of task-orientation versus many-strandedness was dramatically present. It was, in the first place difficult for the leprosy worker to tell the official that it was none of his business. The official held a much higher position than the leprosy worker, and the latter simply had to answer because that was part of the hierarchical code.

Secondly, the fact that the official could discuss these matters with the leprosy worker in the presence of the two patients (whom he did not know because they were not from his native village) shows how accepted it is to enquire in great detail about the health of others. This holds true especially when the one inquiring is higher in social status. He or she is considered to be responsible for the well-being of his inferiors. It is also obvious that illness is considered a public affair. It is something that concerns the group as much as the patient and the doctor, though such diffuse and many-stranded behavior can lead to negative results when it concerns socially stigmatizing disease like TB, leprosy and venereal disease. People will try to evade a public announcement of their illness and abstain from treatment.

When there is only one state-controlled system of medical care it is to a great extent possible to control patients in order to guarantee continuous treatment. The same holds true for vaccination programs, as the results in the eradication of infectious diseases in countries like China and Cuba show. The further implications of a diffuse and many-stranded orientation are, however, not solved with the introduction of one centrally supervised medical care system. There is, moreover, another side as well. It is a marked trait of all professional medical treatment in India that there are always third parties (relatives, friends, or neighbors) present when a patient consults a doctor. This is a result of climatic, economic as well as spatial reasons, but it also represents an approach. It is normal that others join in the conversation between the doctor and the patients (see also Djurfeldt and Lindberg, 1975: 162).

In the Western world being ill as well as getting cured concern the patient and the doctor. It implies a strong single-stranded relationship. It is of course generally accepted that a doctor should know about the personal circumstances of his patients in order to get the right anamnesis. But such knowledge about the individual patient is part of a task-orientation: classifying the illness and prescribing a cure.

The ill-effects of the Western medicalization of life and "the transformation of the doctor from artisan exercising skill on personally known individuals into a technician applying scientific rules to classes of patients" (Illich, 1975: 24) have received much attention in recent years.

There is no doubt that the positive results of Western medical technique cannot be seen apart from the tendency to depersonalize diagnosis and therapy: to make man into a "machine" whose proper working is thought to be dependent on the flawless functioning of its parts. There is little need to discuss here the unwanted side-effects of this typically Western approach to illness. But when we consider the social aspects of medical care in India these questions need to be thought over.

The group-aspect as well as the decidedly particularistic accents are after all, also, components of the "human" element in Indian medical care. Though it may create tensions it is nevertheless true that there is much comfort (and healing-power) in the attendance of a group to a sick person. And similarly the feeling that the doctor treats you because of what you are, can contribute more positively to the improvement of health than the idea that he treats everyone exactly the same. This poses obviously a dilemma.

Better organization and a certain bureaucratization will certainly improve the technical quality of health care, but it is necessary to evaluate in what ways such changes are related to aspects of the traditional as well as a new social setting.

I have discussed in what ways the accentuation of status can be seen as a means to manipulate diffuse and mutally obligatory human relationships and how refraining from task-orientation can be seen as an integral part of this interpretation of relationships. Such behavior is unquestionably a result of the over-all structure of Indian society. But even a quick and fundamental change of that over-all structure will not directly change the sort of approach discussed here. Health problems are not only technical or political or economical alone (Djurfeldt and Lindberg, 1975: 15) but also socio-cultural in nature. And in order to cope with these problems it is necessary to take into account various relevant aspects.

REFERENCES

BANERJI, D.

1974 *Health Behavior of Rural Populations: Impact of Rural Health Services—A Preliminary Communication.* New Delhi: Centre of social medicine and community health.

BHATIA, J.C., DHARAM VIR, A. TIMMAPAYA and C. CHUTANI

1975 "Traditional Healers and Modern Medicine." *Social Science and Medicine* 9: 15-21.

BLAU, PETER M.

1967 *Exchange and Power in Social Life.* New York: Wiley.

BREMAN, J.C.

1974 *Patronage and Exploitation: Changing Agrarian Relations in South Gujarat, India.* Berkeley: University of California Press.

CENSUS OF INDIA

1971 *District Census Handbook.* Series 5. Part X-C-1 Valsad District. Part X-A-B, Valsad District. Ahmedabad: Rajratan Press.

COHN, BERNARD S.

1971 *India: The Social Anthropology of a Civilization.* Englewood Cliffs, New Jersey: Prentice Hall.

DOYAL, LESLEY and IMOGEN PENNELL

1976 "Health, Medicine and Underdevelopment." *Economic and Political Weekly* 11: 1235-1246.

DJURFELDT, GORAN and STAFFAN LINDBERG

1975 *Pills against Poverty: A Study of the Introduction of Western Medicine in a Tamil Village.* London: Curzon Press.

FOSTER, G.M.

1961 "The Dyadic Contract: a model for the Social Structure of a Mexican

Peasant Village." *American Anthropologist* 63: 1173-1193.

GEZONDHEIDSZORG IN NEDERLAND

1973 "Ziekenfondsen en de strijd van de arbeidersbeweging voor goede sociale voorzieningen," pp.110-189. In Frans Huysmans, Paul Juffermans, Bert Lagro, Bob van Niekerk, Frans Smits and Henk Vlaar (eds.), *Gezondheidszorg in Nederland*. Nijmegen: Sun.

HASSAN, K.J.

1967 *The Cultural Frontier of Health in Village India*. Bombay: Manaktalas.

ILLICH, IVAN

1975 *Medical Nemesis: The Expropriation of Health*. Bombay: Rupa.

KING, MAURICE

1966 *Medical Care in Developing Countries*. London: Oxford University Press.

MAMDANI, MAHMOOD

1972 *The Myth of Population Control: Family Caste and Class in an Indian Village*. New York: Monthly Review Press.

MARRIOTT, MCKIM

1955 "Western Medicine in a Village of Northern India." In Benjamin Paul (ed.), *Health, Culture and Community*. New York: Russell Sage Foundation.

MARU, RUSHIKESH M.

1976 "Health Manpower Strategies for Rural Health Services, India and China: 1949-1975." *Economic and Political Weekly* 11: 1253-1268.

PAREKH, BHIKU

1974 *Colour, Culture and Consciousness: Immigrant Intellectuals in Britain*. London: George Allen and Unwin.

SRINIVAS, M. N.

1969 "The Social System of a Mysore Village." In McKim Marriott (ed.), *Village India*, pp. 1-35. Chicago: Chicago University Press.

TAKULIA, HARBANS S., CARL E. TAYLOR, S. PRAKASH SANGAL AND JOSEPH D. ALTER

1967 *The Health Center Doctor in India*. Baltimore: John Hopkins University Press.

VAN DER VEEN, KLASS W.

1972 *I give Thee my Daughter. Marriage and Hierarchy among the Anavil Brahmans of South Gujarat*. Assen: van Gorcum.

1974 "The East-West Encounter; Cooperation and Communication in an Indo-Dutch Research Team." *Sociologische Gids* 21: 375-392.

1976 "Urbanization, Migration and Primordial Attachments." In C. Baks and E. Hommes (eds.), *Modernization, Stagnation and Steady Decline. Sociological Contributions on Social Change in South Gujarat*, pp. 27-70. Utrecht: University of Utrecht (Mimeograph).

WERTHEIM, W.F.

1974 *Evolution and Revolution: The Rising Waves of Emancipation*. Harmondworth: Penguin Books.

WOLF, ERIC

1966 *Peasants*. Englewood Cliffs, New Jersey: Prentice Hall.

1969 *Peasant Wars of the Twentieth Century*. New York: Harper and Row.

S.B. MANI

FROM MARRIAGE TO CHILD CONCEPTION: AN ETHNOMEDICAL STUDY IN RURAL TAMIL NADU

ABSTRACT. Through a study based on observation and interviews with traditional birth attendants, parturient women and indigenous medical practitioners, the prevailing ethnomedical beliefs and practices regarding sterility, fertility, conception, gestation and abortion in rural Tamil Nadu is described. Treating the ethnomedical scene as a microcosmic representation of the larger cultural universe, an attempt is made to explore the basic value orientations that shape the world view of the villagers as well as the cognitive structure underlying the ethnomedical setting. Relevance of such cultural themes as segmentation and harmony, dependency on astrology and cyclical concept are emphasized to provide a proper understanding of the ethnomedical panorama.

"COW'S MILK TO A NEW MOTHER?" EXCLAIMED ELLAMMA, A MIDWIFE from the barber caste in a Tanjore village, to my question why the young, weak mother was not given cow's milk to help regain her strength. "No, *Iyyā* (a respectable Tamil word for 'sir')" continued Ellamma, "cow's milk is 'cold' and if the woman who has just given birth to a baby drinks it, both the mother and the child will develop 'cold' fever and they will have diarrhea and *kavam* (*kapha*-phlegm or mucus). For at least one week after delivery the mother is not allowed to drink coffee with milk in it. The child is given just warm sugar water for three days before it is allowed to breastfeed."

"But Ellamma," I retorted, "how can you give raw milk of a donkey to the newborn on its first day but not its own mother's milk?"

Ellamma in an assertive voice replied, "You see *Iyyā*, for the first few days after delivery, the mother's milk is curdled and spoiled. Further, a newborn child has a 'cold' body constitution and we have to keep the child warm. Donkey's milk is so 'hot' that if you leave the raw milk in a container for one hour, you can see worms crawling all over. That is why we give donkey's milk to the newborn baby on its first day. To keep it warm. If we don't get donkey's milk we can give goat's milk, but this milk is not as 'hot' as donkey's milk. Water buffalo's milk is also 'hot,' but who wants a child with a water buffalo's brain?"

I repeated, "The milk of a donkey, a goat and a water buffalo is 'hot' but that of a cow is 'cold'?" Ellamma nodded her head and turning to another barber woman enjoying our conversation said convincingly, "Now *Iyyā* understands."

Did I understand the logic behind Ellamma's argument? I should. Because, as Ellamma put it, I am "college educated." There have been many instances in the course of my field work in Tamil Nadu villages when I have been made to understand that goat's meat is "hot" but sheep's meat is "cold"; fish that are caught in fresh waters are "cold" while those from the ocean are "hot" and such fruits as mangoes, papayas and pineapples are "hot" while certain species of bananas, citrus fruits and pomegranates (*Punica granatum*) are "cold."

I have also been made to "understand" more than once that a barren woman is "cold." However, she can conceive by visiting a modern (allopathic) doctor or a local homoeopathic doctor, by eating the tender leaves of margosa (*Melia azidirachta Indica*), by consuming the powdered bark of the tulip or the portia tree (in warm water or buttermilk), by sacrificing a male goat or a cock to the local deity, by having coitus on or near full moon days, by consuming a small piece of the umbilical cord from a new baby, by worshipping a cobra, by going around the *pīpal* tree (*Ficus religiosa*), by abstaining from sexual intercourse on some important religious occasions, by consulting an astrologer, or by simply waiting for the "right" time to come.

There is an extraordinary melangè of ideas, beliefs and behaviors of a prescientific, scientific, commonsensical and cosmological nature that a novice trying to understand the concepts of illness and health in the rural Indian socio-cultrual matrix often finds unfathomable, capricious and illogical. To a casual observer, the practice of medicine in village India appears to be irrational and even contradictory and seemingly there is no connection between belief and behavior and between etiology of illness and therapeutic procedures. According to Beals, the rural Indian health care system appears to be a "buzzing, blooming confusion" (1976: 198).

Medicine, as practiced in India is pluralistic, in the etiology of illness, diagnostic methods, therapeutic procedures, and therapists (Beals, 1976; Carstairs, 1955; Fuchs, 1964; Gould, 1965; Lewis, 1965; Marriott, 1955; Opler, 1963 and Taylor, 1976). This pluralism is perhaps due to an infinite variety of ways, often confusing and perplexing, by which what Leslie (1976) calls the "great tradition" medicine has established itself in the Indian social setting due to parochialization and regional and local cultural accretions. In spite of variations, a detailed analysis of the Indian medical system as practised in India reveals some uniformities in the cognitive system underlying these variations. Thus we are able to make comparisons of health practices between different regions, different castes and even different individuals and arrive at some broad generalizations that have program implications.

It would be an unnecessary exercise in pedagogy to review in this paper the roots and the development of Indian medical systems (see Basham, 1976; Kutumbiah, 1962; Zimmer, 1948). Suffice to mention here that the cognitive system underlying the Indian health system stems from the Hippocratic theory of binary opposition between "hot" and "cold" and "dry" and "wet" humors and Caraka's *Āyurvedic* theory of harmony or balance between three primary *doṣas* (flaws, irregularities or defects). The three primary *doṣas* include bile or gall (*pitta*), gas or wind (*vāta*) and phlegm or mucus (*kapha*). While what constitutes good health or illness may vary from region to region, the etiology of illness is traced to an imbalance or disharmony in the bodily *doṣas* and humors. It is axiomatic in the world view of the Indian villagers that the *doṣas* and humors should be kept in homeostatic balance in order to avoid illness or restore health. This world view guides and sometimes even controls the everyday life, both physical and moral, in village India. In brief, the world view of the Indian villagers towards health and medical systems rests squarely on the Hippocratic humoral theory and the Āyurvedic *tridoṣa* theory.

In the Indian context we see a merging of the humoral and the *doṣa* concepts. Often "hot" and "dry" conditions excite *pitta doṣa* while "cold" and "wet" conditions accentuate the catarrhal qualities thus exciting *kapha doṣa.* As in Guatamala, the dichotomy between "hot" and "cold" received more importance in the Indian health scene while the qualities of moisture occupied a secondary position (Logan, 1973). Foods have also been classified as catarrhal (those which excite *kapha doṣa* leading to an increase in phlegm or mucus), bilious (those which accentuate *pitta doṣa*) and flatulent (those that will affect *vāta doṣa* by increasing gas or wind). "Hot" and "cold" humoral qualities do not solely refer to the *innate* or alleged characteristics of particular foods. They also refer to actual temperature of foods at the time of consumption. For example, a person who has cold or cough is advised to drink hot or boiled water. However, the same boiled water when cooled before drinking is believed to further accentuate the *kapha doṣa.* Like the foods, a person's body constitution is also classified into *vāta*, *pitta* and *kapha*. A person, say with *pitta* body constitution, is advised to go easy on hot and dry foods so as not to excite his particular *doṣa* and cause illness. He is also warned not to expose himself to fire or hot climatic conditions or involve himself in activities that are considered "hot." On the other hand, he is allowed to consume more than average amount of those foods whose humoral qualities are considered to be in complementary opposition to his particular *doṣa*.

Illness and Ethnomedicine

The position taken in this paper is that illness is culturally conditioned and culturally mediated and that for a proper understanding of the concept of "illness" one must examine the prevailing belief and action systems that are culturally defined and held to be "true" in a community. One should not and cannot understand illness *solely* in terms of modern germ theory. Obeyesekere (1976) uses the term "cultural disease" to emphasize the point that sickness in a person should be culturally interpreted. Fabrega's (1972) distinction between "illness" and "disease" seems relevant here. According to Fabrega, "illness tends to be viewed as a cultural category and as a set of culturally related events...behavioral and phenomenologic indicators are usually employed to define a state of illness...(on the other hand) disease (is viewed) as an abnormality in the structure and/or function of any system of the body, and evidences of biological system malfunction serve as indicators of disease" (1972: 167-68). In this paper primary emphasis is given to illness and ethnomedical rather than disease and bio-medical aspects of etiology, diagnosis and therapy of a person's sickness.

Anthropological literature on medicine is replete with terms such as "indigenous medicine," "traditional medicine," "native medicine," "folk therapy," "primitive medicine," "magical medicine," and "sacredotal medicine" to distinguish medical practices that do not resemble modern, Western medical practices. In this paper the term "ethnomedicine" is preferred over other terms as this term is comprehensive and does not lend itself to the criticism of ethnocentrism as the term "primitive medicine" would. Ethnomedicine "refers to those beliefs and practices relating to disease which are products of indigenous cultural development..." (Hughes, 1968:88). Ethnomedicine, as used in this paper, is not limited to a description of the curing of illness but also includes beliefs held by the people regarding illness etiology. Like illness, ethnomedicine is bedded in the social matrix of a community and should be treated as an integral part of the society's value system and organizational structure. In brief, illness and ethnomedicine are defined in terms of the world view of the "patient" and the community.

BACKGROUND

Information presented in this paper froms a part of a larger anthropological field investigation conducted in rural Tamil Nadu during 1975-76 and the summer of 1977. This investigation was conducted to examine the roles played by the traditional birth attendants in the delivery of maternal, child health and family planning services and supplies. The field study focused on the training and utilization of the traditional birth attendants as change agent aides or as "physician's extenders" in the delivery of modern health and family planning services to remote, less literate and hard-to-reach rural population. Although data were collected on a number of research questions, the prevailing beliefs and practices regarding sterility, fertility, pregnancy, gestation and abortion are described in this paper. An attempt is also made to delineate the basic value orientations or the key patterns in the cognitive system underlying these ethnomedical beliefs and practices.

Information presented here was obtained through interviews with traditional birth attendants, parturient mothers and indigenous medical practitioners. The geographical area of research covered several districts in Tamil Nadu, but field research was primarily focused in the districts of Chingleput and Tanjore.

From Marriage to Child Conception

Getting married

Happy is that man whose children are all married and has seen his grandchildren, surely establishing the family line. It is the responsibility of the family members, and a father's obligation, to see that every capable person in the family is married. Getting married, establishing smooth interpersonal relationships with the affinal relatives on the husband's side, especially with the mother-in-law, and giving birth to a child within a resonable amount of time can be said to be important concerns of every normal female in rural Tamil Nadu. Given the high rate of infant mortality, anxiety over the health of the new born can be added to the list of concerns. In spite of government regulations, an average female in rural Tamil Nadu is married before the prescribed minimum age for marriage.

Fear of sterility

From the moment a woman is married, the young bride and her relatives are in a state of anxiety and uncertainty regarding the woman's ability to bear children. Pressures mount if a woman fails to conceive within a reasonable amount of time after her marriage. Often the burden falls on the young bride to prove her worth by having childern. "The dreaded possibility of being barren is a nightmarish specter for a woman who has not borne a child...the mark of her success as a person is her living, thriving children" (Mandelbaum, 1974: 16). A barren woman is often the object of public and private gossip, scorn and pity. A young bride often takes precautionary measures to assure success and enhance her fertility through elaborate rituals, fasting, prayers, pilgrimages and dietary regulations.

In rural Tamil Nadu, sterility is considered to be an illness. Interviews with traditional birth attendants and parturient women elicited a wide range of response on the etiology of sterility, ranging from purely biological or physiological to primarily cosmological. Many indigenous midwives reported that a sterile woman will be advised to go to the Primary Health Center or to see a modern (allopathic) doctor for a medical examination, including checkup for possible venereal disease. Generally speaking, the midwives felt a sense of helplessness in "curing" sterility than in dealing with abortion.

There was a general consensus among the indigenous midwives and parturient women that a barren woman has a "cold" body constitution. It is important to mention here that in rural Tamil Nadu, the female qualities are associated with "cold" and male qualities with "hot." A normal woman is believed to have a slightly "colder" body constitution and is therefore not expected to show any overt signs of sexual interest in her husband. On the other hand, it is the husband, whose body is believed to be "hot," who should initiate sexual advances. Generally speaking, "hot" bodies are sexually more easily excitable than "cold" bodies. As a consequence a sterile woman is believed to have an excessively "cold" body. Therapy therefore consists of efforts made to restore the equilibrium between the "hot" and "cold" humors in the woman's body.

The imbalance between the complementarily opposing humors can be due to pluralistic causes: dietary habits, climatic changes, body constitution, temperament of the individual, flaws in one's horoscope, activities of the supernatural agents as a result of violations in the moral and religious codes, evil eye or simply *karma.*

In rural Tamil Nadu a sterile woman is advised not to unduely expose herself to excessive cold climatic conditions nor to indulge in "cold" producing activities. During her menstrual period (which helps in getting rid of the bad and poisonous blood), a woman is considered to be "hot." Efforts are made to induce menstruation in a sterile woman through emmenagogues. The most common emmenagogue used is a paste of sesame seeds assumed to be extremely "hot" and if used by a pregnant woman, may lead to abortion. Another common emmenagogue is a paste of black cumin seeds and unrefined jaggery (usually dark brown in color). A sterile woman is also encouraged to consume "hot" foods such as vegetable oils (particularly sesame oil), unrefined sugar, spicy foods, chicken, goat's meat, eggs, papaya, mangoes, pineapples and jackfruit and "hot" vegetables like pumpkins, unripe bananas and green peppery. Occasionally, women in the lower castes are advised to consume country liquor to make them "hot."

Another prevailing belief is that sterility is caused due to worm infestation in the "stomach." Hence attempts are made to get rid of the worms through laxatives or purgatives made of local herbs. The paste of tender leaves of margosa tree (*Melia azidirachta Indica*) is used frequently to remove the worms. Other substances used for the same purpose include the bark of the *jāmun* tree (*Eugenia jambolana*) (locally known as *nāga maram*) and the bark of the tulip or the portia tree. Bark of these trees are sun-dried, powdered and mixed with hot water or buttermilk and taken orally on alternate days for three months. These substances, particularly the leaves of the margosa tree which are extremely bitter, are believed to kill the worms that cause sterility in women. Many women reported that one can also get herbal medicines from the local medical shops that specialize in indigenous medicines. The indigenous midwives in the Nilgiris district informed that they often advise sterile women to approach the members of the Kurumba and Thoraiyar tribes who are believed to be experts in curing sterility through herbal medicine.

In a Tanjore village a homeopathic doctor, whose wife was a midwife, offered this prescription for sterility. The bark of the *pīpal* tree (*Ficus religiosa*), leaves of the wild margosa tree, the bark of a medicinal herb (*Daemia extensa*) and the leaves of a small fence climber, locally known as "fence cotton" (*Abrus precatorius*) should be ground together and the juice extracted from these should be mixed with sesame oil and administered orally for about three months. During the course of this medication, the woman is asked to be on low salt and low tamarind diet (salt and tamarind are considered to be "cold" foods). The woman is advised to abstain from coitus during new moon days, and to have sexual intercourse during or close to full moon days. The same doctor also informed that he often prescribed a homeopathic medicine called "sorino" to the sterile woman's husband to increase his sperm count.

There also is a strong belief in Tanjore and Coimbatore districts that sexual intercourse is an activity that makes a person "hot." Hence sterile women are asked to increase the coital frequency and also encouraged to prolong the duration of the sexual act. They are advised to eat cashewnuts, almonds and rock candy in order to increase their sexual passion and thus prolong coitus.

Too many children and children born too close to each other are often considered to be a fault of the woman. Only "hot" and sexually active women will have such fertility achievements. Likewise, a man with an overwhelmingly "hot" body is believed to be easily excited, often has intercourse, wastes an enormous amount of semen and hence usually becomes weak and fathers weak children. In other words, over-indulgence in sexual intercourse drains a man of his energies and may even drain away his life (Carstairs, 1961; Gould, 1969; Mandelbaum, 1974; Mani, 1970; Nag, 1972; Poffenberger and Poffenberger, 1973; Wyon and Gordon, 1971). It is a common belief among the higher caste members, who are generally vegetarians, that the members of the lower caste produce a large number of children because they eat meat which is "hot" and as a result have frequent sexual intercourse. A celibate is respected. He is able to conserve his energy by restraining from the sexual act and thus is able to prevent the loss of his semen, the "energy of his life." In order to reduce his sexual excitability, a "hot" person is commonly advised to drink cow's milk, eat lots of "cold" fruits and refrain from meat and liquor. Examples of *Yogis* and *Gurus* are often cited to emphasize the point that these men are physically strong and spiritually active because of their vegetarian "cold" foods and therefore are able to abstain from sexual activities.

Some recourse to enhance fertility in rural Tamil Nadu resembled imitative and contagious magical rituals. One of the midwives said that she often advised a sterile woman to swallow a small piece of a fresh umbilical cord from a newborn baby. This piece of the cord was to be inserted in a ripe banana and the whole thing was to be consumed. A gryllus insect, swallowed with a banana segment is also believed to cure sterility. The midwife claimed that she herself has successfully administered these "cures" to several sterile women in the area. Gryllus insect is locally known as *piḷḷai pūcci* (the literal translation of which is "baby (not small) insect." This linguistic sympathetic association with a child or baby perhaps underlies this particular type of "cure." A Tanjore Iyer family presents another example of imitative magical rites. A pregnant woman during her fifth or seventh month of pregnancy undergoes a ritual (for pregnancies only) called *vaḷai kāppu* (adorning bangles). After the initial religious rituals are over the pregnant woman is asked to sit on a wooden plank and she ritually adorns herself with bangles (usually glass bangles). A sterile woman is asked to sit on the same plank and like the pregnant woman is asked to wear lots of bangles. After the entire ceremony is over, the *sāri* of the pregnant woman, worn by her during *vaḷai kāppu* rituals, is wrapped around the sterile woman. Such imitative practices are believed to make the superhuman agents bless the sterile woman with a child.

In Ramnad and Coimbatore districts several such fertility-enhancing rituals suggest the law of imitation. In these districts barren women were asked to make toy cradles from a piece of cloth and tie them to a sacred bush using stones or pebbles to symbolize babies. Many women pray to Lord Muruga or to Lord Sri Venkateswara to help them conceive. These women will buy small bronze or copper or images of *bāla* Krişņa (Krişņa as a crawling baby) and go on a pilgrimage to Palani (famous for Lord Muruga) or to Tirupathi (the seat of Lord Sri Venkateswara) and offer these images to the gods by dropping them in the temple *huṇdis.* Such rituals are believed to have promising results.

In a village in Chingleput district people sacrifice cocks and male goats to the village deity to seek his blessings in curing sterility. Only male animals are sacrificed, suggesting a logical association of male qualities with sterility therapy. As mentioned before, male qualities in Tamil Nadu villages represent "heat" which is believed to be a good cure for a sterile woman who is "cold."

Many rural women believe that sterility is due to *doṣam* (defect or a flaw). This *doṣam* need not be restricted to their body. It can also be in their horoscope, in the diamonds of their jewellery, in their newly-built or newly-occupied house. In order to correct this flaw, the local astrologer is consulted and necessary compensatory and corrective rituals are performed. Sometimes the local medicine man or the magician (*manthiravāthi*) is consulted to detect the origin of the *doṣam.* After determining its origin, the magician will chant some *manthirams* (sacred hymns) and prescribe proper curative rituals. The *manthiravāthi* often gives a sterile woman a piece of ripe banana, believed to have magical curative powers, which is to be consumed immediately.

Wrath of the superhuman agents due to rupture of harmony with them is also believed to result in sterility in a woman. This disruption may be caused by the woman herself or by any of her or her husband's relatives, in this or in her previous births. There is a firm belief that killing a cobra will cause an imbalance in harmonious relations with the superhuman world. The cobra (snakes in general) is a very important and sacred fertility symbol, so is also Śiva Linga (Śiva in a phallic form). The cobra is usually adorned by Lord Śiva. Hence, sterility in a woman is believed to be due to harm inflicted to a cobra by one of her relatives in this or in the previous births. A sterile woman is frequently advised to pray to Śiva and offer milk to the cobras. She is also asked to go on a pilgrimage to Rameswaram —an important place of abode of Lord Śiva. Thus, by praying to Lord Śiva and the cobra (by extension to all the poisonous insects such as scorpions and poisonous centipedes known as *pūrān*) the ruptured harmony with the superhuman agents is believed to be restored. Sterile women are also encouraged to go around the *pīpal* tree (*Ficus religiosa*). In Tamil Nadu one can observe several stone images of cobras installed under the *pīpal* tree which is also believed to be the abode of cobras, hence the rite.

Other suggested therapeutic course of action to overcome childlessness include fasting, restricted diet, salt-free diet, feeding young children, feeding and giving gifts to the Brahmins, visiting *gurus* and *mahātmās* (sacred, pious and holy men), personal sacrifices, animal sacrifice, eating holy ash, and removing the evil eye. If all these ethnomedical efforts fail, perhaps the time is not "right" and one has to simply wait.

It is important to note here that in this discussion of sterility, the husband is seldom blamed for the inability of his wife to bear a child. It is commonly believed that a man simply cannot be sterile because his body constitution, as nature has made it, is "hot"; he is sexually active and, consequently, fertile.

Conception

A normal and a healthy woman, whose *doṣas* and humors are in perfect harmony and who has lead a normal moral and ethical life is often blessed with beautiful children. Any disruption in this harmony—either between the *doṣas* and humors or between the woman and her social and cosmological world—will make a woman either very "hot" or very "cold." A "hot" woman will experience frequent abortions or will give birth to a large number of weak children. On the other hand, a "cold" woman will be unable to conceive. As mentioned earlier, efforts are made to restore the balance between the *doṣas* and the binary opposition of the humors and also to normalize relations with the superhuman agents in order to cure a sterile woman.

A woman would conceive when her body is normal. She is advised to have sex on those days when her body is believed to be normal. For example, a woman is asked to refrain from sexual intercourse on days when she takes an oil bath which has a "cooling" effect. A woman is also asked to abstain from sex on important social and religious occasions so as not to invite the displeasure of the superhuman agents. It is generally believed that conception takes place during warm nights rather than during cold and dark nights. A homoeopathic doctor suggested that if a woman has coitus during the full moon day and if that day falls between the first day of a woman's menstrual period and the next fifteen days, conception is assured. He continued, "It will be a waste of semen for a man to have intercourse with his wife during new moon days (or during waning period of the moon) when the nights are dark and cold. Even if the woman should conceive, the child will be a girl."

There is a firm belief that conception can occur only on certain days and on certain times of the day. Casual sexual relations will not result in conception. Timing of the coitus should be carefully planned to make certain that the woman will conceive. This will depend upon her body constitution, days of the moon, position of the celestial bodies, position of her and her husband's birth star and astrologically auspicious days and time. These days and times are supposedly known to elderly persons, the village priest and the local astrologer; their advice and guidance are sought on these matters.

Pregnancy: its detection and staging

Very few women go to indigenous midwives or to local doctors to find out whether they are pregnant; nor are they eager enough to establish the stage of pregnancy. Pregnant women often call upon a midwife or visit the doctor at the local Primary Health Center or a hospital soon after the birth pain has started. As a result, certain complications during pregnancy frequently go unnoticed or undetected until much later. These cases include twins, breech deliveries, transverse lie, cephalo-pelvic disproportion, etc.

The ethnomedical diagnostic procedures for detecting and staging pregnancy are pluralistic—again ranging from purely physical to predominantly cosmological. A Tanjore village homoeopathic doctor claimed that the best way to detect the early stages of pregnancy is through feeling a woman's pulse on her wrist. Basically there are three types of pulse (*nādi*): *vāda nādi*—indicating acid humors or gas elements and is felt by the forefinger; *pitta nādi*—indicating bilious humors and felt by the middle finger; *sleśma nādi*—indicating phlegmatic elements and felt by the ring finger. In a non-pregnant woman, the *vāda nādi* and the *sleśma nādi* would beat smoothly and uniformly (similar to the walking of a peacock). If the woman is pregnant, at least for forty days, the beat of the *vāda nādi*, and in particular that of the *sleśma nādi*, would be intermittent indicating changes in her phlegmatic elements (perhaps a cold woman is slowly getting warmer). He also pointed out that normally he would inject the urine of a woman suspected of pregnancy into a live white toad collected from a banana tree. If the toad turns to a red blood color it means the woman is pregnant. There would be no reaction if the woman is not pregnant. According to the doctor this test is good for pregnancies that are at least forty days old. Another method for detecting pregnancy is an examination of the nipples of a woman. A woman's nipples would change to red as soon as she is pregnant. After ninety days of pregnancy the redness would disappear and they turn to brown or dark brown. With a glitter in his eyes, he claimed that the information on the "nipple examination method" is not available in any standard homoeopathic text book and that he learnt this method through personal experience. Another method he infrequently used was to examine the hairline in the pubic region; a pregnant woman will have curly hair. Since a pregnant woman is fertile, likewise her pubic region will also become fertile and will have profuse hair growth.

Many indigenous midwives and parturient women responded to the question, "how does someone detect pregnancy?" by saying that "we *know* when we become pregnant." Further probing revealed that they suspect pregnancy if they miss a menstrual period, if they have morning sickness, if the breasts enlarge, if the facial skin turns pale, if their feet swell, if they crave for unusual food items and if they are uninterested in sexual intercourse.

In order to determine the month of pregnancy, the midwives normally asked the woman about her last missed menstrual period. Some women count the pregnancy month from the nearest new moon or full moon days of the last missed period. They also mentioned about keeping track of their pregnancy month from the nearest festival, agricultural activities such as seeding, transplanting and harvesting or some important village event.

Some midwives claimed that one can find out the stage of pregnancy by an examination of the abdomen. If the fetus is above the navel the mother is more than six months pregnant; if the fetus is below the navel and if it feels like an unripe fruit it is less than five months old. Some midwives also mentioned that they can calculate the month of pregnancy by feeling the fetus with their middle finger inserted through the vagina. This way a pregnancy that is more than seven months old can be detected easily.

Sex determination. There is usually some anxiety in the mother, as among her relatives, regarding the sex of the unborn. If it is her first pregnancy, a mother prefers a boy to a girl. Most indigenous midwives and parturient women admitted that the sex of the child is determined by god and a woman will get a child according to her fate (*thalai ezhuttu*—literally translated as "head letters"). However, there are a number of cultural beliefs and practices that can ensure the sex of the fetus can foretell the sex of the unborn.

In order to ensure the sex of the child one desires, timing of the sexual act as well as the temperament and the body constitution of the couple at the time of coitus are important. If the husband or the wife was angry at the time of coitus, the chances are that the child conceived at that time will be a male. Anger is believed to excite the "hot" elements in a person. Likewise, if the body constitution of the husband, and more importantly that of the wife, was "hot" during intercourse, again the child will be a male. If intercourse takes place during full moon days and during the waxing period of the moon, the child will be a male. If conception takes place during the waning period of the moon or during new moon days, which are believed to be "cold" and dark, the child, naturally, will be a female.

If a woman is already pregnant, she can still make sure that she can deliver a child of the desired sex. A pregnant woman desiring a girl should stand out in the open during new moon days in order to make her body "cold," enabling the growth of a female fetus. If a woman desires a male child she should go out during full moon days. To the question, "can a woman get a male child if she stood out in the hot sun to make the fetus 'hot'?," a midwife replied that the rays of the sun are too hot and this will result in an abortion. A male fetus is believed to be smaller than a female fetus. Hence a woman should eat less during pregnancy to make sure that she can give birth to a male child. Naturally a woman will deliver a female child if she ate more during her pregnancy.

There are many ways of foretelling the sex of the unborn. An indigenous midwife claimed that by examining the shape and the size of the abdomen of a pregnant woman she could foretell the sex of the fetus. According to her, generally speaking a male child is smaller than a female child at the time of delivery. Hence if the abdomen of a pregnant woman is small during the seventh month of pregnancy she will deliver a male child. If the abdomen is large, it will be a female child. If the abdomen is conical it is a male fetus; if it is round it is a female fetus. If one feels the heart beat of the fetus on the right side (of the pregnant woman) it is a male; if it is felt on the left side it is a female. It is interesting to note that the right side is associated with the male principle while the left side with the famale principle. A wife must always be on the left hand side of the husband, especially during ritual occasions.

According to the homoeopathic doctor in a Tanjore village, a woman with a male fetus will have an above-normal body temperature while a woman with a female fetus will have below-normal body temperature. A normal temperature for a woman is taken to be 98.6°F.

A large number of midwives reported that a male child will be born earlier than the expected date of delivery. If the delivery is postponed beyond the expected date, it is "sure" to be a female child. They also informed me that a male child at birth will be lesser in weight compared to a female child and that a male child requires more attention and care than a female child during the post-natal period.

According to a woman in Chingleput district, one can discover the sex of the fetus by observing a pregnant woman when she gets up from a sitting position. If the pregnant woman puts her left hand down to push herself up while getting up, she will have a female child. If she uses her right hand for the same purpose, she is going to have a male child. If she puts her hand between the two legs while getting up she will have a boy but if she puts her hand on her side she will give birth to a female child.

Preventing conception

Mechanical and chemical contraceptive usage is still limited in rural Tamil Nadu. However, most women were aware of modern contraceptive methods due to extensive family planning program efforts made by the government. The most commonly mentioned method of birth prevention was male sterilization. In spite of limited use of modern methods, there are numerous indigenous methods and beliefs regarding conception control. A woman is believed to conceive when she is "hot." She is therefore advised to avoid coitus those days when her body constitution is "hot" to prevent conception. Some of these days include full moon days, waxing period of the moon, and days immediately before and after her menstruation. Menstruation is believed to occur when a woman's body is "hot" and the menstrual blood is discharged to make the body normal in terms of body humors.

A woman is also advised to refrain from sex when she or her husband is intoxicated or on those days when they are "hot" and spicy foods. Most women were of the opinion that abstinence was the best way of preventing conception. There is a common belief that a sterilized male is a "cold" male and having sex with him will not lead to conception. She also reported that having coitus on days when a woman takes an oil bath will also prevent conception. An oil bath is believed to "cool" a woman.

Some indigenous contraceptive methods include using margosa oil before coitus, using a mixture of salt and tamarind water after coitus (as a douche), ejecting the sperm from the uterus by gently jumping immediately after coitus or by manipulating the abdomen (uterus introversion?), and inserting a piece of cloth in the uterus before coitus. Many women reported that condoms are not acceptable as a contraceptive method. They believed that only those who go to prostitutes use condoms. Further condoms are made of rubber and this tends to produce heat during coitus. It is assumed that this heat leads to venereal diseases. The etiology of skin diseases such as rashes, blisters, boils, measles and chicken pox is also traced to "heat."

The homoeopathic medicines to prevent conception include a mixture of a zinc compound with the leaves of a thorny bush (*Ziziphus jujuba*) and the leaves of wild licorice. This mixture is burnt to ash and is mixed with butter or buttermilk (made from cow's milk) and consumed orally. This mixture is believed to make a woman "cold" thereby preventing conception. Women desiring to prevent conception are also advised to drink lot of buttermilk mixed with salt.

Abortion

Generally speaking, the indigenous midwives and the local medical practitioners hesitated to admit that they encouraged or performed abortions. It appeared that they normally discouraged abortion unless it was absolutely necessary. This would include cases of illegal conception, pregnant widows, rape and danger to the health of the mother if she delivered a baby.

The midwives believed that if they performed abortions on normal pregnant women, the midwives' own children or the children of their relatives would be born with physical deformities. Parturient women considered abortion on normal women a moral sin that would disrupt the harmonious relations with the supernatural agents. Generally speaking, abortion was considered unnecessary. The midwives believed that only those women who are "hot" get easily sexually excited and unnecessarily invite trouble. Normal women, in their opinion, will have a lot of self control and would not seek abortion. Due to the prevailing value system there is a complete censure of unmarried pregnant women either single or widowed.

One out of two midwives admitted that they have been approached for abortion, but most of them pleaded ignorance regarding indigenous methods and medicines for inducing abortion. They reported that normally a woman seeking abortion would be advised to approach a city doctor or a doctor in the Primary Health Center.

The homoeopathic doctor in a Tanjore village mentioned that he gave homoeopathic medicines such as Kasibigom, Abis Q and Pulsatilla Q (a mixture of tincture and water taken orally by women) for inducing abortion. He also claimed that these medicines are effective when pregncianes are less than two months old. For pregnancies beyond this time these medicines are ineffective.

The commonly believed etiology for abortion is the excessively "hot" body of the pregnant woman. In order to prevent abortions, the women's bodies must be kept normal. By exciting the "hot" elements in a pregnant woman's body one can induce abortion. In order to cause abortion, efforts are made through mechanical, herbal and dietary means to increase the body "heat."

The most frequent method of abortion mentioned by the local midwives is "stick insertion" (*kucci vaikkiradu*). In this method, a small stick (usually a match stick) is tipped with a piece of cloth and this tip is smeared with the latex of *Callotropics gigantea* (locally known as *kaḷḷi* or *yerccan chedi*). This treated stick is inserted through the vagina until it touches the fetus. It is left in place for a day or two. This is believed to be a sure way of inducing abortion in women who are less than four months pregnant. Latex of other plants (*thanga araḷi, kombu kaḷḷi*, etc.) are also used for inducing abortion. According to one midwife, "the woman will get stomach pain and will develop high fever and after the fetus is aborted these symptoms will disappear."

In Coimbatore district a woman desiring abortion is asked to consume sesame seeds, soaked overnight, to induce bleeding and abortion. In addition, a paste of dry ginger (*sukku*) and sesame seeds is administered orally to a woman for six days to abort the fetus. Bamboo shoots and unrefined jaggery taken orally are also believed to be effective abortifacients. A decoction of long pepper, dill (*Anethum sowa*), bark from a local tree (*māvalinga maram*) and turmeric (*kastūri*) is given to a pregnant woman for about a week. This decoction will make the fetus very "hot," resulting in abortion. It is interesting to note that some of the ingredients used in this decoction also form part of an elaborate medical mixture (known as *kāya marundu*) given to the mother soon after her delivery. *Kāya marundu* is widely used in Tamil Nadu and there are shops specializing in this medicine. This mixture is believed to heal the wounds that are caused during delivery. A mother is considered to be "cold" soon after her delivery and she must keep herself warm and *kāya marundu* does just that.

In the Nilgiris district, the midwives obtained herbal medicine to induce abortion from the native Kurumbas and Thoraiyar tribes. They also ask women seeking abortion to consume large quantities of oats and rye, boiled in water. Other methods of inducing abortion include swallowing camphor inserted in a piece of ripe banana, oral consumption of a paste of mustard and jaggery (jaggery made of palmyra sap), eating boiled green papaya, excessive consumption of "hot" fruits such as mangoes, pineapples, papaya and jackfruit (*Artocarupus integrifolia*), and eating "hot" vegetables such as bitter gourd and pumpkin.

In Chingleput district an extract from a paste of *marutāni* leaves (*Lawsonia spinosa*) is administered orally to induce abortion. It is interesting to note here that these leaves are used for a dye and one can see women and young girls using *marutāni* paste to decorate their palms and fingers. This paste when applied externally on the palms and fingers is believed to make the body "cold" while its juice taken internally is believed to make the body "hot."

Mechanical methods of inducing abortion include riding on a bicycle through a rough dirt road, jumping from a wall, climbing steps, climbing a ladder, putting pressure on the "stomach," jerky movements caused by the husband during coitus and lifting heavy weights.

In general, abortion is considered as a sinful act—an act that would anger the supernatural agents. It is also believed to be an act of immoral women. The line of argument given by an elderly Iyer woman in a Tanjore village is that abortion is frequently practiced by women in the lower castes. Lower caste women eat all kinds of meat and "hot" foods. Such dietary habits make these women sexually easily excitable and as a result they often get into trouble through extramarital intercourse. This is the reason for frequent abortions among the women of lower castes and it is not a problem among the women of higher castes who are vegetarians.

Prevention of abortion

All the above-mentioned conditions and activities that are believed to result in an aborted fetus would naturally be avoided in order to prevent abortion in a pregnant woman. As mentioned above, since abortion is associated with "hot" elements, to prevent abortion a pregnant woman should be careful not to excite the "hot" humor in her body. She is asked to refrain from eating "hot" and flatulent fruits and vegetables, avoid spices, fats and vegetable oils, abstain eating chicken, eggs and goat's meat and completely avoid liquor and products made of sesame seeds. She is also advised to keep away from continuous exposure to fire, sunlight and to avoid strenuous work and lifting of heavy objects. Among the Badagas in the Nilgiris district, a pregnant woman is asked to keep away from cemeteries and cremation grounds and not to cross a temple in order to avoid the wrath of the supernatural agents.

A pregnant woman fearing abortion is asked to consume such "cold" foods as buttermilk made of cow's milk, citrus fruits, foods with salt and tamarind and in general "cold" fruits and vegetables. A pregnant woman is also advised not to have coitus as it is believed to be a heat producing activity. A pregnant woman is prohibited from going to places where she has never been before or talking to strangers for fear of the evil eye. She is also asked not to go to slaughter houses or see animal sacrifices. These may have sympathetic effect on her fetus.

Young banana trees and coconut trees will never be cut down in a house in which a pregnant woman lives. These trees, particularly the young ones, are treated as babies (*piḷḷai*) and any harm done to them will also affect the fetus.

Gestation

A woman who has missed her menstrual period is not taken to the hospital or the local midwife to ascertain pregnancy. Very little attention is paid during the early months of pregnancy. Only during the later months in her pregnancy, usually after the sixth months, does a woman get attention. No special nourishing or nutritious foods are given to a pregnant female. On the contrary, a pregnant woman is advised not to eat fatty or nutritious foods for fear that the fetus may grow too large resulting in complications during delivery. A pregnant woman is believed to be very delicate and is easily affected by even a slight imbalance in her humors. Drastic change in her diet and climatic conditions make her vulnerable to illness.

There are many dietary restrictions, taboos and rituals to be observed by a pregnant woman during the later months in her pregnancy. Generally speaking, a pregnant woman is believed to have an above average "hot" body. Hence she is advised not to eat "hot" foods or indulge in "heat" producing activities for fear of abortion. As mentioned previously, coitus is believed to be "heat" producing; hence, a pregnant woman is asked to abstain from intercourse from the third month of pregnancy onwards. A pregnant woman is advised to avoid strenuous work and bad temper. She is asked not to eat excess of "cold" foods so as not to excite her phlegmatic elements.

A woman who is pregnant is encouraged to eat foods that are non flatulent and are easily digestible. These would include tender vegetables and certain kinds of ripe bananas. In Chingleput district it was noted that a pregnant woman was not allowed to consume leafy vegetables, particularly the leaves of *Muringa Indica* (often known as the drum-stick tree), for fear that these leaves and greens may get "entangled" with the umbilical cord of the child in the fetus. In general, dietary restrictions are much stricter for a woman after her delivery as compared to during her pregnancy. She is advised to keep proper balance of her *doṣas* and humors in order to have a safe delivery and a healthy child.

A pregnant woman is careful not to do evil things or get involved in activities that would make the supernatural agents unhappy.

Since every woman would like a wholesome child without any physical deformities, women in their late pregnancy are advised to refrain from such activities as killing, hurting, cutting, clipping, breaking, tearing, etc. These activities are believed to have sympathetic effects on her fetus resulting in a deformed child.

The celestial bodies, particularly the sun and the moon, are believed to have profound effects on the people, especially on the fetus. A pregnant woman is asked to strictly observe certain religious prescriptions during eclipses. It is a common belief that during eclipses the sun and the moon develop *doṣam* (defects) and are incomplete (*bhinnam*). Eclipses are believed to bring harm to a pregnant woman if she exposes herself and would cause deformities in the fetus. Eclipses are also believed to be evil and to pollute people. Generally, people do not eat or drink during eclipses for fear of indigestion and one must take a purificatory bath before eating.

Finally, every woman in Tamil Nadu would like a child with a fair complexion. In order to achieve this aspiration rich people often advise their pregnant women to consume large quantities of saffron mixed with hot milk or with rose water. Saffron is believed to affect the skin of the child in the fetus making it fair. Poor people try to achieve similar results through consuming small quantities of red brick powder or powdered red stone or holy ash (usually whitish grey in color). Pregnant women are careful to avoid dark skinned fruits such as black grapes, black berries (*Solanum nigrum)* and black or dark pink fruit known as *nāga pazham* (*Eugenia jambolana*). Consumption of these fruits is believed to result in a dark-skinned baby. It is also believed that a child conceived on a full moon day will have a fair skin. In short, a normal woman with proper habits and with a proper balance of her humors and *doṣas* will have a normal and a healthy bady.

Conclusions

The initial impression one might get is that the prevailing ethnomedical beliefs and behavior regarding sterility, ferility, conception, gestation and abortion are illogical, bewildering and even contradictory. However, a closer examination of attitudes and actions regarding illness etiology, nosology, symptoms, diagnostic procedures and therapeutic strategies reveal that the underlying value orientations that shape the world view of the villagers and influence their social relations in everyday life also affect their cognitive system underlying the ethnomedical scene. In other words, the constituents of the ethnomedical panorama seem to epitomize the general value systems, organization and the philosophy of the larger universe of the Indian culture.

What are these fundamental value orientations that are characteristic of Indian culture in general and Tamil Nadu culture in particular that have relevance in shaping the ethnomedical behavior? Opler (1945) has given an analytic model that helps to analyze and understand health beliefs and practices. He calls these basic value orientations "themes" (1945) which are believed to influence and direct behavior along certain lines (1968). Just as themes influence people's thoughts and behavior in a particular society, they also exert influence and rationalize their behavior in the ethnomedical arena.

Themes of *segmentation* and *harmony* seem to have a powerful influence in structuring the nature of rural Tamil Nadu culture. The universe, in the villagers' world view, is segmented into smaller units, each unit with a distinct function assigned to it. The physical layout of the village, social structure and organization (*varṇa, jāti* and *jajmāni* systems), time (*yugās*), individual life (*āśramas*), souls, body parts, sexual qualities, foods, days of the week and times of the day, directions, rituals and the supernatural agents are all segmented and ranked. Although the universe is ranked, it is also seen as having an order to harmony between these segments. It is essential that a person learns to live harmoniously with various elements.

Like the Indian universe, the ethnomedical scene is also segmented. Etiology of illness, nosology, symptoms, diagnostic methods, therapeutic strategies and the therapists are segmented. In addition, body humors and *doṣas*, temperament, sex, body constitution, celestial objects and foods that are believed to have important effects on the health of an individual are meticulously classified according to their humoral qualities. Illness is believed to be due to physical causes, climatic or seasonal changes, culinary habits, flaws or irregularities (in a person's horoscope when he has astrological bad times—*graha doṣa,* in his previous birth, *karma doṣa,* in the new residence or in the diamonds in one's jewelry), immoral and unethical behavior of the individual, scourge of the supernatural agents or a combination of these. There is a strong conviction that illness is due to lack of harmony in the body humors and *doṣas.* It is believed that the humoral balance which is regulated by a person's sex, temperament, food habits, body constitution, climatic conditions, *karma,* astrological and cosmological forces can be thrown out of order resulting in illness. For example, sterility may be due to various reasons: the husband's low sperm count, worm infestation in the woman's "stomach," low frequency of coitus, "cold" body constitution, excessive consumption of "cold" foods, exposure to cold environment, wrong timing of the sexual act (which should take place on full moon days or during the waxing period of the moon when nights are believed to be "hot"), sins committed by the woman or one of her relatives in the previous births, flaws in her or her husband's horoscope, or simply, the wrong time for conception. Generally speaking, sterility is believed to be due to disharmony in the woman's *doṣas* caused by her excessive "cold" humoral element.

Therapeutic procedures are basically geared towards maintaining or restoring the homeostatic balance between the humoral elements and the *tridoṣas.* A "cold" woman will fail to conceive, while a "hot" woman will have abortion or give birth to weak children. Hence care should be taken to see that perfect harmony is restored between the body humors and *doṣas* in order to avoid illness or regain health. This harmony could be effected through restoring balance in the relationships with the supernatural agents through rituals, prayers, pilgrimages or sympathetic magical rites. Conception could be achieved through propitiating the supernatural agents through fasting, *mathirams* (sacred hymns), pilgrimage to Tirupathi and Palani, worshipping the cobra, performing sympathetic rituals such as making a toy cradle and tying it to a sacred bush, wrapping the sari of a pregnant woman around a sterile woman during *vaḷai kāppu* and offering images of baby *Kriṣṇa* to the supernatural agents. A woman can also conceive through physical manipulation of her internal and external surroundings through medicine, consuming "hot" foods, environmental changes and getting involved in activities that are considered to be "hot." Such efforts are believed to restore the humoral balance in a woman. Advice on medicine, diet, and the moral and spiritual regimen of life is given to an ill person to regain the ruptured harmony of the humoral elements. Thus, in the world view of the Tamil villager, health is not considered a normal state of the human body but as a state resulting from the requisite harmony that arises from compromise between the complementarily opposing humors and *doṣas.*

Dependency on astrology is another important theme that has relevance to the understanding of the ethnomedical behavior. Celestial bodies, particularly the sun, the moon, Saturn and Mars, are believed to have important influence on the life of people and the unborn. Horoscope plays an important role in one's moral, ethical, social and economic life. In order to be successful in a new venture, procedures must be initiated during astrologically good times that befit a person's birth star. His horoscope is used to determine this particular time. Congruence in horoscopes between the bride and the groom is the first essential step in the successful culmination of marriage and in the happiness of life after marriage. This theme permeates the ethnomedical scene as well. Sterility may be due to flaws in the woman's or her husband's horoscope or the woman's birth star may be going through a phase that is not good at this time (*graha doṣa*). Like the human body and foods, celestial bodies, particularly the sun and the moon, are believed to have symbolic humoral qualities. The sun is "hot" and overexposure to sunlight would make the fetus "hot" and lead to abortion. The full moon is "hot" and women desiring children or a male child are advised to have intercourse on full moon days. Children conceived on new moon days are generally girls; like a woman's body constitution, new moon days are "cold." The sun and the moon which are believed to be defective during eclipses (*bhinnam*) are believed to likewise cause deformities in the fetus if a woman exposed herself during an eclipse. Ritual baths during new moon days and eclipses are mandated, failure of which would result in illness. In order to avoid illness or regain normal health through restoring the equilibrium between *doṣas* and humors, a person is advised to initiate activities on auspicious days and times. Fasting, going on a pilgrimage, visiting a city doctor, performing purificatory and compensatory rituals and even the first sexual intercourse of the newly married should be carefully planned according to the time fixed by an astrologer or a learned Brahmin. Often, medicines prepared during certain phases of the moon are believed to bring promising results.

Cyclical concept is another Indian theme that influences the world view as well as the ethnomedical behavior of the villagers. Time is seen as cyclical rather than linear. There is an emphasis on repetition, recurrence and reassurance. A person sees himself as a passive participant in the scheme of things. Illness is seen as a punishment meted to an individual for wrong deeds in this or in previous births. Illness is due to a person's *karma doṣa*. All he can do is to accept what is given to him and perform compensatory rituals and purification ceremonies or simply wait for the right time to come. The theme of cyclical concept may explain fatalistic attitudes towards illness therapy. This theme, along with the idea of reincarnation of souls, could underlie some ethnomedical beliefs and practices that appeal the supernatural agents and cosmological forces through prayers, fasting and pilgrimages.

Ethnomedicine, as practised in rural Tamil Nadu is based on some basic value orientations which also shape and influence the world view of the villagers. While their behavior and beliefs may appear illogical, unscientific and sometimes in direct conflict with the established modern medical practices, failure to understand the behavior from the villagers' cognitive structure might impede efforts to formulate an acceptable rural health strategy. The indigenous health care "vessel" is not empty. Any attempts at improving the health care system in rural India through the introduction of modern medical practices should be sensitive to the already existing complex network of ethnomedical beliefs and practices.

REFERENCES

BASHAM, A.L.

1976 "The Practice of Medicine in Ancient and Medieval India." In Charles Leslie (ed.), *Asian Medical Systems*, pp. 18-43. Berkeley: University of California Press.

BEALS, ALAN R.

1976 "Strategies of Resort to Curers in South India." In Charles Leslie (ed.), *Asian Medical Systems*, pp. 184-198. Berkeley: University of California Press.

CARSTAIRS, MORRIS G.

1955 "Medicine and Faith in Rural Rajasthan." In Benjamin D.Paul (ed.), *Health, Culture, and Community*, pp. 107-134. New York; Russel Sage Foundation.

CARSTAIRS, MORRIS G.

1961 *The Twice Born: A Study of a Community of High-Caste Hindus*. Bloomington, Indiana: Indiana University Press.

FABREGA, JR., HORACIO

1972 "Medical Anthropology." In Bernard J. Siegal (ed.), *Biennial Review of Anthropology*, pp. 167-229. California: Stanford University Press.

FUCHS, STEPHEN
1964 "Magic Healing Techniques Among the Balahis in Central India." In A. Kiev (ed.), *Magic, Faith and Healing: Studies in Primitive Psychiatry Today*. London: Collier-Macmillan.

GOULD, HAROLD A.
1965 "Modern Medicine and Folk Cognition in a North Indian Village." *Human Organization* 24: 201-208.

GOULD, KETAYUN H.
1969 "Sex and Contraception in Sherupur: Family Planning in a North Indian Village." *Economic and Political Weekly* 4: 1187-1192.

HUGHES, CHARLES C.
1968 "Ethnomedicine." *International Encyclopedia of the Social Sciences*, 10: 87-93.

KUTUMBIAH, P.
1962 *Anceint Indian Medicine*. Madras, India: Orient Longmans.

LESLIE, CHARLES
1976 "Introduction." In Charles Leslie (ed.), *Asian Medical Systems*, pp. 1-12. Berkeley: University of California Press.

LEWIS, OSCAR
1965 *Village Life in Northern India; Studies in a Delhi Village*. New York: Vintage Books.

LOGAN, MICHAEL
1973 "Humoral Medicine in Guatamala and Peasant Acceptance of Modern Medicine." *Human Organization* 32: 385-395.

MANDELBAUM, DAVID G.
1974 *Human Fertility in India: Social Components and Policy Perspectives*. Berkeley: University of California Press.

MANI, SRINIVASA B.
1970 "Family Planning Communication in Rural India." (Unpublished Ph. D. Dissertation). New York: Syracuse University.

MARRIOTT, MCKIM
1955 "Western Medicine in a Village in Northern India." In Benjamin D. Paul (ed.), *Health, Culture and Community*, pp. 239-268. New York: Russel Sage Foundation.

NAG, MONI
1972 "Sex, Culture and Human Fertility: India and the United States." *Current Anthropology* 13: 231-237, 260-263.

OBEYESEKERE, GANANATH
1976 "The Impact of Ayurvedic Ideas on the Culture and the Individual in Sri Lanka." In Charles Leslie (ed.), *Asian Medical Systems*, pp. 201-226. Berkeley: University of California Press.

OPLER, MORRIS E.
1945 "Themes as Dynamic Forces in Culture." *American Journal of Sociology* 51: 198-206.
1963 "The Cultural Definition of Illness in Village India." *Human Organization* 22: 32-35.

1968 "The Themal Approach in Cultural Anthropology and Its Application to North Indian Data." *Southwestern Journal of Anthropology* 24: 215-227.

POFFENBERGER, THOMAS and SHIRLEY POFFENBERGER
1973 "The Social Psychology of Fertility Behavior in Village in India." In James Fawcett (ed.), *Psychological Perspectives on Population*, pp. 135-162. New York: Basic Books Inc.

TAYLOR, CARL E.
1976 "The Place of Indigenous Medical Practitioners in the Modernization of Health Services." In Charles Leslie (ed.), *Asian Medical System*, pp. 285-299. Berkeley: University of California Press.

WYON, JOHN B. and JOHN E. GORDON
1972 *The Khanna Study· Population Problems in the Rural Punjab.* Cambridge: Harvard University Press.

ZIMMER, H.R.
1948 *Hindu Medicine.* Baltimore: Johns Hopkins University Press.

PART THREE

INDIGENOUS SYSTEMS OF HEALING AND CURING

MARK NICHTER*

TOWARD A CULTURAL RESPONSIVE RURAL HEALTH CARE DELIVERY SYSTEM IN INDIA

ABSTRACT. The detailed study of a South Indian health arena revealed that illness specific patterns of resort exist in respect to villagers' utilization of multiple therapy systems. While allopathy has become popular for the treatment of many types of illness, it is not always chosen as an initial or primary source of medical aid. Multiple variables including cultural beliefs, age, economic capacity, education, and practitioner accessibility influence lay medical decisions (Nichter 1978). On the basis of these general findings and a study of indigenous medical practitioners, in respect to their use of eclectic medical resources, a number of recommendations toward the improvement of rural health care delivery have been proposed. It is suggested that the practice of medicine be culturally responsive and that physicians be trained to communicate with their patients within their conceptual framework. It is also suggested that existing indigenous medical manpower be maximized by short-targeted training programs designed to reinforce regional patterns of resort and medical need. Cooperation between modern and indigenous medical practitioners is encouraged. In this regard, it is emphasized that cooperation will depend upon a sharing of basic medical resources and knowledge, an understanding of basic cultural concepts of health and healing, and mutual respect between pluralistic practitioners. Mutual respect is a prerequisite to the establishing of a workable rural referral network. It will require an appreciation by practitioners of each other roles and responsibilities. Anthropologists are encouraged to participate in the health sector by providing health planners with baseline data on regional health arenas and by actively participating in medical education programs.

*I wish to thank the National Institute of Mental Health, Bangalore for support and assistance during my field work during the period of May, 1974 to March, 1976.

BANERJI HAS WRITTEN THAT THE POPULARITY OF THE UNQUALIFIED registered medical practitioner (RMP) is contingent upon the fact that modern medical aid is not readily available to villagers:

> The RMP are in effect created as a result of the inability of the PHC dispensary or other qualified practitioners of western medicine to meet the demands for medical care services in the villages (1974: 1341).

The suggestion that a greater number of qualified doctors and more efficient Primary Health Centers (PHC's) would serve to eliminate the popularity of indigenous therapy systems and RMP is over-simplistic. It is based on the faulty assumptions that the biomedical model is suitable to India's cultural context without significant modification and that qualified medical personnel recognize villagers' socio-medical needs and are capable of meeting these needs.

A recent study conducted by the researcher examined villagers' use of modern, eclectic, and traditional medical practitioners in a region of South India (South Kanara) where each of these practitioners was accessible to villagers. It also examined the practice of medicine by a representative sample of these practitioner types. The study came to the following general conclusions:

1. Most villagers are pragmatic in their choice of medical aid. In most cases of illness, a villager's first concern is to seek symptomatic relief from whatever medicine is readily available within economic constraints. In areas where modern medicine has recently become available, this aid has been accepted after an initial period of exposure. However, the use of allopathic medicine is constrained by cultural factors including indigenous notions of body physiology, etiology, and diet.
2. The acceptance of modern medicine has not meant that traditional ideas of disease etiology have been superceded or that the cultural ramifications of specific illnesses have disappeared. This is apparent when immediate palliative treatment cannot be realized or when the illness is long term.
3. It is misleading to speak of a general acceptance of allopathic medicine for the villager's choice of medical treatment is far more subtle than this. Definite patterns exist as to the types of

curative treatment villagers will choose to utilize for different illnesses. Patterns of resort are dependent on multiple factors including economic and educational variables, the influence of local practitioners, the cultural significance of an illness, and the strategic use of illness as a means of role manipulation and/or expression of anxiety.

4. Traditional and eclectic rural practitioners treat a number of illnesses which are not brought to doctors in their initial stages. Among these illnesses are a number of children's illnesses. It was found that many adults who used allopathic medicines for their own ailments chose to use indigenous medicines for their young children.

5. Patients having long term illnesses or psycho-social problems are generally willing to engage in longer relationships with traditional practitioners than with busy doctors who are less sympathetic and who by and large do not understand the social meaning of illness and the sick role.

6. Established rural RMP and traditional practitioners, *vaidya*, are part of a rural referral network which links them with astrologers, sorcerers (*mantravadi*), possession cults, etc. Although these specialists are somewhat competitive, they offer each other mutual support and thereby legitimate each others' roles. They are pragmatic and refer cases beyond their competence to other practitioners and specialists. Cases are directly referred to allopathic doctors when a relationship of mutual respect existed between a local allopath and RMP.

The details of the South Kanara study have been presented elsewhere (Nichter, 1977; 1978). What is focused upon in this paper are some tentative recommendations toward improving rural health care delivery which health planners might explore in greater detail. Topics to be discussed include innovative medical education, the training of indigenous practitioners, the setting up of referral networks, the use of allopathic medicines by registered medical practitioners, and basic research priorities in the social sciences. I will emphasize that improved rural health care delivery will depend on a mutual understanding between physicians and patients and cooperation between India's pluralistic medical personnel. Understanding will depend on a comprehension of local health ideology while cooperation will depend on an appreciation of each practitioner's rôle, skills, and relationship with his/her patients. It will be stressed that regional studies in health ideology and patterns of resort in the layman's use of curative services are of immediate importance to health planners. They will provide baseline data upon which training programs and referral network may be assessed or instituted. The skeletal remains of numerous pilot projects and training schemes should be evidence enough that a close look at the ground is in order before leaping into the future with new plans.

INDIANIZING MEDICAL EDUCATION: A CONSIDERATION OF INDIGENOUS HEALTH IDEOLOGY

The failure of India's modern medical schools to prepare graduates for rural medical practice is widely recognized and it is an issue of current political debate. The key subject of social medicine which should prepare graduates for community work has been described by Banerji (1973) and Taylor *et al.*, (1967) as "stale, stagnant, and uninspiring." A survey I conducted of one hundred young medical graduates corroborated this description. It was found that a large majority of graduates rated social and preventive medicine as their least valuable and most boring course. Informants who planned to pursue PHC careers noted that their courses had not touched upon the realities and exigencies of rural medical practice. The major reason for this, as Banerji has noted, is that most of the teachers of these courses are themselves out of touch with village life; most have been trained overseas or in Indian schools which have relied solely on Western texts.

Critics have questioned both the aptitude of today's doctors to deal with rural patients and their attitudes toward these patients and rural work in general. Committees such as the Gore Committee have been delegated to investigate how medical education can be made more relevant to India's needs. So far, few practical proposals have been made. Several recent reports have suggested that doctors should be trained in the social sciences to broaden their social outlook, but as Jeffrey (1976) has noted the report was vague and the value of training doctors in general sociological theory is dubious.

Doctors and health staff would greatly benefit by an understanding of the conceptual framework of rural patients. What needs to be taught is not sociology in general, but the sociology of Indian health ideology and medical culture. Emphasis must be placed on such subjects as the use and meaning of the hot-cold idiom, the layman's use of *doṣa* (humoral) terminology, local notions of disease etiology, food classification, the symbolic aspect of medicine, the semantics of illness, the patient's expectations of a diagnostic session and so on. A familiarity with such subjects would make for a greater rapport between patient and doctor allowing the doctor to assess and diagnose a patient's illness better by knowing how to question him/her. Moreover, the use of local concepts could enable a doctor to explain to patients how they have contracted an illness and why they should follow his instructions.

Doctors and health staff could be trained to teach modern health ideas in a manner which the villager can understand. Instead of ignoring the villager's perception of health as balance and illness as imbalance, medical staff might better be trained to work with the balance metaphor. If villagers view medicine as hot or cold and they understand curing in terms of reinstating a balance of heat or humors, why is it not possible for doctors to work within or at least accomodate this framework. Research in South Kanara found the *doṣa* and hot-cold framework to be flexible and capable of explaining many basic bio-medical concepts.

I would suggest that doctors and health staff be trained to work within the existing cultural context instead of disregarding cultural parameters entirely. Medicine is a social as well as a natural science and health education must prepare medical staff to act as "cultural brokers" as well as fighters of microbes. The formulating of education programs responsive to existing health ideology is of high priority and should be encouraged. In this regard, medical students and health staff would benefit from courses based upon field studies which have investigated the cultural importance of bodily symptoms, health customs, disease etiology, etc. Social scientists with a background in the health sector should participate in medical education programs and utilize field data in their courses.

Sociological orientation should produce a doctor with a greater appreciation of his patient's problems and a greater ability to communicate with his patients. It is doubtful, however, that it will change the doctor's values or attitudes towards his profession. If the attitudes of doctors and health staff are to be altered, then the entire structure of the medical profession must be altered. This entails a change in both the material institution and the career of medicine in India.

Many health planners have emphasized that symbolic modernism in the form of sophisticated medical technology must be underplayed if medical education is to be centered on rural medical problems. Medical goods and services must be shifted to the rural areas in proportion to population and need. As important as the issue of resources is the issue of manpower. The manpower issue involves not only increasing numbers of physicians in rural areas, but determining what their role will be. The special nature of the physician's work, his domain of personal knowledge and status, must be defined in relation to alternative and auxiliary sources of medical aid and not in isolation.

THE TRAINING OF INDIGENOUS PRACTITIONERS

At the same time that medical education is being orientated toward rural health care delivery problems, programs must be developed to train indigenous and allied medical personnel in the use of essential medical resources and the value of preventive health measures. If supportive supervision and cooperation between government health personnel and indigenous practitioners could be fostered during training programs, then referral networks could be established. A few suggestions toward this end may be made.

Research was conducted to determine if village and town RMPs would be interested in knowing more about the treatment of those illnesses and mental disturbances which they commonly encountered. Village practitioners with a steady clientele expressed the greatest desire to receive further training and establish referral channels for cases which they were not successful in treating. Few of these practitioners, however, had a desire to be formally attached to the Government. Most stated that such an affiliation would be detrimental to their medical practices. They were afraid, for example, that they would be pressured by the Family Planning Program to bring in sterilization cases.

An investigation was carried out to determine the conditions under which these practitioners would cooperate with a rural medical training scheme. According to their stipulations, such a scheme would have to be kept separate from the Family Planning Program. Furthermore, training courses should be periodical, of short duration, and performed in rural areas rather than in large city hospitals.

I would suggest that these courses be conducted at renowned

temples, an ideal place for the integration of the old and new. Some of these temples have already set up medical units and employ doctors both for humanitarian reasons and for purposes of tax status. These temples might readily consent to have training programs held on their premises. Practitioners would be more likely to attend courses held at renowned temples because an association with such a temple would add to their own status and a visit would be attractive to them.

Training courses held at such renowned temples would be prestigious and the integration of science and tradition at these temples would foster the attitude of traditional modernism to which many RMP already subscribe. It would, moreover, allow these practitioners to preserve their dignity as opposed to being subjected to paternalistic training programs conducted in hospitals where they would be treated without status and respect.

The success of such training courses would be in large part determined by the selection procedure used to group practitioners into categories based on their experience, present knowledge, and education. It is doubtful that adhoc courses would be popular. A course designed for quasi-educated RMP would be beyond the comprehension of uneducated folk practitioners and courses designed for these latter practitioners would be condescending to the former type of practitioners. In order to group practitioners in each region appropriately, survey work would have to be carried out in each area to determine prospective candidates. Survey work which I conducted on the distribution and basic characteristics of medical personnel in one PHC zone in South Kanara was carried out with the occasional assistance of PHC staff and took four months to complete (Nichter: 1978).

In reference to possible training programs, more favorable response was generated for courses to be based upon the treatment of specific types of illnesses than for general courses without a specific theme. Training courses might be organized around subjects like children's illnesses, skin diseases, respiratory diseases, and so on.

Toward a Referral Network

The success of doctor-RMP referral relationships will depend primarily on mutual respect; respect gained from an appreciation of each other's roles. Provisions might be made so that when a RMP refers a patient to a government doctor, his patient is given special attention in accord with, and thus affirming, the RMP's status. Moreover, the patient might be directed back to the RMP if his condition requires follow-up treatment which the RMP is capable of administering.

Considering a PHC's small radius of effective influence, (Taylor, 1967; Nichter 1978) the establishment of such referral relationships might be an important step in improving rural health care delivery coverage. However, two major impediments stand in the way of promoting such referral relationships. First, RMPs do not wish to send patients to PHC doctors who have private practices because they do not wish to loose their patients entirely. PHC doctors with private practices on the other hand, would not wish to give recognition to RMPs because this might undermine their own practice and status. This problem is critical in areas where competition is keen and where RMP practice in close proximity to the PHC. Guidelines on a government doctor's private practice will have to be set and RMP will have to be reassured that doctors are not undermining their practice. RMP on the other hand will have to be convinced not to over extend themselves in areas of medicine where they have no competence. In this regard, legal restraints would be of little consequence. It is most likely that when a rural RMP with a steady clientele is able to recognize complications and when he realizes that his status as a practitioner rises more with a referral than with prolonging a cure, he will exercise his best judgement.

The second difficulty is in convincing government doctors of the positive value of maintaining good relations with RMP in rural areas. This may be accomplished more easily once studies on patterns of resort in the use of curative services have been carried out, the polemic surrounding the RMP's right to use allopathic drugs has been clarified, and training courses in the proper use of essential drugs have been initiated.

RMP AND THE USE OF ALLOPATHIC MEDICINE

> It is evident from the data...that folk practitioners and folk traditions play an important role in certain specific illnesses, but non-institutionally qualified indigenous medical practitioners dominate the scene by virtue of their ability to capitalize on such factors as paucity of qualified practitioners; making themselves

> readily available; providing medicines in accordance with local customs, beliefs and demands and freely imitating the qualified allopaths in the use of medicines...it would be normal to expect that the indigenous medical practitioner will continue to play a significant role in providing medical care to rural people for sometime to come (Kakar, Murthy and Parker, 1972: 290).

It is past the time to debate whether or not RMP should be allowed to use potent allopathic drugs. The fact is that a significant proportion of India's medical population using allopathic drugs are RMP. Unknowingly, many of these practitioners are misusing potent drugs for want of better training. Training these RMP in the proper use of commonly administered allopathic drugs is of high priority.

Recently, the Government has placed emphasis on the training of PHC staff in curative skills so that they may become multi-purpose health workers. Although this idea is laudatory, the fact remains that there is not enough government medicine to supply PHC doctors, let alone their staff. It is suggested that at least as much emphasis be placed on training RMP who have allopathic medicine at their disposal and who are already actively using it (for better or for worse) due to patient demand.

Consider for example the plight of a recent graduate of a school of ayurvedic medicine who has not received formal training in the use of allopathic medicine. If patients want strict ayurvedic treatment they generally frequent elder ayurvedic practitioners first, unless a young practitioner comes from the family of famous *vaidya*. Many villagers consider a young ayurvedic practitioner to know little more than an experienced patient. While they do not credit a young ayurvedic practitioner as being proficient in the use of ayurvedic medicine and knowledgable in *shastra*, (Science), they give him far more credit if he uses allopathic medicine. This is so because allopathic medicine is viewed as a new source of technical knowledge.

Diploma holders, in ayurveda or homeopathy, whether or not they are trained in the use of allopathic medicines, are forced by prevailing conditions to use these medicines to a significant extent. To exist in a competitive medical market a diploma holder must make use of fast acting allopathic drugs. Over 50 per cent of an average practitioner's patients will not return for further treatment after two days if notable symptomatic relief is not experienced. Long courses of treatment are expected of established ayurvedic pundits, but not practitioners who are primarily perceived as sources of symptomatic aid.

THE PHARMACEUTICAL INDUSTRY AND TRAINING PROGRAMS FOR RMP

It is clear that untrained RMP and diploma holders in homeopathy and indigenous systems of medicine will increasingly make use of allopathic drugs. Given this situation, it is in India's best interests to provide these practitioners with rudimentary training in the use of basic allopathic drugs. The question arises how such courses should be organized and what incentives rural practitioners should be offered for attending such courses. In terms of organization I have placed emphasis on an initial practitioner survey and assessment in terms of popularity and sophistication (by Western standards). Toward this end, it might be beneficial to glean the records of pharmaceutical companies operating in various regions of India. Preliminary research into the activities of pharmaceutical representatives revealed that these representatives maintain detailed records on popular practitioners (diploma holders) located in their field zones. Moreover, health planners might want to explore the future role of pharmaceutical companies in respect to their involvement in the rural health sector. Some basic data collected in South Kanara may better define this involvement.

In South Kanara, the pharmaceutical industry has a significant financial interest in the RMP. In order to document the extent of this interest, I composed a list of 206 practitioners of allopathic medicine visited by medical representatives in the rural area of five taluks: Puttur, Sullia, Bantval, Beltangadi, and Mangalore taluks. Data was then collected on the size of their practice and their popularity in respect to other nearby doctors. An analysis of this data indicated that:

1. Established RMP (having some diploma) were often as popular as qualified doctors when both practiced in the same locale.
2. RMP were of immense importance as a market for the pharmaceutical industry.

Consider, for example, the ratings given to 206 practitioners served by medical representatives covering the areas:

TABLE 1

THE POPULARITY OF MBBS DOCTORS AND DIPLOMA HOLDERS

Popularity	*MBBS*	*Diploma Holders*
Very popular	62 (57%)	35 (36%)
Popular	42 (39%)	52 (53%)
Average	4 (4%)	11 (11%)
	108	98

According to these figures, 47.6 per cent of the practitioners visited by medical representatives have been trained in *ayurvedic* or integrated medicine. Thirty-six per cent of their most propserous clients fall in this category and 55 per cent of the clients they considered popular. Moreover, these figures are low for they do not include diploma holders who were supplied drugs indirectly by chemists and RMP not possessing medical diplomas and thus not served by medical representatives.

If this data is indicative of the importance of the diploma holder and (untrained) RMP to the pharmaceutical industry in other sectors of India, then the Government might justifiably request that pharmaceutical companies supplying medicines to non-MBBS practitioners contribute toward their ongoing training. I am not suggesting that such commercial concerns directly set up training courses themselves, as this would naturally result in product advertisement, but rather that they contribute to government-organized training programs. One function of these programs would be to educate the practitioner as to available products on the medical market, their merits and limitations, and their relative costs. Such orientation might in turn cause pharmaceutical companies to compete for the sale of low-cost drugs to rural practitioners.

What about incentives? I have noted that interest already exists in the rural medical sector in regard to ongoing education. If education programs were responsive to cultural principles, logistically attractive, of suitable length, and not overly paternalistic then they have a good chance of succeeding without offering payment incentives. What might be more attractive are medicine subsidies for practitioners attending ongoing courses designed to educate them in the proper use of basic medicines. Subsidies might facilitate an evaluation mechanism instituted to assess the effectiveness of training programs and practitioner skills.

I am not suggesting that such a program would put a halt to quackery. Surely, quackery and commercial medicine will exist in India despite the efforts of training courses and/or sanctions. However, interviews with numerous rural RMP revealed that a significant number of these practitioners openly criticize the amoral nature of allopathy and state that allopathy does not constitute a comprehensive system of health care. However, they are not against technical innovations and consider allopathic medicine a useful form of technology.

CONCLUSION

Banerji (1973) has poignantly criticized foreign social scientists and their Indian colleagues for having misled health planners by convincing them that far more cultural resistance to allopathic medicine exists in India than is actually the case.

Banerji is correct in attacking the myth of cultural resistance; a myth more commonly propagated by administrators to rationalize planning failures than by anthropologists in their descriptions of health behavior. However, it would indeed be a mistake to stress the villager's acceptance of modern medicine at the loss of recognition of:

1. Villagers beliefs about disease causation, prevention, and cure, and how these beliefs influence medical decisions.
2. The importance of traditional medical cultures in many Indian villages and the role these medical cultures play in maintaining individual as well as social welfare.
3. The positive value of traditional practitioners and RMP as agents of social change (cultural brokers) as well as an allied medical resource.

If India is to develop a more adequate health care delivery system, then health planners will have to consider:

1. How modern doctors can be educated to (*a*) be more sensitive to villager's needs and ideas so that they can function more effectively in diagnostic sessions, (*b*) how they can be trained

to pass on valuable health ideas to villagers in a manner which they can understand, and (*c*) how modern medical aid can be meaningfully integrated into the villager's world so that it will be used effectively.

2. How traditional and modern medical cultures can be made complementary so as to offer villagers more comprehensive health services. Moreover, how cooperation between heterogeneous medical practitioners and traditional specialists can be promoted and referral relationships established.

3. How traditional practitioners and RMP can be trained to fulfill a more valuable role in rural health care. How they can be taught to improve upon the services they already offer to villagers; services which villagers often choose to make use of even when alternatives exist.

Responsive health planning and medical education will require intensive anthropological research into regional health sectors. Such research may assist planners in the assessment of manpower, resources and training needs, the organization of health care delivery programs and the evaluation of planning objectives and outcomes.

REFERENCES

BANERJI, D.

1973 "Health Behaviour of Rural Populations." *Economic and Political Weekly* 8: 2261-2268.

1973a "Social Orientation of Medical Education." *Economic and Political Weekly* 8: 485-88.

1974 "Social and Cultural Foundations of Health Service Systems." *Economic and Political Weekly* 9: 32-34.

JEFFREY, R.

1976 "Sound and Fury Signifying Nothing." *Economic and Political Weekly* 11: 92-93.

KAKAR, D., S.K. MURTHY and R. PARKER

1972 "People's Perception of Illness and of Illness and their use of Medical Care Services in Punjab." *Indian Journal of Medical Education* 11: 286-91.

NICHTER, M.

1977 "Health Ideologies and Medical Cultures in the South Kanara Areca-nut Belt." Unpublished Ph.D. Dissertation. Edinburgh: niversity of Edinburgh.

1978 "Patterns of Curative Resort and their Significance for Health Planning in South Asia." Paper delivered at the Conference on Global Health. Cleveland, Ohio: Case Western Reserve University.

TAYLOR, C., H.S. TAKULIA, S.P. SANGA and J.D. ALTER
1967 The Health Center Doctor in India. Baltimore: Johns Hopkins University Press.

DAVID G. MANDELBAUM

TRANSNATURAL CURING

ABSTRACT. In coping with the universal problem of illness, people generally use both secular and religious, transnatural practices. Villagers in India and Sri Lanka typically make a sharp distinction within their transnatural relations as between the transcendental and the pragmatic. In a comparative analysis of curing practices, certain topics can serve as a frame for comparison. These are diagnostic procedures, pathogenic causes, pathogenic agents, therapeutic agents and therapeutic procedures. To illustrate the use of this frame, data from Africa, South America, and North America are cited. Finally, the important distinction between healing and curing is discussed.

PEOPLE USE THEIR RESPECTIVE RELIGIONS FOR VARIOUS PURPOSES; restoring the sick to health is commonly an important one. In examining this use of religion, the existing studies of ethnomedicine, such as those by Ackerknecht (1942a, 1942b), Hallowell (1935, 1963), and Hughes (1968), provide us with a base from which we can begin. Illness, these studies agree, is a problem with which people must cope in all societies and all have developed regular means of doing so. What is considered to be illness, however, varies among cultures. One group may consider a particular condition of body and mind to be quite normal that another group may take to be abnormal and diseased. But whatever definition of illness is held, and whatever ideas about treatment are implemented, the ideas concerning abnormal states of health always imply concepts of what is normal and natural.

In coping with illness, many peoples of the world use some means they consider to be more empirical and secular, within the command of man, and some which they relate more to powers beyond man, in the keeping of transnatural (supernatural) forces. But they do not necessarily make a sharp division between the spheres of the natural and the transnatural. Thus Hallowell has written of the Ojibwa,

"Instead of any fundamental dichotomy, there is rather, a basic metaphysical unity in the ground of their being." Yet the Ojibwa do distinguish two classes of persons, human and "other-than-human-beings," and they similarly separate occurrences that are more in the expected, ordinary course and those in which other-than-human-beings are involved (Hallowell, 1963: 267, 272).

Some ailments are treated with drugs and techniques that are within the power of men to prescribe and apply. Other ailments, usually the more intractable ones, require efforts to obtain the direct intervention of transhuman forces. These are the transnatural curing practices with which we are here concerned.

Villagers in India and in Ceylon generally make a marked distinction within their religious activities. They have one set of practices and practitioners for individual, personal needs, especially for curing; they have another set that are used for the general maintenance and welfare of society. I attempted to formulate these differences in a paper (1966) in which the one set was termed the pragmatic complex of religion and the other the transcendental complex. Tribal peoples of India do not usually make the distinction in as marked a degree as do caste villagers. In both India and Ceylon those who have had a modern education are inclined to decry the pragmatic complex and some of them want to abandon it. A developmental context for understanding these differences was suggested in the paper.

This formulation has yet to be broadly tested with further evidence from South Asia, but if it does indeed hold generally to be true there, it should be interesting to consider whether transnatural curing can be understood in a similar context among peoples in other parts of the world. We may also ask whether there are distinctive characteristics of transnatural curing in whole civilizations and across large culture areas, characteristics that may stand in contrast to patterns of curing in other areas.

Answers to these two broad questions may clear the way for a deeper kind of analysis. Matters of health and illness concern people everywhere and so our answers can lead to much more than just trait taxonomy and the charting of distributions. They may help illumine social and cultural dynamics in various societies, possibly including our own. In putting these questions to data from several areas, we begin by sketching curing and religion in India and then in Ceylon.

Transcendental and Pragmatic Uses of Religion

Throughout India, Hindu villagers tend to use different forms and practitioners for the pragmatic functions than they do for the transcendental functions of their religion. The pragmatic complex is used mainly for curing but also for other individual needs, such as the location of a lost valuable, or personal victory in a local struggle. The transcendental complex is used to ensure the long-term welfare of the group, to explain and maintain the social institutions, and to guide the individual through the life cycle. Initiations, weddings and other life-cycle transitions are usually carried on through the transcendental complex.

The two complexes are different in form, each with its distinctive deities and rites. The transcendental deities are depicted as having universal sway and their messages for mankind are conveyed in scriptures, especially in the Sanskrit texts. Transcendental rites are regular events in a fixed ceremonial cycle, conducted in great religious centres as well as in the village locality.

The supernaturals of the pragmatic complex, by contrast, are thought of as being more local in power and residence. Their messages, and accounts about them are given in the local vernacular, in folklore rather than in scripture. While the transcendental deities are neutral or benign or capricious, those concerned with pragmatic issues are more likely to be jealous and readily malevolent. Pragmatic rites are often impromptu, performed when the need arises.

The practitioners of each complex are usually different people with differing attributes. Those who lead in the transcendental rites are religious technicians, priests who hold their office through hereditary right. Priests are commonly from one of the Brahmin *jatis* (caste groups). They are expected to be exemplars of ritual purity; clients maintain a stable, continuous relation with their domestic priests.

The practitioners of the pragmatic complex achieve their role rather than having it ascribed to them. Each of them demonstrates some special, personal communication with transhuman forces. He may be a diagnostician or an exorciser or a general therapist; in many parts of India he helps to cure the sick by becoming possessed and transmitting the voice, diagnosis, and prescription of a supernatural power to the ailing person and his family. The prestige gained by such a shaman is his own, it is not shared by his kin and *jati*. His clients are not in a formal relation to him, they call on him as their need impels and his reputation attracts. He is a demonstrator and channel of transhuman power rather than an examplar of ritual purity.

The shaman-curer is generally from the lower *jatis* of village society though people of the higher *jatis*, the women especially, call on him to help heal a sick person. The priests of the transcendental complex are from the higher *jatis* since only their men were permitted to study the sacred texts and to be versed in the scriptural rites. All villagers agree that the transcendental deities are superior to the local godlings but most also agree that the local supernaturals cause a good deal of the sickness that afflicts people.

Villagers employ the two complexes in a complementary manner, each for its own purposes. Traditionally there was little rivalry between the practitioners of each. The Brahmin priest did not denounce the services of the shaman and, the shaman, whether in possession or not, did not oppose the priest and his rites.

While each complex is distinct, there may be considerable overlap between them. For some purposes, as when a childless couple pray for a son, their offerings will be addressed to every conceivable source of religious power. Some villagers may petition a high god for a fairly pragmatic purpose and priests often advise that transcendental rites be performed as personal prophylactic safeguards. Local spirits may be invoked to look after some cause in the community's welfare. Occasionally the voice issuing from a shaman in possession will identify himself as one of the scriptural deities, although in most cases the voice announces that he is a local godling. While the great majority of those who can become possessed and are consulted for curing are from the lower *jatis*, sometimes a Brahmin will become known as a shaman. Some rites include elements of both complexes. A calendric rite held in the home of a Brahmin family in Delhi has been reported by the Freeds (1962) who graphically describes the behavior of those participants who became possessed by the goddess.

There are also scriptural means for meeting personal needs. Astrology is one; another is the indigenous Ayurvedic (or Unani) system of medical practice. Villagers consult Ayurvedic practitioners for certain ailments; they also use the services of a shaman for the good he can do, for particular kinds of sickness and also when other curing attempts fail. Increasingly they are also coming to allopathic physicians, those trained in scientific medicine.

Rites and deities of the pragmatic complex have sometimes been shifted into the sanskritic roster and, conversely, a god from the high pantheon may be transformed, in a particular locality, into a local spirit of pragmatic employment (cf. Marriott, 1955, pp. 211-218). The shrine of a godling may become so popular as to require a priest-like caretaker and religious technician in addition to the shaman. Such transpositions alter the details within each complex as locally observed; they do not usually alter the general distinction between the two complexes.

Followers of devotional movements have little recourse to the pragmatic complex because such a movement requires that its devotees concentrate all their religious expressions and relations within the sect. But followers of such movements in India have in time generally reverted to the usual practices and have turned again to pragmatic practitioners when a child or a close kinsman falls seriously ill.

Muslim villagers observe the distinction in some degree. They make use of Muslim scriptures and learned men for urgent practical needs but they also resort to local shrines, the tombs of locally venerated holy men, for pragmatic boons. Villagers of different formal faiths commonly seek help from the same local spirits. A Hindu villager who would never enter a mosque for prayer might well bring his sick child for curing to the tomb of a local Muslim saint. Similarly a Muslim villager may seek the help of a Hindu shaman without any fear of betraying Islam in so doing.

Tribal peoples in India commonly distinguish between the two uses of religion but do not separate them as markedly. Thus in the tribal tradition of the Kotas of the Nilgiri Hills, priests and diviners (shamans) are different persons and fulfil different functions, but both invoke the same deities for their respective purposes and take part in the same rites (Mandelbaum, 1954; 1960). Just as tribal peoples maintain fewer specialized roles and functions than do villagers in the civilizational tradition, so do they generally have less specialization in their religious beliefs and practices.

Buddhist villagers of Ceylon, by contrast, observe a more thorough separation of the two complexes than do Hindu villagers of India. They also use the two in complementary fashion and consider both to be necessary—though not at all equal—aspects of their relations with transhuman power. The transcendental, Buddhist part of their religion is unquestionably the superior and all acknowledge that the pragmatic spirits, rites, and officiants exist only by the grace of the Buddha. Buddhist monks provide prophylactic services and may participate in curing rites, but a Sinhalese Buddhist rarely petitions the Buddha for worldly purposes. He addresses the lesser spirits (some of them with the names and symbols of Hindu high gods) for mundane purposes of curing and personal gain (Obeyesekere, 1963: 151-152; 1970). Sinhalese villagers consider that the curing rites enable sick people who are troubled by worldly desires and pains to turn their full efforts, after they are cured, to Buddhist, other-wordly contemplations (cf. Ames, 1963, 1964; Yalman, 1964: 117-118; Spiro, 1966: 93094).

In both India and Ceylon the pragmatic complex tends to include the more mechanical, "magical," ways of manipulating supernatural forces and the more coercive techniques for dealing with supernatural beings. In both areas also, the contemporary movements of religious reform, led by members of the educated elite, advocate that all of the pragmatic complex be spurned as unworthy superstition, incompatible with reformed religion and scientific medicine.

The separation of transcendental from pragmatic functions has sometimes been discussed as the differences between priest and shaman. The priest, as Turner summarizes the role, derives his powers from learned and transmitted ritual knowledge; he communicates with the supernatural through regularly performed rites; he is an "institutional functionary." The shaman obtains his power personally by a "divine stroke"; he has direct contact with supernatural forces; he provides services to individuals, especially in curing; he is an "inspirational functionary." Shamans may be diagnosticians, or mediums, or exorcists, or sorcerers, or therapists, or any combination of these and other specialities (Turner, 1968: 438-439). The term shaman applies to all those who are believed to have special, personal relations with transhuman forces and can direct such forces to affect the lives of men (cf. Eliade, 1964: 297-299).

In several of the discussions of priest and shaman, a developmental sequence is suggested. Thus Lessa and Vogt note that shamanism is "more usually found in the loosely structured food-gathering cultures" and that priests and priesthoods are "characteristically found in tightly structured and relatively elaborate food-producing—usually agricultural-societies. . . ." These authors add that in simpler cultures shamans and priests tend to be interwoven and that only in more complex societies does the priest emerge as a sharply defined specialist (1965: 451-452).

An emphasis on the functions of a religion rather than the functionaries may show more clearly that both purposes are maintained at various levels of social development, though in simpler societies there is generally less separation between them than in more complex societies. The educated in modernizing societies commonly want to eliminate the inspirational functionary as curer and to rely solely on the institutional curing functionary who derives his capabilities from the transcendental realm of science.

The distaste for shamanism is not, however, a product only of modern circumstances. Considerable disfavor is shown in the Old Testament for the inspirational functionaries who tried to cure sick people, although a different attitude is expressed toward inspirational functionaries who addressed themselves to the ills of society and to other transcendental matters. This difference in attitude has been obscured because the same term, *nabi*, is used for prophet and for shaman.

The developmental sequence illustrated for India and Ceylon (Mandelbaum, 1966: 1183-86) has been suggested for several other areas although it has as yet not been clearly depicted for any. Such formulations would be aided by an analytic frame that could be used to sort out the data on curing practices within a culture or an area as well as for comparisons among cultures and areas. Six aspects of curing seem suitable as elements for such analysis and comparison.

Questions for Comparative Analysis

Studies of curing practices in India emphasize the kind of regularities that medical anthropologists have so impressively shown to hold true among a great variety of peoples. To cite just the two papers on Indian villagers in the book edited by Benjamin D. Paul (1955), the article by Carstairs tells that the village patients he observed wanted two quick benefits from the therapist, "that the affliction be given a name and so become less terrible," and that the curer quickly utter his prediction, "He will get well." Carstairs tells how he came to be convinced of the therapeutic capability of the shaman (Carstairs uses the term "priest") in "letting sick people feel that they were not alone and helpless but part of a succoring community, both real and supernatural" (1955: 131). Observers of curing in many societies have similarly noted the therapeutic good that often comes from giving a sick person the sense that humans and supernaturals have been rallied to his aid. McKim Marriott ends his paper on medical practice in a north Indian village with a conclusion that is now familiar and uncontroverted. "The successful establishment of effective medicine here appears to depend largely on the degree to which scientific medical practice can divest itself of certain Western cultural accretions and clothe itself in the social homespun of the Indian village" (1955: 268).

Such generalizations are significant, but it would also be useful to know whether there are curing concepts and practices that are widely shared in India and how they compare with curing in other areas. It may be, of course, that there are no such common elements and that any formulation of curing characteristics can hold good only within much narrower geographic and social bounds. Yet certain ideas about bodily states are upheld by very many of India's people. One prevailing idea is that social rank is related to what members of a group ingest and how it is ingested. Another common concept is that ritual pollution entails social isolation and that some of the main sources of pollution are contacts with bodily excretions and with death. Since there are those characteristic concerns about bodily states, it seems at least possible that there are characteristic ideas about bodily illness and restoration.

In tracing a profile of curing characteristics we need several axes of inquiry, questions that can be asked on transnatural curing wherever it is carried on. These questions should focus on broad processes rather than on detailed traits and should have to do with such general matters as whether illness is thought to be the result of a transgression by the sick person, of aggression by others, or of some particular combination of both. The principal avenues of inquiry suggested here can be listed under these headings: prophylactic measures, diagnostic procedures, pathogenic causes, pathogenic agents, therapeutic agents, therapeutic procedures. Other and better headings may well be brought out in later discussions, but we can begin by using them to examine curing practices among Hindu villagers in India.

Prophylactic measures

These are the means of warding off disease and injury, of preventing illness. In India both priest and shaman can provide shielding through charms, amulets, and protective spells. In addition, the performance of most transcendental rites is thought to have a general prophylactic effect. In a village near Delhi, the local disease-sending spirits are treated more like a transcendental deity when they are propitiated annually in a general, prophylactic ceremony. "At times of specific sickness in a family, it was always necessary to protitiate the specific goddess for the sickness; but for welfare in general the supreme goddess was the all-powerful one" (Freed and Freed, 1962: 165-266). While a shaman, as well as a priest, can provide a prophylactic device, it seems that villagers are inclined to draw more from the transcendental complex in providing group prophylaxis.

Diagnostic Procedures

In attempting a cure, an Indian shaman usually invokes a tutelary spirit to make the diagnosis. After that has been announced, the spirit is asked what is to be done to cure the sick person. Diagnosis and prescription are usually given through the same person; there is little separation of these functions as there is in some other cultures. If the diagnosis indicates a transgression against a transcendental deity, then the cure will entail some special offering for that deity, perhaps using the services of a priest.

In the practice of Ayurvedic medicine, taking the patient's pulse is a central feature of the diagnosis. It involves more than just the pulse beat; the practitioner is alert to tendon tremors and also gets a quick perception of the patient's state of being. Diagnosis is expected to be quickly forthcoming and prescription to be given forthwith (cf. Marriott, 1955: 259).

Pathogenic Causes

Two root causes of illness are recognized in Indian village tradition: one stems from physiological disharmony, the other from disharmony in the patient's relations with other people or with supernaturals. The idea of physical disharmony is a central tenet of Ayurvedic medicine. It holds that the three fundamental substances of the body are bile, wind, and mucous; that illness results from an imbalance (Opler, 1963). The common complaint of village men that they feel weak is often diagnosed as an excessive loss of a man's limited supply of semen, causing an imbalance in the body (Carstairs, 1955: 123-125). Illnesses rising from imbalance are usually thought to be the result of the patient's own ill-advised or intemperate behavior.

The other cause of illness is believed to come from others, either from aggressive malevolence by a human or a spirit, or from the patient's inadvertent infringement on an irascible supernatural. An evil person may bewitch the victim or hire someone to do so. He makes him sick by sending an intrusive spirit or, less often, an intrusive object into his body. Of the five supernatural causes of illness listed by Clements (1932), only the idea of soul loss seems not to be very common in village India. Breach of taboo is usually a breach of the prerogatives of a particular supernatural. Transgressions against social taboos, of a kind that a caste council judges, seem to be left more in the jurisdiction of a council than for immediate retribution by supernaturals. Of the other causes noted by Clements, sorcery is viewed as being done through the intrusion of spirits or objects. The ghost of an ancestor may cause trouble to a person, but ancestral spirits are not a stock source of illness in South Asia as is common in much of Africa.

While an attack by a spirit can bring on bodily imbalance, ailments diagnosed as physiological disharmony are commonly attributed to the patient's own sexual or dietary indiscretions. Carstairs tells of villagers whom he tried to treat, in his capacity as a medical doctor, for their common complaint of "weakness." In many cases he concluded that the "complaints were the expression of chronic anxiety engendered by feelings of guilt." Release from this burden of guilt was obtained mainly through performance of transcendental rites of purification together with strict dietary precautions (1955: 123-126).

Illnesses attributed to malevolence from man or spirit are more often treated through the pragmatic complex. The diagnostic categories used by village practitioners are loose, and if one course of diagnosis and treatment fails, others are sought—a circumstance not unknown elsewhere (cf. Gould, 1965: 207). Certain kinds of illness are attributed to anger of supernaturals. Smallpox is thought to result from the displeasure of the disease-producing goddess. And those who suffer from what would be labelled as psychiatric disorders in Western medicine are also thought to be the victims of malevolent or angry spirits who have entered their bodies, perhaps sent by evil persons.

Patients plagued by intrusive spirits have been studied in several parts of South Asia; these studies yield certain similar findings. Sick people who show symptoms of being in the grip of intrusive spirits are commonly persons sorely beset by difficult social relations. The difficulties are mainly with close kin or within the caste group. The curing procedures make the sick person the center of much solicitous attention and assure him that whatever unacceptable impulses have raged through him and whatever antisocial behavior he may have displayed are not at all his fault but are the manifestation of forces that have picked on him and are working through him.

These victims are more often women than men. Harper estimates that between 10 per cent and 20 per cent of all the women in the group he studied became so seized at some time of their lives. He notes that among these Havik Brahmins of Totegadde village in Mysore, men who are under social stress can do something to relieve the stress. If necessary they can leave the joint family, but women do not have similar avenues for relief. They respond to social stress by fasting, or considering suicide, or by becoming possessed (Harper, 1967: 167-175).

The consequences of witchcraft beliefs have been studied in another village in Mysore State (Epstein, 1967). There too, those who show signs of being bewitched are reported to be people under great social tension. Not only are many of the victims women, but all accusations of being witches are against women. In this village new tensions rose when, through a set of unusual circumstances, some women became moneylenders. Witchcraft accusations against them, Epstein concludes, served to regulate their more rapacious conduct as moneylenders and so strengthened the traditional social structure by rectifying this aberrant behavior. Moreover the woman accused is herself considered to be the victim of an evil force that impelled her to practice witchcraft (*ibid.*, p. 154). So she too can be reintegrated into society through the proper rites.

A case study by Gananath Obeyesekere describes a woman under spirit possession in a village of Ceylon. The author shows why the curative ritual helped her to recover. She had difficulty in coping with her aggressive and sexual drives and spirit possession was her attempt to solve intolerable psychological conflict. By giving vent to symptoms of being possessed she was able to give expression to her repressed feelings. The cultural beliefs about possession provide a cognitive structure that can serve to replace or to substitute for private fantasy. In the role of a sick person, this woman could reject her normal social roles; a prime goal of the curing rites is to reintegrate her into the social structure. "In the modern West mental illness is often looked upon as idiosyncratic pathology; here it is transformed into a publicly intelligible cultural idiom." The Western patient who shows hallucinatory symptoms "would be alienated from his culture, whereas his Sinhalese counterpart would not" (1970: 104, 109).

Several cases of spirit possession in a North Indian village near Delhi have been described by Ruth and Stanley Freed. Their reports are much like those we have cited from villages in South India and Ceylon. In reviewing other studies from North India, the Freeds found that illness believed to be from spirit possession is basically uniform in symptoms and therapeutic procedures that complete across the large region from Punjab to Calcutta. They conclude that complete recovery seems to be the rule although they mention some cases in which the curative rites did not succeed (1964: 168).

Cases of spirit possession reported from a village in eastern Uttar Pradesh are broadly similar in etiology and cure (Opler, 1958). There is a strong and prevailing anxiety about health in the village. The villagers do not meet illness with fatalistic composure; they do all they can to cure their sick. Beliefs and rites about possession are means of doing something about illness. Opler comments that the rites are perhaps as good a therapy as can be managed there for psychogenic ailments. "Ghosts do not wander aimlessly through Indian village culture. They gather at points of stress and attack the soft spots of the social order. To follow their movements is to learn a good deal about social order" (1958: 566). The converse may be just as important. Understanding the stresses in the social order, in Indian villages or in other societies, may be an essential means for understanding some kinds of illness.

Pathogenic Agents

Beliefs about vectors of illness follow on ideas about the causes of illness. Indian villagers are not untreated by different kinds of practitioners. One man from a village near Delhi is quoted as saying "Doctors, *vaids*, and curers, who have goddesses in their power, will each give a different explanation. The pundit would say that it is due to the influence of bad stars, while the curer would say that the person was under the influence of evil spirits" (Lewis, 1958: 297).

Ayurvedic practitioners are likely to emphasize faulty diet as a main cause of illness, especially as rising from an imbalance or from a wrong combination of foods of the "hot" category and those of the "cold" category (Hasan, 1967: 157-158; Hitchcock and Minturn, 1963: 279; Lewis, 1958: 300). But most villagers also recognize that certain kinds of illness, certainly those in which the patient displays the traditional symptoms of being possessed, are the doing of an intrusive godling or ghost or other supernatural elements of the pragmatic complex.

Envy is dangerous to the envied. A jealous person may either deliberately set the harmful effects of the evil eye on his victim or do so inadvertently merely through the baleful force of envy. The latter concept resembles the idea of dangerous, non-personal power found in other cultures but not otherwise prominent in illness attribution by Indian villagers.

Therapeutic Agents

Most villagers are quite eclectic in their choice of therapist. To cure their sick, the members of a family will try all within their means —Ayurvedic, Allopathic, Homeopathic, and shamanistic practitioners as well as vows, offerings, and charms. The choice of a particular therapist depends in part on his reputation for success, piety, disinterest about his own enrichment and corresponding concern for the patient's welfare (cf. Freed, 1966: 481; Marriott, 1955: 261; Gould, 1956: 207). In one village of Uttar Pradesh an important communicator of curing information is the itinerant specialist in cleaning wax from ears. He also carries medicines, even-handedly dispensing Ayurvedic medicaments and Anacin (Khare, 1963: 39).

The choice of one kind of therapist rather than another also hinges on the nature of the illness. If a woman screams with the voice of an intrusive ghost, there is little point to taking her to a physician in the city. Further, poor people of lower *jati* are far less likely to use allopathic "doctor medicine" than "village medicine" (Gould, 1957: 510-513). Another study of the Rajputs, the dominant Rajput of a village in Uttar Pradesh, relates that sick women rarely consult physicians, not only becuase they have more faith in transnatural curing, but also because women of the higher *jatis* are not supposed to move out of their domestic seclusion to visit a physician and be examined by him. There is a greater mortality rate for female than for male children in the village because as the authors observe, girls are not neglected, "But the villagers always expect quick results from medical treatment and will change doctors if the cure is not effective. With a girl—particularly if the family is poor—they will become discouraged sooner, and if she fails to recover may stop treating her" (Hitchcock and Minturn, 1963: 283).

Shamans are consulted for curing by many, even though educated people and those who are strong proponents of modern reform movements such as the Arya Samaj are reluctant to resort to them (cf. Freed and Freed, 1966). The search for cure tends to ignore social and religious barriers. A patient of high *jati* rank may consult a shaman of low *jati*. As we have noted above, Hindus make vows at the shrines of reputed Muslim saints and consult Muslim curers. Similarly, Muslims afflicted by serious illness may try Hindu shamans (cf. Hasan, 1967: 146; Fuchs, 1950: 273; Beals, 1963: 47-48).

Therapeutic Procedures

Since Indian villagers consider control of ingestion to be critical for group as well as personal status, it is not surprising that controls and restrictions of diet are part of almost every kind of therapy. Shamans rarely use sucking procedures to extract intrusive objects (a dangerously defiled object may seriously pollute the shaman) though there are some who practice snake bite cure through sucking (cf. Carstairs, 1955: 113).

Smallpox vaccinations have often been resisted, mainly because villagers believed that the angry goddess of smallpox might be further infuriated by vaccinations (cf. Gould, 1965: 205-210; Marriott, 1955: 253). But injections have become very popular throughout village India. Not only do some Ayurvedic practitioners now give injections but other kinds of practitioners do also. During an influenza epidemic in a village near Delhi, Hindu holy men brought penicillin in and gave free injections to more than half the village population (Freed and Freed, 1966: 682).

In curing, a shaman usually invokes his own tutelary spirit to diagnose the illness and prescribe the therapy. The tutelary spirit, speaking and acting through the shaman in possession, may try to drive out the intrusive spirit or may prescribe remedial measures, or may even refer the patient to another kind of therapist. Dealing with an intrusive ghost or godling does not require the kind of awe that usually accompanies prayers to a transcendental deity. The shaman may threaten, scold or bargain with the intruder (cf. Freed and Freed, 1964: 156; Dubois, 1928: 388). Spells (mantrams) commonly figure in shamanistic curing. One such spell recorded by Father Stephens Fuchs in his account of an untouchable *jati*, is addressed to a variety of deities and includes the words (as translated by the author) "Save! But if you don't cure the patient, I shall pierce the private parts of your mother!" (1950: 272).

In a careful count of all religious observances held during a full year (1955-56) in a village of about 2,000 people, there were forty shamanistic rites. There were also six instances in which residents of the village had curing rites performed for them elsewhere (Opler, 1959: 224). Several patients may be diagnosed or treated in a single session, so there is no dearth of cases for study in any part of India or Ceylon. But there is no study, to my knowledge, of the whole spectrum of curing practices within any one village. Nor do we have data on what kinds of persons choose what types of therapy and in what order, with what results. But while the evidence now available is quite limited, it does indicate certain regularities. There are the consistent (though not absolute) differences from tribal groups, to caste villagers, to educated peoples in their respective separation of the pragmatic from the transcendental complex of religion. There are the curing beliefs and practices, as those about intrusive spirits, that seem to be characteristic in villages throughout the extent of Indian civilization.

From this South Asian vantage, we examine supernatural curing among some other peoples.

Africa

The literature on supernatural curing among African peoples is extensive and a number of the studies bring major theoretical issues into focus. I take for illustration the studies of just two tribes, the

Nyima of the Southern Sudan and the Ndembu of northwestern Zambia.

S.F. Nadel tells that the Nyima number 37,000; their social organization entails small families and nonlocalized clans. Their traditional political organization lacked chieftanship and such political leadership as there was devolved on the three kinds of religious specialists (Nadel, 1946: 476). The nature of these roles reflect the distinction between the transcendental and the pragmatic aspects of Nyima religion.

The most venerated religious office is that of the Rain Maker who is thought to secure rain, health, and fertility for the whole Nyima tribe. He formerly guided the tribe in war and established peace between the Nyima and other tribes. The Rain Maker holds his office by right of descent, as a gift from the benign Supreme Deity. There are also hereditary Hill Priests who officiate at rites concerned with the continuity of life. These priests may, in addition, possess tutelary spirits.

In contrast with the two kinds of priest are the shamans, each of whom has a familiar spirit. The spirit speaks through the shaman in trance and divines auspicious times or warns of dangers or diagnoses the causes of illness. A shaman does not perform therapy but may refer a sick person to a medicine man who is knowledgeable in more secular forms of curing. Nadel observes that in comparing the shaman and Rain Maker, we grasp a fundamental aspect of the Nyima religion. The Rain Maker offers guidance of a general and often predestined order, the shaman offers *ad hoc* help for everyday perplexities. Spirits are capricious, they may be evil or good. The supernatural force represented through the Rain Maker is benevolent, moral, certain.

This dichotomy, Nadel concludes, "underlies the whole edifice of Nyima religion—as it underlies all religious systems." This is so because all religion offers, in whatever disguise, the certainty of a physical and moral order; and all religions must offer, too, a loophole for all that conspicuously eludes or contradicts that order" (1965: 475-467). Since this idea fits well with my own suggestions derived from South Asian data, I am not unsympathetic to it and would like to see it tested on broad evidence from Africa and elsewhere. For one matter, Nadel mentions that the Nyima are classed among the "Nuba" tribes of the Southern Sudan. Of the 18 Nuba tribes whom he visited, only six had shamans. How do the others provide for the "loopholes" in belief and for the curing of the sick?

Nadel further suggests that Nyima shamanism contributes to mental health, not by absorbing abnormal personalities and giving them a social niche as shamans, but rather by "absorbing stresses which might result in mental derangement." His comparative statistics of insanity and emotional instability among the Nuba groups do not give any clear results but Nadel concludes that "it is possible that shamanism both exploits *and* canalizes neurotic predispositions so that they remain relatively stable and confined to one sphere" (1965: 478). Yet it is also possible that the beliefs about malevolent spirits, whose attacks shamans try to undo, may help create neurotic predispositions. Additional comparative study of religion among the Nuba groups might clarify the social features that favor separation of the two complexes of religion.

The Ndembu, as described in an illuminating series of books and articles by Victor Turner, also have a relatively simple social and political organization. They are shifting cultivators, number some 17,000 and are an unusually mobile people. Individuals and families move frequently; families and villages often split.

The Ndembu makes some distinction between the two uses of religion, but much less so than do the Nyima. Their supernaturals include a remote High God and highly important ancestor spirits who may give or withhold good things. There are also spirits, mainly malevolent, who are thought to act as the familiar spirits of witches and sorcerers. Medicines can be used to work either good or evil by practitioners who know the relevant rituals. Diviners are consulted to ascertain the causes of illness, misfortune, and death. A diviner is believed to be possessed with the spirit of a divine ancestor when he trembles and shakes his divining basket during a consultation.

Ndembu life-cycle rites are in the transcendental mode, as such rites usually are, and the curing rites are more in the pragmatic pattern. Diviners are not used for life-cycle rituals. In these rites, Turner notes, certain crucial principles of Ndembu society are renewed and replenished whole in the curing rites these principles are seen to be under challenge. Life-cycle rites anticipate and seek to ward off strains and tensions, the rituals of affliction "seem almost 'designed' to contain or redress them once they have begun to impair seriously the orderly functioning of group life" (1968a: 280).

Illness is thought to be caused through supernatural forces directed by destructive persons. So witchcraft and sorcery are always suspected when a person falls seriously sick. Some ailments are so common that no immediate suspicion arises, but if the sick person becomes seriously or chronically ill, then suspicion grows and a diviner is consulted. The diviner commonly pins the reason for the illness to tensions with the local kin group, either because of punitive action by an ancestor spirit or because of a grudge held by a living relative who resorts to sorcery. He carefully questions the patient and probes for social reasons for his distress. "Divination, therefore, becomes a form of social analysis, in the course of which hidden conflicts are revealed so that they may be dealt with by traditional and institutionalized procedure" (1968a: 46; 1967: 300-301).

The diviner advises that certain rituals be performed to expunge the evil influence and a senior practitioner of the rite is engaged to do so. He collects a group of assistants, each of whom has previously undergone the same rite, as patient or novice. This "cult-association" then performs the ritual for the sick person. Turner points out that these association have important intergrating effect in Ndembu society. "Since individuals move freely from one village to another, since villages themselves change sites often under shifting cultivation, and since there is no strong political centralization under a hierarchy of chiefs and officials, the system of cults helps to bond together the loosely organized Ndembu tribe" (1968: 16).

In his discussion of the Ndembu medicine and treatment of disease, Turner poses the question of why they continue to follow such methods of treatment. There is a high incidence of illness and mortality among them, as among the other people of Africa. The lack of feasible alternatives is a main factor; Turner gives three other reasons. One is that many sick people recover regardless of the treatment given and the recovery is attributed to the treatment. Another is that the curing procedures do have beneficial effect in cases of psychogenic illness rising from social conflicts. The other reason is that the curing rites are part of "a religious system which itself constitutes an explanation of the universe and guarantees the norms and values on which orderly social arrangements rest" (1967: 356).

This observation parallels the concept of the complementary, mutually reinforcing relationship of transcendental and pragmatic rites in a total system of religion (Nadel, 1946: 476; Mandelbaum, 1966: 1183-1184). As seen from a South Asian vantage, Ndembu curing rites appear to be much more central to the whole society than is true in an Indian village. Supernatural curing in India seems more directed to helping the person, isolated by sickness, recover health and so reweave the strands that bind him into his group. Among the Ndembu there seems to be equal concern with repairing the fabric of society as well as the health of the patient. Turner comments that the diviner's role as up-holder of tribal morality and rectifier of disturbed social relationships is a vital one in a society without centralized political institutions (1968: 51). Does the diviner then, not fulfil similar social functions in African societies that have more elaborate political organization?

Or is the emphasis on social repair in curing rites especially characteristic among African peoples? The widespread importance given to ancestral spirits suggests a special concern with the viability of social relations. In their introduction to thirteen studies of spirit mediumship in Africa, Beattie and Middleton note that ancestral spirits are believed to affect living people strongly in all the tribes covered except in two Islamicized groups. "Ancestors, the ghosts of dead neighbors and kin and of ancient kings and hero-gods, powerfully symbolize the essential social forces of familial, neighborly, and political obligation, and the systems of authority usually associated with them" (Beattie and Middleton, 1969: xx).

Some comments on these questions are made by Mary Douglas in the course of a review article of Turner's books. She compares Turner's account of Ndembu diviners with Levi-Strauss' analysis of shamans among American Indians. Both authors, she notes, would agree that the diviner seeks through the symbolic apparatus to create harmony between different layers of experience and that he cures by locating discrepancies and realigning the patient's subjective attitudes to a socially acceptable standard.

But the practitioner described by Levi-Strauss "is the wonder-working shaman of the American shamanistic tradition" who dazzles by the skill of his conjuring and the force of his personality. This shaman works directly on the patient, impressing him with the wonder of his personal power. Other social relations play small part in the curing effort.

"Victor Turner's shaman is also a conjuror" but this is a minor element; the Ndembu diviner's style "rather suggests a psychiatric social worker" (1970: 305). The question of each observer's special perspective is raised and quickly answered. "No doubt at all, ritual healing and social structure are very different, between America and Africa. If Levi-Strauss had been instructed at an impressionable age by Ndembu teachers he would have written differently." This recalls to Mary Douglas that Lowie objected to Durkheim's thesis on the basis of Lowie's knowledge of Plains Indian cultures. Perhaps Durkheim would not have developed his full theme if he had knowledge only of the Plains Indians. "So it is interesting, to suppose that Turner's approach to the rites of affliction, so strongly Durkheimian in feeling, would never have been developed if he had worked under the instruction of American Indian shamans" (1970: 306).

SOUTH AMERICAN INDIANS

Surveys of curing rites and of shamanism among the tribal peoples of South America agree that there is notable similarity in these practices (apart from the ancient Andean civilizations) throughout this vast area. Ackerknecht says that the healing rite is remarkably uniform from the Caribbean Islands to Tierra del Fuego and that the similarities "far outweigh difference between the tribes" (1949: 621, 626). Metraux writes that "the treatment of the sick was practically identical from the West Indies to Tierra del Fuego" (1949: 595).

Among all these peoples, the surveys conclude, the shaman is a central figure in his social group and his central function is curing. Shamans commonly serve other purposes as well, but their prestige is based mainly on their abilities to cure. A shaman may also perform functions for the general welfare of the group, of the kind we have called transcendental functions, such as warding off the attacks of spirits, organizing ceremonies, performing fertility rites, divining the location of fish, game and enemies, leading in life-cycle rites (Metraux, 1949: 595-596; Eliade, 1964: 3230332). Little, if any, separation is made between transcendental and pragmatic functions in practitioners, ritual forms, or deities.

The standard curing rite, Ackerknecht observes, develops in four main steps. First there is a prelude of singing and the purification-fumigation of the patient with tobacco smoke, generally from the shaman's cigar. Then the shaman goes into a state of trance possession. In the next stage he massages the patient and eventually extracts an intrusive object, generally by sucking it out. Finally he applies medicines externally and internally. Throughout the procedure the shaman is very much the active agent, "the whole ceremony represents always a battle between the shaman and the forces of disease" (Ackerknecht, 1949: 626).

His success in the struggle is thought to lie in his ability to control spirits. Among some tribes, a shaman is believed to have special familiar or tutelary spirits, but generally a powerful shaman is believed to be able to summon spirits of various kinds through the compelling force of his personal capacity (Metraux, 1949: 568; Murphy, 1959: 30). Shamans often have a considerable knowledge of herbal drugs; the pharmacopoeia of Western medicine was enriched through the addition of such indigenous drugs as coca and ipecac. Ackerknecht tells that South American Indians also invented the rubber-bulbed syringe and the narcotic clyster for enemas but does not indicate whether these were used as part of the supernatural curing ritual (1949: 627-630). As for a shaman's ability as physical therapist, at least one anthropologist has recorded personal observation of a remarkable cure (Murphy, 1959: 39).

Though medicines and massage are part of the standard treatment, the prime cause of any serious illness is thought to be an attack by a supernatural power, usually instigated by a malevolent sorcerer. Suspicion often rests on alleged sorcerers from a neighboring tribe, rather than among one's own kin. The three most common diagnoses are those of an intrusive object, an intrusive spirit, or the loss of the patient's soul through a sudden fright or by abduction. Breach of taboo as a cause of illness is said to be rare among South American tribesmen (Metraux, 1949: 594-595). In sum, illness among these peoples is diagnosed primarily as the result of aggression by others rather than derelictions by oneself or discord among close kin.

In the more complex culture of the Incas, curing was differently done, with considerable elaboration of a transcendental complex. Ackerknecht notes that in Inca belief the dominant cause of disease was sin; the primary concomitants were "disturbances in the socio-religious structure"; and a main remedy was confession. A close kinsman could enmesh a patient in illness through the kinsman's sin and if the Emperor should fall sick, the whole people had to confess.

The state enforced public hygiene measures, as those concerning pure water, sewage disposal, drink and diet. There were even attempts to unify and standardize the healing profession. But just who the healers were is not clear. Apparently some priests did diagnoses through divination; there were also shamans who followed the standard curing procedures among the tribal peoples. There are only vague hints about the differentiation made by the Incas between the institutional and the inspirational functionaries (Ackerknecht, 1949: 633-642). The more ample ethnographic information on the Aztecs of Mexico indicates that they did distinguish clearly between priest and shaman-curer (Soustelle, 1962: 191-200; Bray, 1968: 182-185).

NORTH AMERICAN INDIANS

Studies of curing among North American Indians depict a more diverse situation than has been formulated in the surveys of the curing rites of South American tribesmen, though it is not clear to me wherther this stems from the different development of the respective tribes or of the respective literatures. Certainly the main elements of ritual curing in South America are widely known among North American tribes. Smoking, singing, massaging, sucking out intrusive objects, driving out intrusive spirits, rescuing strayed or stolen souls are commonly used in the curing rites of North American Indians.

The idea of a personal, tutelary spirit guardian is also common, as is the belief that many persons in a community, not only a chosen few, may have direct and personal contact with transnatural power. The concept of immanent supernatural power is a strong one among many of these tribes. Their emphasis seems to focus on how the individual can plug himself into that power, perhaps more than on how that power can be deployed to benefit social relations. As is true among many peoples of the world, supernatural power is thought to be highly dangerous; it can be used for evil as well as for good, and can damage the recipient if he does not know how to handle it properly or is careless with it (cf. Vogel, 1970 13-35; Eliade, 1964: 297-312). There were, of course, some cultures that had more complex and societally-oriented curing practices; among these were the Pueblo tribes of the Southwest, the Creeks, and the Iroquois.

From the many studies of North American Indian curing, I select three (all from the Southwest) to illustrate some of the problems that have been examined.

In Ruth Underhill's monograph on ceremoinal patterns in the

greater Southwest (1948) there is a survey of shamanism and curing in this area. The conclusion points up "the development of a visionary into a priest and of his simple rite into a communal ceremony." Underhill suggests a possible course of development from the shaman-curer of the simpler cultures, to the Apache case in which "the sucking shaman still exists, but often he has been fused with the ritualist who cures by memorized songs and rites." The Navaho chanter, according to this author, is a full-fledged priest. And the curing societies of the Pueblos are at the other side of this course of cultural development (1948: 40, 50-51). It may be that more telling conclusions could be derived from such a survey if the emphasis were more, as we have noted above, on functions than on functionaries, on results as well as on roles.

A study of witchcraft and curing in Cochiti Pueblo by J. Robin Fox discusses a broad spectrum of curing practices. Fox tells how certain illnesses are engendered by the nature of the society. Cochiti culture allows for the expression of illness and provides means of mobilizing help for the afflicted. Their curing system "is not the result of individual insight but rather of the slow working-out of cultural patterns over the centuries and the achievement of a kind of adjustment that, given the cultural premises, is very successful." But the medicine societies and the clans are not operating as they did and this affects their ability to cure. The old social causes of illness remain potent. So the Cochiti must cope with traditional kinds of illness but with much diminished results from any traditional type of cure (Fox, 1964: 283-284).

The values held by five southwestern groups are described and compared in *People of Rimrock* (Vogt and Albert, 1966). Two are Indian societies, Navaho and Zuni. The others are Mormons, Spanish-Americans, and Texas homesteaders. The chapter by Robert Bellah in this book compares the five religious systems. The two Indian tribes, Bellah observes, find the answer to the problem of life in an all-embracing harmony of the natural and the supernatural. The three Christian groups find the answer in salvation. They are other-wordly in orientation while the Navaho and Zuni are almost entirely this-wordly.

Navaho and Zuni contrast sharply in their curing rites. The Zuni religious emphasis is on transcendental concerns. Curing is largely amalgamated into societal and group ceremonial patterns. The Navaho emphasis is so strongly on curing that the great ceremonials are almost all curing rites. "If Zuni religion is preoccupied with success, one might almost say that Navaho religion is preoccupied with failure. Zuni religion is primarily concerned with seeing that everything stays right; Navaho religion is primarily concerned with righting things when they have gone wrong" (Bellah, 1966: 247). The author raises the question as to what this formal concern with illness means for Navaho life. It is a question worthy of further study, as is the broader enquiry into the differential emphasis on illness in the rites and doctrines of various religions.

I must here omit the other peoples in this survey, Chinese and Mexicans and Puerto Ricans in the U.S., except for these brief comments.

Shamans practiced in Chinese villages though, according to one source, the educated people despised and rejected them (Hu, 1960: 113-114). That rejection has probably been intensified under the present regime. It should be interesting to consider contemporary Chinese culture in the light of how transcendental and pragmatic needs are being met.

Margaret Clark's *Health in the Mexican-American Culture* includes an observation that raises some general questions. She notes that the people she studied did not feel much personal responsibility or guilt about their own illness or that of members of their family. "Among the Spanish-speaking folk of Sal si Puedes, the patient is regarded as a passive and innocent victim of malevolent forces in his environment" (1959: 197). To what degree is such an attitude inimical to widespread use of scientific medicine? Further, to what degree is a complex technological culture necessarily based on widely and strongly held notions of individual responsibility?

HEALING AND CURING

Some of the problems inherent in carrying on a technologically intricate culture appear most vividly in matters of illness. Modern scientific medicine has made great differences in the lives of people throughout the world. Practicing shamans everywhere recognize the power of that secular system, but they also recognize its limitations, hence they can continue to offer their services, whether in the capacity of traditional shaman or in some newer kind of therapeutic role.

The limitations of modern medicine have been ably stated by practicing physician, Eric J. Cassell (1970). Dr Cassell points out the differences that should be recognized between disease and illness and, especially, between curing and healing. Disease, he writes, is something an organ has; illness is something a man has. Illness is a man's feeling that he is incapacitated, that he is unable to function as he would like to and as others would like him to. Disease is defined in our culture as a disturbance of the organs or body fluids that entails structural alteration or biochemical change.

Curing involves the restoration of a diseased part to functional integrity or the stopping of a disease process. Healing, Dr. Cassell asserts, is the returning of the whole person to a sense of fitness and ability, to a state of being in which "he can go and do." The two processes are always interrelated but in modern society they have been invidiously separated. Because of the great technological complexity and success of modern medicine, doctors tend to see their role as curers of disease more than that of healers of the sick. Moreover, "patients now wander about disabled but without a culturally acceptable mantle of disease with which to clothe the nakedness of their pain" (1970: 60).

What a healer does and what a curer does not concentrate on, Dr. Cassel continues, is to provide the patient with a safe bridge from the state of being sick to the different world of the well. He restores the patient's belief in his own vigorous capacity, he removes illness from the unknown to the "realm of reason and the known." That is what a pragmatic practitioner mainly does in the societies we have discussed here. He can do so partly because of the patient's belief in his personal abilities and, in India, at least, his personal qualities of compassion and devotion. He can do so also because he can bring the patient back into a desirable relation with the transcendental complex of the culture and back into less strained relations with others in that society. The shaman was often quite effective in this aspect of healing; the modern physician finds it difficult to do so because of the way his role is defined and the way the society is structured. Healing is a highly personal process that "draws upon something within the patient." The modern physician is handicapped as healer because of the distance that commonly is placed between him and the patient, and perhaps even more, between himself and the patient's inner outlook.

Just as the physician finds it difficult to minister to patient's needs that are served in other societies through the pragmatic complex of religion, so do religionists in our society face similar difficulties. Some of the priests and ministers of the established religions recognize that their traditional ways of aiding the ill and the alienated no longer suffice. Some also hold that the alienation is an ailment of the society as well as of the individual and they are attempting to repair both.

If there has indeed been a tendency in the development of many societies to separate these two functions of religion and latterly to separate the pragmatic into oblivion, there seems to be an increasing search to install some new ways of meeting the personal needs of people. How that may be done for healing will differ among the principal culture areas and so it would be well for anthropologists to look into the relevant characteristics of the people of each area.

REFERENCES

ACKERKNECHT ERWIN H.

1942a "Problems of Primitive Medicine." *Bulletin of the History of Medicine* 11:503-521.

1949 "Medical Practices." In J.H. Steward (ed.), *Handbook of South American Indians* 5:633-644. Washington: Government Printing Office.

AMES, MICHAEL

1963 "Ideological and Social Change in Ceylon." *Human Organization* 22:45-53.

1964 "Magical-animism and Buddhism: A Structural Analysis of the Sinhalese Religious System." In E.B. Harper (ed.), *Religion in South Asia*, pp. 21-52. Seattle: University of Washington Press.

BEALS, ALAN R.

1962 *Gopalpur, a South Indian Village.* New York: Holt, Rinehart, and Winston.

BEATTIE, JOHN and JOHN MIDDLETON (eds.)

1969 *Spirit Mediumship and Society in Africa.* London: Routledge and Kegan Paul.

BELLAH, ROBERT N.

1966 "Religious Systems." In E.Z. Vogt and E.M. Albert (eds.), *People of Rimrock*, pp. 227-264. Cambridge: Harvard University Press.

BRAY, WARWICK

1968 *Everyday Life of the Aztecs.* New York: Putnam.

CARSTAIRS, G. MORRIS

1955 "Medicine and Faith in Rural Rajasthan." In B.D. Paul (ed.), *Health, Culture and Community*, pp. 107-134. New York: Russell Sage Foundation.

CASSELL, ERIC J.

1970 "In Sickness and in Health." *Commentary* 49:59-66.

CLARK, MARGARET
1959 *Health in the Mexican-American Community.* Berkeley. University of California Press.

CLEMENTS, FORREST E.
1932 "Primitive Concepts of Disease." *University of California Publications in American Archaeology and Ethnology,* vol. 32, no. 2.

DOUGLAS, MARY
1970 "The Healing Rite." *Man* 5:302-308.

DUBOIS, ABBE J.A.
1928 *Hindu Manners, Customs, and Ceremonies.* Third edition. Oxford: Clarendon Press.

ELIADE, MIRCEA
1964 *Shamanism, Archaic Techniques of Ecstasy.* New York: Pantheon.

EPSTEIN, SCARLETT
1967 "A Sociological Analysis of Witch Beliefs in a Mysore Village." In John Middleton (ed.), *Magic, Witchcraft, aud Curing,* pp. 135-154. New York: Natural History Press.

FREED, RUTH S. and STANLEY A.
1962 "Two Mother Goddess Ceremonies of Delhi States in the Great and Little Traditions." *Southwestern Journal of Anthropology* 18:246-277.
1964 "Spirit Possession as Illness in a North Indian Village." *Ethnology* 3:152-171.
1966 "Unity in Diversity in the Celebration of Cattle-Curing Rites in a North Indian Village: A Study in the Resolution of Conflict." *American Anthropologist* 68:673-692.

FUCHS, STEPHEN
1950 *The Children of Hari.* Vienna: Verlag Herold.

GOULD, HAROLD A.
1957 "The Implications of Technological Change for Folk and Scientific Medicine." *American Anthropologist* 59:507-516.
1965 "Modern Medicine and Folk Cognition in Rural India." *Human Organization* 24:201-208.

HALLOWELL, A. IRVING
1963 "Ojibwa World View and Disease." In I. Galdston (ed.), *Man's Image in Medicine and Anthropology,* pp. 258-315. New York: International Universities Press.

HASAN, KHWAJA ARIF
1967 *The Cultural Frontier of Health in Village India.* Bombay: Manaktalas.

HARPER, EDWARD B.
1957 "Shamanism in South India." *Southwestern Journal of Anthropology* 13:267-287.
1963 "Spirit Possession and Social Structure." In Bala Ratnam (ed.), *Anthropology on the March,* pp. 165-177. Madras: Book Centre.

HITCHCOCK, JOHN T. and LEIGH MINTURN
1963 "The Rajputs of Khalapur, India." In Beatrice Whiting (ed.), *Six Cultures, Studies of Child Rearing,* pp. 207-361. New York: Wiley.

HU, CHANG-TU
1960 *China, Its People, Its Society, Its Culture.* New Haven: HRAF Press.
HUGHES, CHARLES CO.
1968 "Ethnomedicine." *International Encyclopedia of the Social Sciences* 10:87-92. New York: Macmillan.
KHARE, R.S.
1963 "Folk medicine in a North Indian Village." *Human Organization* 22:36-40.
LESSA, W.A. and E.Z. VOGT (eds.)
1965 *Reader in Comparative Religion.* Second edition. New York: Harper and Row.
LEWIS, OSCAR
1958 *Village Life in Northern India.* Urbana: University of Illinois Press.
MANDELBAUM, DAVID G.
1954 "Form, Variation, and Meaning of a Ceremony." In R. Spencer (ed.), *Method and Perspective in Anthropology*, pp. 60-102. Minneapolis: University of Minnesota Press.
1960 "Social Trends and Personal Pressures." In C. Leslie (ed.), *Anthropology of Folk Religions*, pp. 221-255. New York: Vintage Books.
1966 "Transcendental and Pragmatic Aspects of Religion." *American Anthropologist* 68:1174-1191.
MARRIOTT, MCKIM
1955 "Western Medicine in a Village of Northern India." In B.D. Paul (ed.), *Health, Culture and Community*, pp. 239-268. New York; Russell Sage Foundation.
METRAUX, ALFRED
1949 "Religion and Shamanism." In J.H. Steward (ed.), *Handbook of South American Indians* 5:559-600. Washington: Government Printing Office.
MURPHY, ROBERT F.
1958 "Mundurucu Religion." *University of California Publications in American Archaeology and Ethnology*, Vol. 40, no. 1.
NADEL, S.F.
1965 "A Study of Shamanism in the Nuba Mountains." In W.A. Lessa and E.Z. Vogt (eds.), *Reader in Comparative Religion*, pp. 464-479. New York: Harper, Row.
OBEYESEKERE, GANANATH
1963 "The Great Tradition and the Little in the Perspective of Sinhalese Buddhism." *Journal of Asian Studies* 22:139-153.
1970 "The Idiom of Demonic Possession, A Case Study." *Social Science and Medicine* 4: 97-111.
OPLER, MORRIS E.
1959 "The Place of Religion in a North Indian Village." *Southwestern Journal of Anthropology* 15:219-226.
1963 "The Cultural Definition of Illness in Village India." *Human Organization* 22:32-35.

PAUL, BENJAMIN D. (ed.)
1955 *Health, Cultural, and Community.* New York: Russell Sage Foundation.
SPIRO, MELFORD E.
1966 "Religion: Problems of Definition and Explanation." In M. Brandon (ed.), *Three Anthropological Approaches to the St dy of Religion,* pp. 85-126. London: Tavistock Publications.
SOUSTELLE, JACQUES
1962 *Daily Life of the Aztecs.* Stanford: Stanford University Press.
TURNER, VICTOR W.
1967 *The Forest of Symbols.* Ithaca: Cornell University Press.
1968 "Religious Specialists: Anthropological Study." *International Encyclopedia of Social Sciences* 13:437-444. New York: Macmillan.
1968a *The Drums of Affliction.* Oxford: Clarendon Press.
1969 *The Ritual Process.* Chicago: Aldine.
UNDERHILL, RUTH M.
1948 "Ceremonial Patterns in the Greater Southwest." *Monograph of the American Ethnological Society,* No. 13.
VOGEL, VIRGIL J.
1970 *American Indian Medicine.* Norman; University of Oklahoma Press.
VOGT, EVON Z. and ETHEL M. ALBERT
1966 *People of Rimrock.* Cambridge: Harvard University Press.
YALMAN, NUR
1964 "The Structure of Sinhalese Healing Rituals. In E.B. Harper (ed.), *Religion in South Asia,* pp. 115-150. Seattle: University of Washington Press.

R.S. KHARE

FOLK MEDICINE IN A NORTH INDIAN VILLAGE: SOME FURTHER NOTES AND OBSERVATIONS[1]

ABSTRACT—Extending a previous (1963) discussion of folk medicine in a village in North India, this paper offers three interconnected cultural formulations, which seem to characterize the traditional Indian medical system, and which help introduce considerations of indigenous cultural constructs and interpretations in medical anthropology. The village therapeutic system, it is claimed, continues to be predominantly based on such cultural markers as body and being, dava *(medicine) and* dua *(blessings), and* dharma, karma, *and* daiva *and it exploits in practice ethical overlaps and differences between the indigenous and modern Western medical systems.*

I

COMPLEMENTING ONE OF MY EARLIER ARTICLES (1963) WITH THE same title, this paper aims to bring out a dimension of the village medicine that the previous discussion entailed but did not systematically deal with. It is concerned with an aspect of that value system of the Indian villager which guides his entire perspective and approach to the indigenous as well as the modern Western medical systems for treatment. We shall keep our attention on the villager's view to reach an interconnected set of his priorities and meanings as he goes about seeking cures for his diseases. An obvious

[1]This paper grows out of the conceptual concerns that the three articles previously published had been suggestive of in different ways: "Folk Medicine in a North Indian Village," *Human Organization*, Vol. 22, No. 1, Spring 1963, pp. 36-40; "A Study of Intra-Family Problems of Motivation in Relation to Family Planning in India," *Eastern Anthropologist*, Vol. 18, No. 2, 1965, pp. 73-79; and "Family Planning Communication and Motivation: Some Sociological Suggestion," *Family Planning News*, Vol. 7, No. 2, 1966, pp. 19-23 Here, however, we will refer only to the first one.

The writing of this paper was aided by the Research Committee of the University of Virginia.

anthropological point underscored below is that a "folk medical system" represents a configuration of certain fundamental principles and values of the larger cultural system of which it is an integral part, and only in terms of which can any new or alien medical system be assessed and made use of. The villager, an "insider" to the system, may be found to be a highly active (adapting himself, as well as making the Western medical system to change itself to suit his ways) agent in using new cures that he finds effective, and then culturally making sense of these to himself.

Pursuing only selected instances of the above, we will formulate and examine three interconnected characteristics of the "folk medicine" as carried by Gopalpur (the same north Indian village near Lucknow which had formed the basis for my earlier account), and will expand on certain cultural features of these formulations to show how they guide and run through the villager's conception and treatment of the sick (as a body *and* a being), and his sickness. The following observations, however, remain very limited in scope, and are mostly suggestive rather than final.[2]

II

Since body illness in the village is considered to be only one segment of ailments that afflict a human being, the village therapeutic system

[2]As I thus revisit my north Indian village (Gopalpur) studied previously (1958-60) for various purposes, I am helped by the comments of Leslie (1967: 27-42) and Ahluwalia (1974: 401-430). By way of offering comments on my paper they bring forward certain fundamental questions of theory and method in medical anthropology. Such questions, as this paper exemplifies in its own way, must continue to receive more attention. Leslie, for example, places emphasis on knowing more about indigenous agents, centers and networks that carry on the selection and incorporation of medical ideas, treatments, and drugs in an Indian village. I produce here an aspect of this indigenous view. Such information will not only help discover "Folk medicine in action" but it will also show how the folk and modern medical systems functionally and symbolically must situate themselves within the larger cultural system.

Ahuluwalia (1974: 405-406) also sees the value in such a stance, though she normally notes glaring of research in several important areas of "sociology of medicine." What we know is very little and sketchy, and often without any systematic build-up of information in any one area. An exception will have to come from Leslie's work (e.g., see and compare 1967 and 1977), especially in so far as it continues to seek comparable methodological interrelationships between traditional and modern medical systems.

must show a correspondingly "holistic" cultural ethic and perspective.

My earlier paper on folk medicine (1963) had described a composite picture of Gopalpur when it was viewed for those "agencies" that the villagers had thought helped either to cause or control or cure or prevent ailments within the village. To study these agencies was therefore to see how the villagers articulated *their* views of bodily (and other) ailments and their treatments. As the following excerpts from the article (1963: 63-37) suggest, there was varied concern for diseases (or for remaining healthy) within Gopalpur:

> The village has a large Vaishnava temple near the northern border of the hamlet of Gopalpur. There are two places for worshipping Devi. There are three Shiva temples for the same deity. There are places such as trees, platforms, niches and enclosures, where the deity is enshrined. There are also abodes for five local spirits, Latiarey-bir Baba, Bhumiya-bir Baba, Hardeo Baba, Syed-bir Baba, and Pathak-bir Baba. These spirits visit the houses of the villagers at will. Villagers have certain obligations towards all of these spirits at the reaping of the harvests; they have to keep a portion for them of other commodities produced in the village. If they neglect this obligation the spirits inflict disease, possessing members of the family of the one who has broken the rule. But if these spirits are propitiated, they help in curing various diseases in the village. Spirits along with the old medicine-man-priest and a Kayastha exorcist, greatly influence the behavior of the people at times of illness.. . .It is the opinion of many of the villagers that Gopalpur is especially protected by local gods, goddesses, and spirits from the various epidemics and diseases.
>
> In the minds of the people there is a hierarchy of gods, goddesses, and spirits. Local spirits and Sitala are superseded in power and efficacy by the Goddess Durga, while she herself is under the control of Shiva and ultimately all of them submit to the wishes of Lord Vishnu. As noted above, symbols and shrines of all these higher gods have been present in the village for a long time; the Vaishnava temple which was the last to appear on the scene, is the biggest and most frequented.
>
> . . .It may be pointed out that the system of folk-medicine assures the people that (*a*) the system is their own and (*b*) that it provides the people with the "best" and "complete" and "secure" ways of coping with their physical and mental ailments.

This picture of Gopalpur, however, gives only an incomplete idea of the villager's perspective on diseases. One way to make it culturally more complete is to observe that villagers, while thinking and talking of diseases, do not locate them only in one's physical body, though they recognize that the human body (*ādamī kā badan; sarira*) is by its very nature predisposed to ailments, and that this fact should be *accepted* as a part of life (*zindagī*) or "worldly existence" (*saṃsāra*). Those educated in the village say, "it is the *dharma* of the body to grow old, sick, and eventually disintegrate. After all it is made of *mattī* (a metaphorical use of the term that means "earth," refering to those five elements—earth, water, fire, air, and space—of which one's body is made) and it becomes *mattī* (mere dirt) after death." (*Mattī*, let us recall in this connection, is also a powerful synonym for corpse in the region.)

However, as long as one is alive one does not see himself/herself as a mere body, and hence the idea that one can suffer from ailments all of which may neither be located in nor "caused" by one's body. Though only the educated within Gopalpur labelled ailments (taken in their widest sense) as being from three textually specified sources—from the "body" (*daihika*), from "supernatural agents" (*daivika*), and from "natural or material" elements (*bhautika*), this categorization of sources is widely shared by the villagers. The evidence is produced by the villagers as they make their village an abode of such widely different curative agents (see those given in 1963) as priests mendicants, *ojhās, tantrikas, maulvis, and sādhūs* and *sannyasins*. All of these, in the villager's view, are devoted to preventing and/or curing ailments brought about by body and mind (in Sanskrit the distinction is along *vyadhi* and *adhi*) "under the worldly life."

However, an equally important point within such a therapeutic system is that these agents of cure and prevention can be successful only in the same proportion as the villagers as individual persons remain morally, socially, and physically responsible for their own well being. A visiting *maulvī* (a Muslim mendicant often offering Unnani prescriptions to ailing villagers) in Gopalpur would, as a rule, instruct the patient every time he gave medicine or an amulet (*tabīza*) to him: *himmat mardé madadé khudā* (Courage from man makes God help).

Actually, as a social anthropologist may be more easily prone to notice, the above squad of "healers" in Gopalpur is clearly involved, whether directly or indirectly, in taking a total—wholistic—view of ailments on the one hand, and in placing this conception against an equally culturally total view of human beings, on the other. Thus if Gopalpur's medicine-man-priest gave medicines to his patients to treat their bodily symptoms so that he could treat their "souls" (*jīva*, popularly called *jeeu*), visiting *sādhūs* and *sannyāsins* approached the healthy and the sick to inspire them to increase their "devotion" to Rama and Krishna (and sometimes accompanied with instructions for few *yogika* postures—*āsana*) so that their "souls" will be sufficiently "purified" to let their bodies remain healthy.

Put differently, Gopalpur's therapeutic system is so organized as to draw attention to a series of interrelationships between one's body and being (if the later be admitted as a gloss for that *jīva* and/or *ātmā* that villagers variously emphasize). People do not get sick only because their bodies would not work properly, or only because their "souls" are not sufficiently *dhārmika* (although the dharma is ideologically maintained to be the ultimate curer of all ailments). Villagers of Gopalpur clearly saw two situations to take their clues from, One was that a sick person's body, in fact, does show that the disease is located in the body and is cured by taking medicine into one's body. (This is obviously dramatized to them by the Western system of medicine through its hospitals and physician's clinics, and there is no doubt that the villagers are not as incredulous towards it as they might have been in the earlier decades of this century.) Vaidyas and Hakims, much before the modern physicians, also used to convince them of the same but under a different ethic. The other situation that the villagers could not deny was that even the best *sādhū* and *sannyāsin* that they knew would, sooner or later, also get physically sick.

The villager usually explained the latter situation by repeating the same line that an ailing *sādhū* or *sannyāsin* offers him, "It is only the body that is prey to sickness, I am not; I can never be sick. It is the body's *dharma* to become exposed to ailments, so it is after all following its own *dharma*, while I am, mine." The villager, however, finds such an explanation valid "only for the great souls" (*mahātmās*) and not the common man, because the latter cannot separate (or put distance between) the body and being from each other the same way as "these great souls" can. Yet he fully believes in the above explanation; he does think that "real *sādhūs* and *mahātmās*, even when with ailing bodies, are *not* in fact sick in a common way. They are not like common people."

If we were to summarize at this point the range of relationships villagers recognize between body and being reflecting the integrity—the cultural meaningfulness—of their therapeutic system, we find that *sādhūs* and *mahātmās* for them illustrate that polar condition where the strength of being dominates over that of the body. They *ideally* represent this as a cherishable goal for the common villager, but, as often said, "it is not easy to reach for us." Accordingly, the villager would most often place himself in that "middle zone" where both body and being are "to be treated at their respective places," and they thus also emphasize an ethic for a therapeutic system which would handle both of them, as appropriate. However, it is equally interesting that within this "middle zone" exists a range of variation telling us which disease is more body-based, and how, and which is not. (Such a classification, however, must change over time with alterations in the available information and its communication.) In 1963 (pp. 37-38) Gopalpur offered the following profile:

> Diseases are usually ascribed to supernatural causes. However, the extent varies from disease to disease. Jamoga (tetanus) and small-pox are diseases which are highly supernatural in their origin and also require a corresponding supernatural treatment. Cholera, dysentery, and in some measure, tuberculosis are also believed to have at least partial causes seated in the body. Fever is a broad category which creates great concern and anxiety if it is protracted or periodic, but there is no cause for anxiety if it is transitory. It is remarkable that the zone of the causative agents of various diseases widens and usually moves towards the supernatural with the duration of the illness. There is a similar tendency when people generalize about a disease. If a person suffers for three or four days, the cause generally given is cold or indigestion, but if a person has been sick for a fortnight or more, his illness is ascribed to the harmful position of his stars or to the annoyance of some spirit. ...Again, if a person is asked about the general cause of such diseases as fevers, tuberculosis, respiratory diseases, and epidemics in his village, he is quick to point out the inevitable pattern of supernatural control. Only three or

four persons of Gopalpur believe that smallpox has a minor cause in the body also.

There is a corresponding cultural profile for treatment that the villager follows. It essentially runs along *davādāru* (notice the juxtaposition of medicine and "alcohol," as intoxicating, benumbing agent, while symbolizing the entire domain of man-made medical system and its experts) and *duā* ("prayers,") symbolizing that entire zone of "edge-expressions" which is considered endlessly capable of miraculous cures. The villager is very often found under-scoring this approach as "the best approach" since it seeks both human and divine help.

Accordingly, the villager (particularly those who had been hospitalized) becomes puzzled with that therapeutic system (e.g., the modern Western medicine) which once for all rejects handling body and being together, and insists on treating only the body. This is the other polar condition for him, in several ways clearly opposed to the situation represented by his *sādhūs* and *sannyāsins*. As the Gopalpur villagers clearly demonstrated in 1963 (and there is no reason to believe that in the intervening period such a fundamental feature can change), they evaluated all diseases and all available therapeutic systems within their combinatory paradigms of body and being and *davā* and *duā*.

The latter paradigm, in idea and use, is endogenous to the Indian (Hindu, Islamic and possibly even other) social systems. Under the popular conception, *davā* (i.e., the preventive and curative devices of any medical system) grounds itself in *duā*. As the Gopalpur's priest had put it in 1958-59, "*Duā* can work alone and is capable of overcoming all known or unknown diseases human beings suffer from. If *davā* speeds up the cure, it is because it is a form of *duā* itself, nothing beyond it. Healers and their medicines work only when *duā* works behind them. Otherwise, all of us will have become immortals." Thus the condition where *davā* can work totally independent of *duā* as a purely physical agent within one's body evoked skepticism from the common villager.

When the villager's "journey" for seeking actual treatments are followed in the field along the *davā* (d) and *duā* (D) axis, the combinatory paradigm referred to above again becomes amply evident. Since villagers grade *davā* (as d_1, d_2, d_3, and so on) according to its extrinsic efficacy (including who gives it, what it contains, and what it is supposed to do) and *duā* (as D_1, D_2, D_3 and so on) for its intrinsic efficacy (through as well as independent of *davā*, and since *davā* and *duā* are variously sequentially recombined (as in $D_1+d_1+d_2+D_2$, etc.) according to the nature of an illness, villagers' procedures in fact leave behind a "treatment track" which could be summarized by such syntactic chains as the following. (These could obviously be much further elaborated or simplified, depending upon the crudeness or sensitivity of measures employed to denote varied dimensions of the two categories, their internal gradations, and their syntactic relationships. No attempt can be made here to elaborate such points.)

Basic Values of Recombinations: $D>d$ $D=d$ $D<d$

Derived Chains: $D_1>d<D_2<d_2=D<d_1=d_3$ ... a chain offering diminishing place for *davā*.

$d_1\ d_2<D\ d_3<D_1<D_2$ ... a chain offering increasing place for *duā*.

$D_1\supset d_1\ \ D_2>d_2$ ... a chain offering *davā* as a subset of *duā*, and vice-versa.

$[D_1d_1]\rightarrow[D_2d_2]\rightarrow[D_3d_3]$ ... a hypothetical, hierarchical chain where *duā-davā* recombination goes hand in hand at each step.

The *duā-davā* or *davā-duā* basis of a therapeutic system offers to the villager a very wide ranging cultural "curtain" for internal interpretation and meaning. The segment of *duā* (supernatural help) is meant to connect with all such formulations as *dharma* (the Moral Order), *karma* (action), and *daiva* (fate or destiny) have within the Indian system. For the *duā* and *davā* work, as the villagers point out, "only when one's *dharma* and *karma* are befitting and *daiva* is kind and helpful." Even the best medicine would not work until there is *duā* available from the above; and the latter will not be there until one's *dharma*, *karma*, and *daiva* are properly disposed. Gods and goddesses, and spirits and spells—all are guided (i.e., made effective or ineffective) by one's *karma, dharma* and *daiva.* This was one way the Gopalpur priest had put the matter in 1958-59.

If we emphasize a consideration of *dharma* and *karma* as it underlines the village therapeutic system, few further systemic characteristics emerge, which extend and complement my earlier (1963) observations of Indian folk medicine. For example, attention needs to be given to the cultural distribution of access to, and consumption of, the medical help available from the village therapeutic system. Let us discuss it in the background of an appropriate cultural formulation.

III

Since those sick seek their treatment according to priorities that their cultural system and its values set up, the village therapeutic system must reflect these as villagers order their access for treatment.

The fact that villagers see their social groups as thoroughly based on internal value *(dharma-karma)* considerations as are their body and being, offers us a vital connecting axis between the village therapeutic system and the sociocultural system at large. An aspect of this axis which concerns us here is again an extension of the same cultural emphasis that the *davā-duā* complex illustrates, but it is done in a different way than in the preceding discussion.

If villagers approach medical treatments according to their *davā-duā* considerations (and the implied ideas of *dharma, karma,* and *daiva),* they also popularly order their access to treatment in terms of their view of themselves. Consistent with their own *dharma-karma* based cosmology, they order sickness and treatment by distinguishing between the old and the young, the men *(marda)* vis a vis the women and the children *(bibī baccé),* the holy *(sādhu* and *sannyāsin)* and the commoner *(sādhārana loga* or *jīva),* and the commoner and the impious or "the fallen" *(pāpī* or *nīcha).* Actually, such a classification is as much about the social status of these people as about certain properties of their bodies *(sarīra)* and beings *(jīva).* Thus is also a sense made of an usually encountered observation, "Those holy and pious do not get sick like common people because their bodies are under rigorous spiritual discipline." Put in other words, there are three classes of people in relation to illness, as the villagers points out, those who are least exposes to diseases (e.g. holymen), those who represent an average (e.g. the common householder), and those particularly susceptible (e.g. the impious, the old, and the children).

However, as the villagers order these distinctions they are found handling two kinds of cultural criteria, one which simply treats human body as a material object and the other that views it under a dominance of the moral-spiritual principle. Thus, for the villager getting old normally means getting sick more often (or at least they see this as a natural tendency of the body). Similarly do they view the "constitution" of the woman's and the child's body as being responsible for making them generally more susceptible to sickness; a woman's body "has more intricate internal parts and they are made fragile," while a child's body is *kaccī* ("unfirm" or "unprotected" as against the grown-up's, which is called *porhī, paccī),* "just like a small growing fruit" *(*a *batiyā).* A person remaining sick in his/her youth and an old person being free from sickness are therefore an anomaly (one undesirable and the other desirable) within this scheme, and they have to be explained by the *dharma-karma* formulations.

It is soon found out that the villager's perception of the physical in the human body is quickly juxtaposed to, and made sense of, in terms of the moral *(dharma-karma)* ordering of his universe, for it is the latter which still answers his "whys," "hows," and "wherefores" when all other available information fails him. Thus people do not become sick, villagers point out, only because their bodies do not properly function but more importantly because their *dharma-karma* balance predisposes them (i.e., through their bodies) to be sick. This moral-spiritual dimension helps them understand the eternal paradox, "Why am I sick now in this manner? Why does it have to be me?"

The above question is subsumed under that moral paradigm of sickness which states that those with "good" *dharma-karma* enjoy maximum (bodily and spiritual) health. Hence the pious become least sick and the impious, the most. When this order is superimposed onto the first one given to recognizing the *dharma* (as in age and sex differentials) of the human body, the villager's above classification of sickness distribution is approximated. This distributional order may be taken as a widely shared "folk" model which helps the villager explain his own or others' sickness in a repetitive, culturally satisfactory manner.

The *davā-duā* axis of the village therapeutic system, as discussed above, also agrees with the physical-spiritual axis in the human body. Thus also emerges a related "folk" model for patterning access to treatment. Here the villagers logically observe how there are some sick people who may have a priority for treatment over certain other sick persons; how some may be indifferent to a treatment; and how some others (though sick) may even refuse treatment. This is, in effect, to study the "internal" ethics of a non-Western cultural system towards patterning access to and distribution of the total therapeutic services.[3] For example, householders (*bibī-baccéwalé*), who also house the old and the disabled in India, accordingly, would seem to require maximum medical services, while the holy men would need the least, if at all, "for sometimes they refuse any *davādāru* (treatment) because they know they are sick because of certain past bad *karma* and will get well once its effect is worn out and their accumulated spiritual merit (*puṇya*) prevails," in terms of a Gopalpur's itinerant mendicant.

However, besides this positional gradient there are other ethical, intrafamilial considerations which the villagers may simultaneously take into account. *Normatively,* the sick within the system *seeks* (most often through one's near and dear ones), *rather than claims* (as a self-existent right), a treatment for himself or herself. (This remark is to suggest a different personal ethical attitude and premise than in the West.) This is only appropriate given the above cultural (*dharma karma* ordered) etiology of disease; and the sick person is considered particularly unfortunate if he does not have any "helper" (*davādārū karné aur davā pani déné wālā*) around. The sick person is therefore normally accompanied by some other member of the household as he visits the curer. It is the *dharma* ("duty") of the healthy to take care of the sick, and not an optional courtesy.

[3]More attention is evidently required in this area because it will help start a much needed discussion on comparative medical ethics and health delivery systems and their differing underlying cultural principles and assumptions behind the construct of "the sick," the production of appropriate medical help, and their relative distribution in different segments of one's society.

Conceptually, there may be different (but not a lack of) construct of the "Individual" at the back of such non-Western medical systems, and it may have wide ranging implications for the ethics of these medical systems. Conversely, such a discussion may also help expose some comparative conceptual premises of the Western medical system.

Similarly, as the villagers recognize, it is the *dharma* of the less sick to take care of, and yield privileges of treatment in favor of, the more sick. The children and women, in that order, should stand in front of the adult, male householder to receive medical help, even if all need to have, and can afford such services. The old men and women (often also arranged on the basis of kinship seniority) must customarily be given priority by the younger sick members. However, the old may as normally (and quickly) insist to return this privilege to the younger ones, particularly those earning living on behalf of the household. The familiar argument is, "Anyway, we are old and old age means sickness; it just keeps on going in one form or the other (*ék na ek roga lagā hi rahta hai*), so how can we stand in way of a better more effective treatment of my...(son or younger brother, or whoever), who not only will regain his health sooner (being young) but will also go back to his work to earn our bread." With contextual factors, these considerations can acquire a predominantly economic character at one end and a highly normative moral tone at the other.

As villagers thus order their access to the village and extra-village therapeutic system, it can also be argued that they are trying to distribute a scarce service under a culturally rational scheme. The question how would they develop priorities if everybody had equal access to, and the needed money for, "best medical treatment" (which is not, it must be noted, necessarily or only the Western), remains a hypothetical proposition before them. Their answers are equally hypothetical, and sometimes quite suggestive of their world-view. The village priest had remarked, "even then, diseases would not go away; all people will not always be healthy, for these conditions are born out of one's *dharma-karma* [differentials] and not because there are not enough cures and curers available to us."

Similarly, whether better access and economics of the medical services will help *equalize* the availability of treatment to all, remained an open question before Gopalpur villagers. For them social distinctions and differences must remain even then, as the primary school teacher had remarked, "for they come from the human mind (*ādamī ké dimāga kī upaja haī*) and they cannot go away as they are inherent in our thinking." Implied in his remark is of course the crucial point that insufficient and unequal access to medical treatment is not merely a problem of more equitable and equal distribution of scarce medical services, which the government can achieve by locating more medical practioners and their facilities in the region, but it is, rather, basically a condition of human existence, and as such it is of course internal to any therapeutic system.

This total ethic, based as it is on a set of widely shared cultural bases, is not limited to the rural system. It is fact pursued through as the modern Western medical system and its institutions are approached.

IV

When juxtaposed to the ethic of the modern Western medical system, the villager faces a disruption of that sense of overall satisfaction and impartiality which his therapeutic system has traditionally offered. As a consequence he is, in practice, actively involved in adapting this new system to his notions and needs.

In 1963 (pp. 39-40) I had briefly described the diverse channels of communication Gopalpur villagers had available to them to gain an idea of some illnesses and their treatments. The description was evidently all too brief to present significant value concerns of the villagers. We shall take up few such aspects here, but again only selectively, and only in the context of our preceding discussion.

The point that the village therapeutic system, when taken on the whole, gives villagers a sense of better satisfaction that the modern Western system, is not simply a commonsensical, anthropologically relevant observation but it also allows an entry into some vital "value questions" which the folk medicine and its communication system has to handle. One such question, which becomes openly discussed among the villagers, concerns evaluation and comparison of their gains and losses as they go to a "doctor or his hospital." Their reactions clearly fall in two critical areas: the success and failure of the modern Western medicine in handling "difficult illnesses" and its starkly different (even opposed) outlook (*maddê nazar*) towards questions of access and treatment in relation to the villager's indigenous system.

In relation to the question of "success and failure" of one therapeutic system over the other, the villager, as expected, sides with the *overall* (even mythicized) successes of his own system, though he is neither slow nor reluctant to admit the "magic" (*jādū*) of the "doctor's medicine and his knife." Pills and injections (*golī* and *suī*) are repeatedly cited as being clearly superior routes to a dramatic cure.

However, the failures of this new system (as in terminal illness or in "botched-up" cases through doctor's insensitivity and hospital's neglect) are far harder for him to take; they become occasions for a critical examination of the deficiencies of the new system and a recall of, and return to the indigenous system (at least as a first step) during the next illness in the household. Despite this critical attitude, the Gopalpur villager is *not* unmindful of the effectiveness of the "doctor's medicine" any more.

But actually villagers' puzzlement at the "doctor's dispensary" may not be resolved by this factor; it may instead be at a deeper level—in the contrasting models of ethics between the villager's and doctor's approach towards each other. As for his system, it is important to note how he finds it offering him a system of access that, while operating under the conditions of social *inequality* (the *ūncha* and the *nīcha*), *is not free from an idea of equity*. The last feature emerges from that idea of justice or impartiality that is administered in terms of *one's own* stock of helpful or hindering *karma* of the past. "Visible" (human or other) healers become merely "instruments" of that inalienable justice (villagers called it *Bhagwan* or *Khuda kī marzī*) that, as the Thakurpur (one of Gopalpur's hamlet) teacher had remarked, "applies as inescapably to the karma of a Brahman as to an Untouchable. All are ultimately equal before God, for bad *karma* chase a Brahman as relentlessly as they do an Untouchable." In this model, access to an effective curer is dependent on the sick person's good *karma*; unavailability is a sign of one's bad *karma*. In contrast, an access to the Western system, as villagers repeatedly point out by giving their experiences, is held dependent on "having or not having money. It makes all the difference if one wants to go to a doctor's dispensary (*doctor kā dawākhānā*)."

Conceptually, if the village therapeutic system patterns itself after the moral inequality of individuals and social groups, the "doctor's dispensary" and its services most generally follow economic differences between individuals. As the Pasi, Kurmi and Chamar of Gopalpur would repeatedly point out, "One cannot go to a doctor (a popular Hindi corruption for the term in this region is: *dākdhar*) even if one wants to, because he means money—cash money. We most often do not have enough to think about him. He does not, like our 'Panditji' (village priest), accept grain, or our labor, or a deferred payment. He does not reduce or forget what we owe him, as does our Panditji, at least sometimes, under his *dayā* and *dharma* (charity and piety)."

If both the two systems carry an idea of equality and equity, they are distinctly different from each other by definition. The village system posits, as we noted above, an "ultimate" notion of moral (*dharma* ordered) equality and equity, but it is to be pursued through social expressions of thoroughly moral inequalities. The modern Western medicine, on the other hand, brings with it the ethic that all patients are intrinsically equal and are in equal need of treatment and attention, but this aim has to be pursued under a thoroughly economic (contractual) procedure of goods and services, dividing people between "haves" and "have nots" (and subsequently trying, to fill the gaps between the ideal and the practical through "philanthropic" delivery systems).

Accordingly, not only are the two systems two configurations of values but they, under conception, are found to "erode" each other's implied notions of equality and equity. If an antagonist villager finds the doctor's dispensary to be starkly money based, inequitable, and "imperfect" (i.e., as the primary school teacher had remarked, "it can give us a treatment and often cure, but it is still not as satisfactory and satisfying as is our own system), a protagonist of the modern Western medicine finds the Indian social inequality (and its classification of patients and curers and their access to each other) intolerable, "basically wrong."

In *practice* the two systems work under a process of mutual adaptation. Here the two systems show practical compromises at our level and cultural reinterpretations at another. It must be remembered that this process starts from *both*—villagers' and doctors'—sides. Thus, if the villager devises compromises and reinterpretations from his side to accommodate the effective cures and preventions the modern Western medicine has to offer, the doctor does his share of professional and social adaptation. The latter has been inbuilt in India for some time. For, in fact, the modern Western medicine in India means *Indian* physicians trying out Western models of medicine (and medical profession) on *Indian* patients, who, in turn encounter a Western idea and understanding of the sickness and "the patient." The complexity of translation and practical adaptation is obvious. However, our attention here will have to be limited to the villager's side, particularly since he has *not* been a *passive acceptor* of the modern Western system.

As a major step towards such an adaptation, the Gopalpur village *extends* (obviously because he finds that he can do so without any conflict) his *dharma-karma* based notions of sickness and treatment to his doctor's dispensary. He approaches the effectiveness and inequity of the Western system (or whatever else it brings along) as being a part of the *dharma-karma* explanatory scheme. Thus if a villager gets cured by a doctor, it means, most importantly, two things. First, he will be encouraged to try him again during the next illness (and-parenthetically, he will try harder to modify and be modified by doctor's contractual, money-based services), and secondly he will "explain" this success as being ultimately owing to his own good *karma* (or *daiva*). For explaining the success this way helps him explain the doctor's failures as well. If he does not get cured by the doctor, it is *his own* bad *karma*; it is for him a "satisfactory" answer, enabling him, among other things, to keep away from learning the actual internal inadequacies of the doctor's system. This also means "taking services of a doctor from a distance," forging a result-based connection with, rather than being converted to, the new medical system.

This arrangement does not require a sharp displacement (much less replacement) of the village therapeutic system or its ethic by that of the doctor's, as also it does not render the internal cultural explanations any less cogent or redundant. In fact, not only is the ethical umbrella of the *dharma-karma* scheme quickly opened over the doctor's system but it is also applied through and through as the villager's encounters with the Western medicine accumulate over time. Obviously, this approach is most natural for the villager to adopt, even as he may be getting more exposed to (and in some subtle ways even changed by) the work of the Western medicine and its network of institutions.

For example, more and more Gopalpur residents were getting exposed to hospitals or doctor's dispensaries in 1958-59. Some twenty residents—men and women—"had gone to nearby hospitals for more than a day to get cured," and it was considered "a very high number" (out of a population of over 600) for any one year by the Kayastha ex-Zamindar, considering the fact that several of those hospitalizations were "for those illnesses which few years ago villagers would have treated at home." Yet, equally importantly, in all these cases whatever doctor's medicine could or could not do was assessed and explained in terms of the ethics of their village system. This helped the villagers answer questions which the doctor's dispensary raises but, as they said, "nobody answers"—about the distinct demands and special sacrifices it calls for from the patient and his relatives in terms of time, out-of-the-village travel, expense, strange medical procedures on one's body, and a stay in distinctly impersonal hospital surroundings.

The villager makes numerous behavioral compromises in all such areas as he goes to the doctor's dispensary but he does not compromise *his* view of these things. He accepts and explains them his way. This allows him to keep subscribing to his moral ideas of "ultimate" satisfaction and equity that *his* village therapeutic system has provided for such a long time, but *without* sacrificing the improved results of the doctor's medicine. The *dharma-karma-daiva* paradigm enters and evaluates the doctor's dispensary without any qualms. It is, however, a connection that goes both ways. If it opens the access to a new system, it also keeps a distance. It is most often a connection villagers make out of need rather than by a conviction in, or understanding of, the values which Western medicine is based on. This distance also allows the indigenous system to answer (to villagers' satisfaction) those "hows" and "whys" that the villagers need to know even *before* they can make such a limited connection. Conversely, however, it must also strengthen the hold of the indigenous system on the villager's mind, making him see its relevance in contexts that he previously had not thought about.

This way the villager brings his *davā-duā* ethic also into the doctor's dispensary, where patients are found asking the doctors, as an ethnographer quickly notices, not only to prescribe "good" medicines (*acchī davā*) but to give his "blessings" (*duā*) as well. Those doctors who are known to be particularly effective in curing diseases are popularly characterized as people with "art" (*hunar*) and fame (*jasa* or *yasa*) because they are "pure souls" (*puṇya ātmā*). The suggestion is obvious: an effective doctor is effective most importantly because he possesses a particularly good stock of his own *dharma-karma*, and his *duā* goes out with his medicine to cure the patient."[4]

Though the above does not complete in any systematic manner the

[4]It may be remarked that the villager's approach to the "*doctor sahab*" (the term of address he actually uses in north India) is the same in this respect as it has been for long towards his own healers, including Vaids and Hakims. The villager behaves towards him—courtesying and bowing to touch his feet—as he does towards his Brahman priest or a superior who is in a position to deliver ("the seen" and "the unseen" aspects of) what he needs.

villager's view of the Western medicine, it provides an idea of the nature of this connection from his side.

V

Summary and Implications

The preceding discussioin is devoted to bringing forward three interconnected features of the "folk medicine" in a village in northern India, especially as an emphasis on the indigenous categories and perspectives would yield them. The village therapeutic system is found based on certain culturally widely shared notions of interdependence between body and being. Thus we found an emphasis on the *davā* (medicine) and *duā* ("blessings") complex for properly handling the sick and his sickness. There is this culturally "holistic" approach brought out by the villager in treating diseases. Also, as he finds pervasive connections between sickness and health and the masterkey cultural concepts like *dharma, karma* and *daiva,* it allows the anthropologist to show how the indigenous medical system embodies an ethic and a perspective rooted in the cultural system and its values. Its appreciation is found crucial for bringing out the villager's version of the system.

Corresponding to the above emphasis, we find that the villager classifies the sick (in body and being) along a set of social factors (age, sex, social status, etc.) and cultural values (e.g. worldly existence versus the renunciation) for treating him under a set of culturally meaningful priorities. There is thus an internal ethical patterning of access to treatment, which grows out of certain basic values of the Indian sociocultural system and which guides the contemporary villager as he approaches the "doctor's dispensary" as a scarce service.

The villager not only discovers the differences in the approach and the ethics of the two—the indigenous and modern Western medical systems, but he is also actively involved *in his own way* in adapting himself and the new system to his needs. Consistent with the emphasis in the above two features, however, the villager does this by firmly locating himself in the ethics of his own system (and its cultural values). This stance works because he approaches the Western medicine mostly for its results. He goes to this new system with a limited understanding and for purely "getting cured," while also attempting to subsume it under his cultural schemes (and their explanations) "to make sense of what goes on in such places."

The few characteristics illustrated here of a system of meaning that the Indian villager follows probably point towards a necessary field of value research for medical anthropology (cf. Landy, 1977: 1-70), especially if it is interested not simply in questions of "social engineering" but also in deeper, long range questions of how cultural systems of significance and priorities have to support a therapeutic system before it can connect with and adapt to the change the public health planner works for. An effective curing system implies that it should also be culturally satisfactory, equitable, and understandable among the people who seek it.

Becoming concerned with systems of cultural meanings in a folk medical system also means raising some theoretically important, and so far uninvestigated, questions about alternative definitions and constructs of the body and its place in sickness and health. It relates to exploring the idea of "the person" as the next step,and to the logico-empirical versus the moral "individual" as the third step. Assumptions behind the Western medical ethic need to be thoroughly probed under such an approach. They have so far been assumed as universally constant and problem-free. It is probably an over-simplification, especially in such a comparative context as the Indian situation represents. Actually, a study of the comparative ethic of the Western and non-Western medical systems may yield a theoretical pay off that the two systems otherwise variously hide.

REFERENCES

AHLUWALIA, ANEETA

1974 "Sociology of Medicine: A Trend Report." In *A Survey of Research in Sociology and Social Anthropology*, Volume 2. Bombay: Popular Prakashan.

KHARE, R.S.

1963 "Folk Medicine in a North Indian Village." *Human Organization*, 22: 36-40.

LANDY, DAVID (ed.)

1977 *Culture, Disease, and Healing: Studies in Medical Anthropology.* New York: Macmillan Publishing Co.

LESLIE, CHARLES M.

1967 "Professional and Popular Health Cultures in South Asia: Needed Research in Medical Sociology and Anthropology." In W. Morehouse (ed.), *Understanding Science and Technology in India and Pakistan.* New York: State University of New York, Foreign Area Materials Center, Occassional Publications, No. 8.

1977 "Pluralism and Integration in the Indian and Chinese Medical Systems." In David Landy (ed.) *Culture, Disease, and Healing: Studies in Medical Anthropology*, pp. 511-517. New York: Macmillan Publishing Co.

EDWARD O. HENRY

A NORTH INDIAN HEALER AND THE SOURCES OF HIS POWER

ABSTRACT. This study of an eclectic magico-religious medical practitioner of Northern India is a symbolic explanation of the setting in which the curing takes place, the roles of the curer, his public image, and the items and actions of the curing ritual. It shows how this assemblage of symbols establishes expectations of help based on perceptions of the healer and his therapy as powerful, names what is wrong with the patient, suggests the alleviation of sickness-causing agents, and thereby contributes to the cure of the illness. Impressed by the miraculous reputation of the curer, a patient (generally a woman) comes to the ashram the residence of holy men and the site of temples, which is auspiciously located where two streams converge. The curer is both a holy man—a person with ascetically acquired superhuman powers, and a pujari*—temple keeper and steadfast worshipper of the deities represented therein. In this curing the divines the cause of the illness, usually a malevolent spirit, and expels it with magical chants and diagrams, and a symbolically potent wand. Finally he tells the patient how to compound the herbal medicine or how to alter her deit, and assures her she will get well. This mode of healing, in which natural remedies are combined with exorcism, is an expression of a world view which comprehends both natural and supernatural causes of illness.*

THIS IS A STUDY OF AN ECLECTIC MAGICO-RELIGIOUS MEDICAL practitioner of eastern Uttar Pradesh in Northern India. I collected treatment data during six sessions of observation and interviews at the curer's residence, about four miles from my headquarters during a sixteen-month field study.[1] Pertinent beliefs and

[1]The fields research upon which this article is based was made possible by United States Public Health Service Research Fellowships 1 FO1 MH 48987-01 and 5 FO1 MH 48987-02, and through the aid and generosity of friends and associates in eastern Uttar Pradesh. I also want to thank Dr Charles Leslie, without whose encouragement this study would not have been undertaken. Thanks, Charles.

other ancillary data were gathered throughout the period (1971-72). I could not collect data regarding the illnesses which the curer treats—behavioral constraints imposed by the illnesses, stages of onset, progression and resolution and their duration, and visible and behavioral symptoms—because medical practices were not an original concern of the fieldwork, most patients did not live near my headquarters and time was limited.

For many years healing of this type was glossed over as mere hocus-pocus. But recent studies of "primitive" psychotherapeutic treatment of illness such as those in Jerome Frank's *Healing and Persuasion*, Ari Kiev's *Magic, Faith, and Healing* and E. Fuller Torrey's *The Mind Game,* show that such treatment is effective in dealing with the emotional component of illness, an aspect which in some illnesses is as important or more important than physical causes and symptoms.[2] Explanations of the effectiveness of this kind of treatment generally involve reference to one or more of the following symbolic processes:

1. Expectations of help based on perceptions of the healer and the therapy as powerful. Many expectations arise out of beliefs regarding the healer personally, the several roles he plays, the setting in which the curing takes place, and items and actions in the curing ritual. Such expectations reduce anxiety and render the patient receptive to subsequent therapy.

2. Naming what is wrong with the patient. To name the disease, 'is immediately to define it, circumscribe it, tame it, weaken it,' (Shiloh, 1969:377). Again, anxiety is reduced, here because a trusted and respected expert understands what is wrong. The naming process, the fitting of symbol to experience, also provides a patient with a language by means of which otherwise inexpressable psychic states can be expressed, reorganizing the patient's psychic process in a favorable direction. Identification of the offending agent may also activate a constellation of associations, producing catharsis and abreaction (Levi-Strauss, 1967:181-201).

3. Suggestion. Suggestive elements in the curing process can be conceived on a continuum from suggestive symbolism, which overlaps with 'generating expectations...' above, to direct command. Carstairs has written (1955:112) that one of this early failings as a

[2]E. Fuller Torrey's book *The Mind Game*, shows that these three symbolic processes are equally important in Western psychotherapy.

medical practitioner in Rajasthan, in the eyes of the local residents, was omission of the positive prognosis. From such a powerful person as a medical practitioner this is not only the omission of a blessing, but the omission of the command that will end the illness.

The healer under discussion announces that the patient will get well at several points in the curing ritual, and his therapy involves items and actions symbolizing the expulsion or suppression of sickness-causing agents.

The following exposition reveals symbolic objects and actions in rural North Indian culture which are sufficiently potent to mobilize the mind against illness in the three modes outlined above. The first part of the paper describes the context in which the curer operates, the ashram, and its contribution to his curative power. By relating the sequence of events leading up to my introduction to the curer and observation of his treatment, the paper then shows the reputation of the curer transmitted by the general public and his disciples, the roles he plays, his persona, and again, how these factors induce faith in his curing. A brief overview of the clientele precedes descriptions of the curing session. Primary complaints and correlated herbal prescriptions follow it. I review very briefly other kinds of available indigenous medicine to show the eclectic nature of this healer's treatment. A discussion of residual matters regarding faith in this healer precedes the summary and conclusion section.

ASHRAMS

The area in which the research was carried out is on the Indo-Gangetic plain in eastern Uttar Pradesh, about forty miles north-east of Varanasi (Banaras). Compared with western Uttar Pradesh, communications and industry are underdeveloped and the culture is more traditional. The population density in rural areas is about nine hundred per square mile.

Scattered around the countryside in this area are numerous ashrams, which are the quarters of resident *sādhūs* ("holy men"), as well as lodges for itinerant *sādhūs*. An ashram is generally at some remote, but rarely more than a twenty or thirty minute walk from the nearest village. Most ashrams are centered around one or more shrines or temples in which the resident *sādhū* daily worships the deities whose icons are housed therein. On the grounds of this particular ashram there are two sizeable temples, one said to be for the worship of Bholenath, and the other for the worship of Mahadev. Both of these are considered aspects of the deity Siva. The Mahadev temple also contained a small image of Buddha, whose presence no one seemed to think extraordinary. Immediately adjacent to one temple is a man-made hill containing an underground room in which the healer purportedly lived while acquiring his special powers through renunciation.

The ashram is located on the bank of a river near its confluence with another stream. Such confluences are almost always the locations of shrines or temples—the purificatory and life-sustaining attributes of water give it an important place in Hindu practices and beliefs. Within a quarter mile of the ashram are several mother goddess shrines and perhaps coincidentally the edifice used by Muslims for worship on the festival day of Id which closes Ramzan, the Islamic holy month of fasting.

The location at the confluence of streams, as well as its accommodation of temples and *sādhūs,* render the ashram a sacred place, a place where divine aid is close at hand and thus more easily tapped.

The Image of the Curer

I was told by one resident *sādhū* that his guru, whose ashram was several miles away, was *siddh.* This can mean either that he had attained spiritual perfection, or that he had supernatural powers; for the villager, I think the latter is more commonly signified. When I inquired about him in the village in which I was living, a respected Brahman pundit said that "by his command your wishes will be granted" (*unke kahne se āp kā kām pūrā ho jāyegā*). This very phrase was later repeated to me by a *celā* (apprentice disciple) of the *sādhū,* who was a prime transmitter of lore bolstering his reputation. This young man said he was an adopted son of the *sādhū*—his mother had promised the *sādhū* she would give him her first son if he cured her illness, which doctors had diagnosed as fatal. The young *celā* procalimed that his guru was 115 years old. He also mentioned that people went to his temple for *darśan* (beneficial meeting) on Tuesdays and Sundays. (Throughout North India and Nepal much supernatural healing and sorcery are carried out on these days.)

The next Tuesday I made the first of six visits to the healer's ashram. A slight man with light skin and white hair, he moves about constantly and looks at things intently. He rarely smiles. According me the hospitality extended to the *atithī* (honored guest), he had tea brought from the nearby bazaar, offered me cigarettes and sweetmeats and provided a chair for me. I mention these respectful and hospital acts because they show that he was awarding me a high social status. This no doubt prompted the subsequent show of credentials, and determined in part the high-level, theoretical nature of the explanations of this curing which he gave me. His initial wariness eventually diminished but never entirely disappeared.

He began a show of items apparently intended to impress me with his qualifications—an assortment of sacred Sanskrit, Hindi, and Bengali religious texts, testimonial letters, a ten-foot rosary, and other accoutrements. Then, following a ritual bath during which he recited *mantras,* he applied ashes from a sacred fire to his body, and climaxed the brief show with a few embrangled Yogic postures.

In the process, he told me he was called Bhūmidhariā Bābā because he had lived in an underground room in a hill on his ashram for 21 hours a day for 36 years. Bhūmidhariā means "under the ground" and Bābā, a title commonly used by *sādhūs,* "father," "grandfather" or "old man." His name thus has an extraordinary connotation which serves to promote his reputation.

Bābā said that through austerities (not hearing or seeing men; eating only milk and fruit), and by performing devotions and meditation, he had acquired special power. With his power he could cure those that doctors said would die; he had cured a number of people who had wasted much money on doctors before seeking his aid. He referred to his power as *paramātma kā śaktī* (the power of the universal soul or supreme spirit). I suspect that this formulation was one which he would use only for educated persons. Few villagers demonstrated an acquaintance with the monistic and absolutist philosophies employing the *paramātma* concept. It should be noted that Bābā did not mention *iṣt karnā*, the concentrated and repetitious ritual which *ojhās* ("shamans") say they use to recruit tutelary deities. Unlike the exorcism of *ojhās*, Bābā's exorcism did not require him to be possessed by a tutelary deity who, using him as a vehicle, would expel the invading spirit from a patient (cf. Marriott, 1955 : 254).

As for the claim that he had lived underground for 36 years, there were no newspapers or other documents by which to check it. Local residents could only recall that he was born and raised in a village 10 or 15 miles away and had moved to his present location before the uprising against the British in 1942.

Bābā told me that he had spent 16 years in Calcutta as a young man, where he had affiliated with the Lāl Shrī Sampradayā (a monastic order) and had lived with *mahātmas* ("great sages") in Hardvar and Pushkar (famous Hindu pilgrimage and monastic centers). Both claims give credence to his identity as a *sādhū*. In theory the *sādhū's* ascetic and esoteric practices result in freedom of the mind from the distractions of the senses, and reunion with the supreme spirit, the divine absolute. Baba, however, projected the notion (perhaps more meaningful to villagers and certainly more important to his curing) that his underground activities had resulted in the acquisition of supernatural power. *Siddh*, the villagers' attribution mentioned above, carries both meanings. Both *siddh* and *paramātma kā śaktī* connote the Tantric aspect of Hinduism; the importance in the ritual curing of *mantra* and *jantra* (explained below) also alludes to Tantrism.

Bābā's dress instantly communicated his *sādhū* identity and connoted the constellation of associations mentioned above. Like many *sādhūs*, he had entwined rope fibers in his hair, which he wore in a high coil on his head. Instead of the usual white or saffron cotton garments worn by mendicant *sādhūs*, he wore a *kurtā* ("a long-sleeved, loose-fitting Indian shirt") or a long-sleeved Western shirt, a *lingotā* ("loin-cloth") and over these, a long wool jacket-vest (*jhul*). The *jhul* is an item borrowed from the Sufi cults, for which its coarse wool symbolized the ascetic vows of its wearers.

Combined with the role of *sādhū* was the role of *pujārī*, worshipper of the deities whose icons are housed in the temples. Performance of the morning worship of the deities may take several hours. Villagers say that the resident *sādhū's* worship rites please the gods and thus benefit the surrounding area. In return they support the *sādhū* with gifts of produce and cooked food. These donations are meritorious and insure something better in the next life for the donor.

Bābā stressed that he did not do *chikitsa*, the type of medicine practiced by *vaids* and *hākīms*, the practitioners of Ayurvedic and Unani medicine. (Ayurvedic is the classical Hindu medicine, and Unani the classical Islamic system.) But at the same time he employed a primary legitimation used by these practitioners—piety (see Mariott, 1955 : 259). Piety induces the confidence of religious people and thus enhances the power of the curer. The worship of temple deities mentioned above is one expression of his piety. Another is the annual *yagya* (Sanskrit *yajña*) which he holds at his ashram. A *yagya* is a fire sacrifice performed by Brahman priests. Like Bābā's temple worship, the *yagya* is thought to benefit the surrounding area. The sponsor and organizer of the *yagya* (Bābā in this case) thus performs a valuable community service which enhances his prestige. For the villager the word *yagya* not only denotes the fire sacrifice, but connotes the entire milieu of the rites—the accompanying devotional music (*harikīrtan*) performed by volunteers from nearby, crowds of people milling about and, perhaps most importantly, an open feast. Landholders and merchants accumulate ritual merit by donating food for the feast. A *yagya* also serves to acquaint people with, or remind them of, Bhūmidhariā Bābā's abilities and goodness.

The only time I was at all successful in persuading Bābā to talk about how he became a *sādhū*, piety was again a theme. He said that after his father had taught him "devotion to God" (*Bhagvān kā bhaktī*) when he was seven years old, he began seeking, and ultimately found God.

To conclude this section, there is much about Bābā which alludes to his power to heal. At least for a certain segment of the population, his appearance, the daily rituals and devotions he performs, his religious paraphernalia, the ascetic experience of which he speaks, and his pious persona all induce faith in his supernatural healing power. In the following section I discuss the common characteristics of those who can put their faith in him.

THE CLIENTELE

On Tuesdays and Sundays the grounds of the ashram are crowded with people seeking Bābā's help. Some come from a considerable distance, such as one woman I interviewed from Mau, approximately 50 miles from the ashram. Twenty-six (63 per cent) of the 41 patients whose treatments I observed were women, and a majority of these were under 36 years old. Another six were men or boys whose female relatives had brought them there. Totalling these figures, 30 or 78 per cent of these cases involved a woman resorting to Bābā. Why more women than men consult Bābā and practitioners like him is a complicated matter which needs more research, and the following explanations are therefore tentative.

The higher proportion of female patients is, in part, an expression of the difference between male and female sub-cultures which arises from the different domains of male and female activity, the segregation of the sexes, and *pardā* (the complex of institutions whose purpose is to seclude women from public life). Women's roles tend to keep them in their homes and with other women. Men, on the other hand, are required by occupational and other concerns to visit the cities at least occasionally. A substantial number of village men (at least ten per cent) live in the cities in order to earn wages, returning to their conjugal families in the villages only several times a year. This means both that men have greater access to allopathic doctors (more of whom live in urban areas), and that they are more exposed to the modern urban culture in which allopathic treatment is more highly regarded. Another aspect of modern mentality is a diminished belief in the malevolent spirits which are thought to cause the illnesses which Bābā treats. Modern attitudes and values are also imparted in secondary schools and colleges, which are attended by many more village men than women.

Women may also find it easier to relate to practitioners like Bābā because they are rural people like themselves, not city people with unfamiliar ways and disdain for country folk. Also, as Planalp mentioned (1956 : 669), for some women a visit to the *sādhū* or healer may provide an opportunity to escape the boredom and tension of the daily household routine. Thus the seclusion of women in the home and village seems to have much bearing on their preference for traditional practitioners.

Secondly, bearing children is a paramount concern of women in this patrilineal society. A woman is much more respected by members of her husband's family when she has provided the son that will extend the family line. Because practitioners like Bābā are often thought of as specialists in problems related to conception, women are inclined to consult them regarding other health problems as well.

There are other factors which appear to be relevant to the higher proportion of female patients. Gould (1957) has pointed out that villagers go to Western medical clinics for critical or incapacitating dysfunctions, but they tend to go to village practitioners for chronic, nonincapacitating dysfunctions such as asthma, rheumatism and headaches. It may be that more women than men are afflicted with such nonincapacitating dysfunctions. This in turn may be related to the stress inherent in the role of daughter-in-law, and in other female roles in this society (see Opler, 1958; and Planalp, 1956 : 674). The higher cost of allopathic treatment may also contribute to the higher proportion of resort by females to this type of curer.

DESCRIPTION AND EXPLANATION OF THE CURING SESSION

On my first three visits, in an attempt to encourage Baba's confidence, I watched the curing, which took place in the small, dimly lit ante-room of the Bholenath temple, but I did not ask detailed questions. On my last two visits I sat in the ante-room with a cassette tape recorder during the sessions, asking questions whenever possible. Some friends in the village in which I lived later helped translate the recordings. Although I spoke with Baba in Hindi, most of his communications with his patients were in Bhojpuri, in which I never attained fluency.

Bābā sits cross-legged on a wide bench about 20 inches off the floor on one side of the ante-room. His patients squat before him to await and receive treatment. There is no queue system and the most aggressive get treated first. When he beckons, the patient comes before Bābā, touches his feet, and presents him with her donation. It may be money (never more than a few rupees, and often less than one) or produce such as cane sugar or flour. The deference and donation express the attitude of supplication with which patients come to Bābā, as well as his divine superiority.

Bābā then asks *Kyā dukh hai*? which can be loosely translated "What is the trouble?" *Dukh* has a wide range of meanings which includes states of both emotional and physical distress, e.g., sorrow, unhappiness, pain, illness, suffering. The question usually elicits the identification of physical symptoms. The other patients clustered in the ante-room can hear the reply, but patients do not seem ashamed or embarrassed to relate their problems in front of other patients. (This also seemed true of local allopathic treatment.)

In addition to this inquiry, there are six other elements in Bābā's curing: divination; *jhāṛnā* (sweeping); *mantra* (incantation); *jantra* (magical diagram or formula); prescription of *jarībūtī* (curative herbs) and dietary restriction; and award of *bhābhūtī* (ashes from a fire sacrifice).

Divination

Except for headaches and simple colds, Bābā reads the patient's palm to determine what her fate line indicates about illness. This allows him to make a positive prognosis, to implant the suggestion that the patient will recover. If the patient is a young woman he also tells whether her palm indicates children, and occasionally remarks about the degrees of wealth and happiness to be expected. He follows this type of divination by another more complex one. The technique he uses most frequently is to write three letters on a piece of paper and ask the patient to select one at random. This is done three times, after which he concludes, usually, that a *bhūt* (ghost) is responsible for the illness. A *bhūt* is the malevolent soul of a person who died an untimely or violent death, or died in some frustrating situation, such as in a dispute over property or payment.

Bābā would not divulge exactly how this process of divination works, but a knowledgeable Brahman priest gave me the following plausible explanation. The practitioner associates each of three letters with a suspected cause of illness, e.g., *bhūt*, *rog* (disease-causing micro-organisms), or *grah* (the configuration of stars and planets). The assumption is that the cause which is "over" the patient will compel her to select the letter which the practitioner has associated with that cause. Bābā used second and third trials of the divination to specify the locality or source of the *bhūt*.

There are innumerable ways in which a *bhūt* may become attached to a person; the *bhūt* is a universally available scapegoat for illness or any other calamity. A *bhūt* may reside with the family of which the deceased was a member, in the spot where the deceased met his or her death, or in any eerie place like a desolate path or grove. A *bhūt* may be transferred through sorcery and witchcraft, or merely by contact or proximity. One well-known procedure for riddance of a ghost involves encapsulation by ritual in a vessel which is then buried where three paths intersect. The ghost is transferred to the first unsuspecting pedestrian who traverses the spot. Another is to encapsulate the ghost in a pot of food which is then offered to unknowing recipients. Such gifts of food are customary if not obligatory between affines. Given the hostility and suspicion which sometimes exist between affines, in the context of beliefs about *bhūt* transference these pots of food provide a conceptual mechanism through which affines become scapegoats for calamities which have befallen the family.

In most cases of *bhūt* etiology, Bābā specified a *bhūt* whose locus or source, although it seemed plausible, could not be ascertained by the afflicted. For young women he would identify the ghost as one attached to a related family with which the woman had at sometime been in contact, but about which she had no detailed knowledge, such as the family of her mother's father (*nanihāl*). For boys or young men the *bhūt* or *churail* ("a female *bhūt*") was generally one which had "grabbed" him as he walked along some path.

The magical perception that is divination constitutes an overture in the drama of the curing session; by allowing the practitioner to reveal hidden knowledge, it functions to establish him as a person of extraordinary powers in the eyes of the patient and the audience (Murphy, 1964 : 80). It also serves as a cue for Baba's immediate intuition. "The diviner is often a good intuitive psychologist and very much in tune with the peculiar stresses of his culture." He often makes impressive "blind diagnoses" (Prince, 1964 : 111). Finally, divination allows proclamation of imminent recovery, which, coming from Baba, is tantamount to a command for the illness to end.

Jhāṛna

Following the divination, Baba usually strokes the back and upper arms of the squatting patient with his wand for several minutes, reciting a *mantra.* The stroking, called *jhāṛna* ("to sweep, brush") is mimetic magic. Together with the *mantra,* it is thought to drive the aggravating spirit out of the body. The wand is a two-foot-long stick from a *nīm* (margosa) tree. *Jantras* (explained below) are bound to it with strips of red and white cloth. The *nīm* tree has great germicidal and medicinal significance. The villagers who use *nīm* twigs to clean their teeth say that the twigs kill *rog* on contact. Some think that fanning smallpox victims with *nīm* leaves kills the smallpox *rog* as well as cools the patient by soothing the smallpox goddess in him. (Smallpox is thought to be the manifestation of the smallpox deity.) *Nīm* bark, also an important item, is one of the substances included in Baba's herbal prescriptions, at mentioned below.

For headaches and dizziness the stroking is done with a wad of *dūb* or *kus* grass, and confined to the head. Both of these kinds of grass are used by Brahman priests in many of the rituals they perform for their patrons. *Dūb* grass may have special significance because it is perenially green (Planalp, 1956 : 174). Instead of stroking the patient, Baba may exercise the illness-causing spirit by throwing pinches of dirt or ashes from a sacrificial fire at her feet while reciting a *mantra.*

Mantra and Jantra

Belief in the power of magical speech forms over gods and other supernatural forces, as well as the ability of these spells to affect the mundane, is pervasive in South Asia. Such beliefs are fundamental in the Rig Veda and other Vedas dealing with sacrificial rites, and in the Tantric texts. The villager is confronted with *mantras* ("incantations") at every ritual occasion involving a priest or medium of some kind. Also, in rural eastern Uttar Pradesh and probably most of North India there is a variety of curers called *mantravidhs*, each tending to specialize in the treatment of one kind of illness using mantras. Most common are those who treat dog bites, snake bites, scorpion stings and illnesses thought to result from the evil eye.

The *mantra* Baba uses are generally sentence-length phrases made up of Sanskrit syllables. Like most practitioners, Baba incants the *mantras* with more emphasis on speed than on enunciation.

Whereas the power of the *mantra* inheres in the spoken, the power of the other primary technique, the *jantra* (Sanskrit *yantra*), inheres in the written. A *jantra* is a magical diagram or formula. There is a wide variety of formats. One is simply a matrix of numbers, often three by three. There are other types in which symbolically powerful words are written in a certain configuration. Others contain words in a linear arrangement. The power of a *jantra* may be acquired by wearing the paper on which it is written in an amulet (also called a *jantra*) around the neck or upper arm. Another method is to soak the paper in water and drink it. *Jantras* are provided not only by healers such as Baba and some *ojhās*, but by some Brahman practitioners as well, who "give *jantras* for most kinds of sickness, but especially those involving malevolent supernatural powers" (Planalp, 1956:702). The *jantra* is a symbolic reassurance of lasting protection.

Belief in the power of written words is also manifest in other contexts, e.g., the *sāgun*—"omen." In rural India, villagers, often paint *jantras* on the path-side walls of their house. Ram and Sita (two major dieties), and *lābh* ("advantage, benefit") and *śubh* ("auspicious") are the most common. The "magic square" containing a matrix of numbers which when added in any vertical, horizontal or, diagonal row yield the same sum, is also common. It is believed that the sight of such a display at the outset of any endeavor will ensure its success. The use of written *jantras* and amulets, the malevolent spirit etiology, the use of chanting to expel the spirit, and many other elements of the medical system under discussion are also important in folk medical systems of the Middle East.

As Baba finishes the stroking-cum-incantation he again announces that the patient's condition will return to normal. He then verbally issues the prescription and dietary restrictions. Dietary control constitutes a discrete element in Baba's curing, with an elaborate constellation of concepts and beliefs which must be omitted from this already lengthy study. Opler holds that in village India, "...faulty diet is probably the most common explanation offered for illness..." (1963 : 34). He also notes that in the treatment of illness by vaids, "the imbalance [of humors] and sickness are attributed to faulty diet and are considered capable of being adjusted by strict nutritional controls" (1963 : 33). Adjustment of diet is also a nearly universal part of home treatment.

COMPLAINT AND PRESCRIPTION

This section of the paper brings together the most common complaints for which I have reliable data and the associated prescriptions and dietary restrictions. I also include brief descriptions of Baba's treatment in those cases where it departed from the norm described above.

Barrenness and Problems with Menstruation

In two cases the complaint was menstrual problems (*mehanwārī garbar*) and stomach ache (*peṭ kā darad*). The prescriptions was to eat yogurt made from cows' milk for 15 days, and to chew bark from the *babūl* (acacia) tree for nine days. In three other cases where there was no stomach pain the prescription was to grind a leaf from a sterile branch of a mango tree in cows' milk and eat the mixture. In one of these cases Baba also instructed the woman to grind the root of a *sākhpuspī* plant in water and drink the mixture for seven days. Later in an interview he said that *sākhpuspī* combats painful urination, and that a complete treatment for barrenness involves all of the elements mentioned above. (I was unable to identify the *sākhpuspī* plant. Bhargava's *Dictionary* gives a *sākh hulī* plant which is said to be used for medicinal purposes.)

Coughing and Asthma (*Khansi aur Dama*)

Dry ginger (*soth*), green pepper (*pīpar*), chili pepper (*marīc*), cardamon (*chotī lāīcī*), and molasses (*bhelī*) are to be mixed and stored in a jar. The patient is instructed to take two draughts a day for 15 days. A prescription for asthma (*sās pultá haī*): dry leaves from the *pīpal* tree are to be ground and mixed with honey; two draughts a day are to be taken for 15 days.

Headache (*Sir ka Dard*)

Baba asks the patient to bring some *dūb* grass from a spot near his ashram. He winds it together, taps the patient's head with it while reciting a *mantra*, then tells the patient to grind it, mix it with mustard oil, and apply the mixture to the forehead once a day for 21 days. He told one woman with a headache to eat sweets in the morning as well.

Lower Back Pain (*Kariyah Ka Dard*), *and Shoulder Pain* (*Kandha ka Dard*)

Goats' milk and mustard seed oil are to be combined and the oily mixture used in massaging the aching area.

Skin Problems

The following problems (of different patients) received similar prescriptions: leukoderma (a skin abnormality characterized by a lack of pigment in spots or bands, *suphedī* in the vernacular language); sores on the dorsal surfaces of the feet; itchy feet; sores on buttocks. Two women with leukoderma were told to grind the bark of the pipal tree in water and apply the mixture to the affected area. They were also given the following curious dietary restriction: they were to eat no salt on Sunday for a year. One of them was also told to have three *pūjās* performed in the next year. The mother of the boy with sores on his feet was told to apply pipal bark ground in *lainū* (a viscous oil or grease made from clarified butter) to the sores. The mother of the boy with sores on his buttocks was told to apply *nīm* bark ground in sesamum oil to the sores. The man with itchy feet was told to mix ground *nīm* bark, alum, cow dung and water, cook well in sesamum seed oil, and apply the mixture to his feet. Note the use of *nīm* or pipal bark in all these prescriptions. The divine and medicinal qualities of the *nīm* tree were mentioned above; the pipal tree also has both sacred and medicinal significance.

The Use of Herbs

Jerome Frank states that, "... since until recent years most medical remedies were either inert or harmful, the reputation of the medical profession actually rested largely on the power of the placebo" (1964: xi). Frank's chapter on "The Placebo Effect" should be consulted for further evidence of the effectiveness of placebos in Western medicine (1961:65-74). Inasmuch as the effectiveness of the placebo lies in its symbolic power, it is not surprising the Baba frequently uses parts of such sacred plants as the *nīm* and pipal trees and *dūb* and *kus* grass. More detailed ethnography of the uses and contexts of the other herbs in Baba's pharmacopeia would no doubt reveal other subtle associations which give the user faith in them.

Some of the herbs, e.g., the *sakpuspi* plant, may have beneficial physiological effects as well. That an investigation of such herbs may prove very profitable is underscored when we remember that "the whole array of tranquilizers comes from the discovery of the chemical nature of the juice of a plant, Rauwolfia, traditional in the pharmacopeia of India" (Bates, 1958:114).

MORE EXPLICITY EMOTIONAL PROBLEMS

I have associated these two cases because of common elements in prescriptions and because of the relative absence of visible physiological symptoms. In the first case a boy of sixteen or seventeen complained of chronic insomnia, lack of appetite and a feeling of weakness. Baba told the boy to mix garlic juice with asafetida and apply this noxious concoction beneath his eyes and in his nostrils for seven days. This is a kind of aversive therapy. Carstairs interpreted the complaint of weakness as an expression of chronic anxiety engendered by guilt feelings, for which the traditional remedy was a pilgrimage or purificatory rite (1955:125). The element of self-punishment is common to both these procedures and the asafetida-garlic application.

The mixture was also part of a prescription for a woman who had been possessed by a *bhūt* or *bhūts* for several months. She had been "playing" (*khel rhī hai*), which denotes a violent side-to-side oscillation of the head, the usual expression of possession. She often did not recognize kin and friends, and verbally abused those around her. She once threw away all of herclo thes. (For detailed studies of such illnesses see Opler, 1958; Planalp, 1956:662-677; and Freed and Freed, 1964.) Her family, of a Brahman caste, had taken her to a psychiatrist or clinical psychologist in Varanasi, who diagnosed her illness as hysteria but apparently was unable to help her.

Baba brought a small twig, broke it and rubbed the ends of the two pieces on the white-washed wall. These, he said, were to be gently inserted and held in her ears for five minutes a day. He told her accompanying kin to grind together in water a leaf from the *akāś bāwar* plant (also called *amar-bel*—a kind of parasitic plant which I could not identify) and black pepper in water, and feed the mixture to her. He also blessed some *dūb* grass and instructed them to grind it in mustard oil and apply it to her forehead for nine days (the prescription for headache). He restricted her diet to cows' milk, sugar and rice for nine days. Finally, he said they should have a puja performed and feast some Brahmans. The latter procedure is a means of atonement.

This treatment is notable for its range of strategies—aversive, symbolic, herbal, dietary and nurturative. The sticks-in-ears procedure, by requiring daily attention and physical contact, would constitute a ritual expression of the family's concern for the well-being of this woman.

The Final Stage of the Curing Session

After telling the patient how to compound the necessary remedy and what not to eat, Baba gives the patient a pinch of ashes (*bhābhūtī*) from a fire sacrifice, which the patient touches to her tongue. *Bhābhūtī* is another common element of Brahmanic ritual, and the practice of touching it to the tongue is most common at pilgrimage places. It is considered divine because it has been in contact with the divine, and thought to be beneficial in the same way that taking *prasād* ("consecrated food offerings") is beneficial—as a means of deferring to the gods by ingesting that which they have polluted. In the context of curing it suggests a lasting protection.

Before turning our attention from Baba's curing ritual to other subjects, it should be noted that the ritual, itself prescribed by the medical conceptual scheme, in turn validates and reinforces that scheme (see Frank, 1961: 50; Planalp, 1956:662-677 for descriptions of the curing sessions of a somewhat similar practitioner).

The Special Significance of the Puja in Treating Illness

At several points in the above paragraphs it was noted that Baba recommended the patient to have a puja performed. The recommendation is usually made where the illness is particularly troublesome such as in cases of barrenness, or in cases where the illness is one of a series of misfortunes which the family has suffered. Baba may advise the patient to have a puja performed by a Brahman or may tell her to bring the materials for him to use in the performance of the ceremony on an auspicious date which he specifies after consulting his astrological charts.

A puja is a complex religious ceremony which a family usually has performed by its Brahman priest. It is a part of all Hindu rites of passage, but it may also be performed on other occasions of special importance to the family, such as a groundbreaking for a new house, or taking a special vow to elicit supernatural aid in some endeavor. In the context of healing the puja has special significance to the ill person, who is the focal individual in the puja. This person, after a purifying bath, must fast all day and wear new clothing. This is clearly "a dramatic break in the usual routine of daily activities" (Frank, 1961:51). Like the rest of the ritual, it gives the person the feeling that he or she is doing something to combat the illness, which in itself is important. Preparation of sacrificial food and other ceremonial details require the aid of the family members and *parjuniā* (clients of the family), who have specified duties in the puja. The family thus can "convey their concern by participating in the ritual" (Frank, 1961:51). After the puja, the consecrated food is distributed among close relatives and friends of the family, reinforcing or redressing those bonds. The puja would also have the effect of redressing or reinforcing the relationship of the afflicted with the supernatural.

COMPARING BABA'S TREATMENTS WITH OTHER INDIGENOUS TREATMENTS

In order to gain some perspective on Baba's treatments, it is useful to have some idea of other available treatments. Marriott's study (1955:250-262) provides a useful framework for comparison.

The initial response to most of the kinds of problems Baba treats excepting spirit possession is some kind of home treatment, which encompasses a tremendous variety of folk cures and usually involves dietary modification. If this fails, or for certain special problems, the individual will resort to the second type of treatment, that which

Marriott calls "magical medicine." Essentially this is "a body of mechanical techniques that can be directed against invading spirits. Its techniques include the wearing of protective strings and amulets and the expulsion of invading spirits by rituals of exorcism." This class of medical technicians includes the *mantravidhs* and other specialists who use *mantras* to treat evil-eye afflictions, dog bites, scorpion stings and other problems. The villagers are quick to use this type of treatment not only because its techniques are painless, quick and safe, as Marriott points out, but because they have faith in them. I would include in this category the snake bite curers which Marriott considers discrete because he believes they have higher caste and power ranking. A third category of treatment is that practiced by the *ojhā* (see, pp. 290-291). A fourth category is "sacerdotal medicine"—the Brahman priests who "advise their clients to perform certain religious rituals as means of obtaining good health, prosperity, and children...[and] also give astrological advice, which helps their clients time their activities according to astral omens so as to avoid illness and other misfortunes." These priests may also dispense *jantras*, as mentioned above. Secular medicine comprises the Ayurvedic and Unani systems mentioned above, as well as the herbalists (see, for example, Planalp, 1956:699).

Both the combination of persuasive components which comprise Baba's roles and public image, and the various procedures incorporated in his treatments are highly eclectic. He is encompassed by none of the above categories, yet shares elements with each. Like the magical medical technicians, he exorcises by *mantras* and protects with *jantras*. Like the sacerdotal curers, he reads Sanskrit and advises his clients regarding ritual needs and the astrological timing of important undertakings. Like the *ojhās* he is a bit wild looking and is supposed to effect his cures through a supernatural power acquired by unusual ritual means. He utilizes herbs like the herbalist and prescribes diet like the *vaids* and *hakims*.

In both his public image and his treatment, Baba is a *bricoleur*. The analogy is one of Levi-Strauss's (1966:16). The contemporary bricoleur is a handyman who assembles from available odds and ends a device to perform a required function, i.e., he takes available units provided by tradition and assembles them in a novel way to build an effective system. Baba has assembled roles, a public image and a comprehensive set of cures which his patients find persuasive.

OTHER FACTORS IN FAITH

In addition to all of the meanings attached to Baba and his healing which suggest success, there are other cognitive factors which lend support to his reputation. One is the *post hoc ergo propter hoc* (after that threfore because of that) logic which is common among uneducated (and a good many educated) people. Remission of symptoms no doubt does occur in many cases that Baba treats, and this reinforces faith in him. Another factor is that successes are more significant and longer remembered than failures. These two principles were nicely summed up in one villager's comment: "They go to the *sādhū* and take the *bhābhūtī* and if they get well they say it was the *sādhū's bhābhūtī*. If they don't they just forget it." Ironically this same informant later asked if he could have some magical herbs which Baba had given me. Additionally, in those cases where illness does persist it is easily blamed on a breach of prescription or dietary restriction, or not wearing a *jantra*. Or the illness is attributed to fate, or God's will. People are reluctant to say they have consulted a healer or other practitioner when the illness persists, for that would imply that they have spent money foolishly or have not followed the healer's instructions. Thus failures are not broadcast as are successes.

There is skepticism of Baba and curers like him, but I found that it was quite like the skepticism of the Azande reported by Evans Pritchard in *Witchcraft, Oracles and Magic among the Azande* (1937:183-185). Most of my acquaintances believed that there are a few entirely reliable practitioners, but that most are quacks. But in the case of any particular practitioner, they are never quite certain that he is one of the reliable ones. These differences of attitude are not merely differences between one individual and another, but are also differences of attitude of the same man in different situations, as seen in the case above.

When a problem is pressing, particularly if other alternatives have failed, a person will try an alternative which at an untroubled time he or she would intellectually dismiss. To be doubly certain, some people will consult a range of practitioners, as in the case of a Sanskrit scholar I know who after being bitten by a dog sought treatment from an Ayurvedic practitioner, an allopathic doctor, and Baba.

Summary and Conclusions

Recent studies in various disciplines indicate that many illnesses have an emotional component and that curing can take place through effective treatment of this aspect of the illness. Therefore, understanding of the folk healer's effectiveness requires consideration of his pertinent mental culture (magico-religious ideology and ritual symbolism); the roles of the curer; and the image of himself which the curer projects. In this case etiology consists of two primary beliefs: that illness is caused by a malevolent spirit which can be exorcised, and that it may also be due to incorrect diet. The curer treats the latter with dietary prescriptions and restrictions to restore corporal balance. Underlying exorcism of the afflicting spirit is the assumption that the more ways power can be implemented to drive out the spirit, the better. The efficacious *mantras*, mimetic sweeping out with a doubly effective charm-wound wand of a sacred wood, charms to effect and ensure expulsion, fire sacrifices which enlist the aid of more powerful supernatural forces, ingestion of consecrated ashes, and his own powerful commands comprise a compelling drama. The setting of the treatment in a temple at a particularly sacred location is also doubtly auspicious. The curer's role as curer is reinforced by his role as *sādhū*—a divine and powerful personage. The curer projects this role aspect via his distinctive attire and through other *sādhū* activities such as Yoga and application of sacred ashes to his body. His role as keeper of the ashram's temples and regular devotee of the deities whose icons are within also suggest advantageous relations with the supernatural. His piety is expressed through sponsorship of annual community-benefiting fire sacrifices, as well as through his daily worship and charitable medical treatment. Other aspects of the curer's public image which fall outside of the role requirements identified above create further faith in his power. These include his literacy, his stern demeanor and the many stories which circulate via his disciples regarding his miraculous abilities and achievements—his remarkable age, his 36-year subterranean austerities, and the adopted son bequeathed in payment for his mother's miraculous cure. His repeated apparent successes also reinforce faith in his powers. The combination of all of these persuasive elements induces in the patient a state of heightened suggestability and expectation, which are focussed and given momentum by Baba's identification of the miscreant spirit, ritual expulsion of it, and pronouncement that the illness will cease.

An important axiom of Medical Anthropology is that "...man's behavior before the threats and realities of illness is necessarily rooted in the conception he has constructed of himself and his universe" (Pellegrino, 1963:10). In the cosmos of many rural Indians several supermundane realms interpenetrate the realm of everyday human life. Supernatural entities—gods, godlings, and the malevolent spirits of the dead, play a part in the condition of every human. Illness can be their work or the work of mundane factors; it is never clear which. Healing in which natural remedies, such as herbal and dietary prescriptions, are combined with various approaches to the control of the supernatural is a logical expression of that local world view, and in turn reinforces it.

REFERENCES

BATES, MARSTON
1958 *Gluttons and Libertines; Human Problems of Being Natural.* New York: Random House.

CARSTAIRS, G. MORRIS
1955 "Medicine and Faith in Rural Rajasthan." In Benjamin D. Paul (ed.), *Health, Culture, and Community*, pp. 107-134. New York: Russell Sage Foundation.

CROOKE, WILLIAM
1968 *The Popular Religion and Folklore of Northern India.* (Originally Published in 1896.) Delhi: Munshiram Manoharlal.

FABREGA, HORACIO
1971 "Medical Anthrolopology." In Bernard J. Siegel (ed.), *Biennial Review of Anthrolopology* 1971. Stanford: Stanford University Press.

FRANK, JEROME D.
1961 *Persuasion and Healing; A Comparative Study of Psychotherapy.* Baltimore: The Johns Hopkins Press.
1964 "Foreword." In Ari Kiev (ed.), *Magic, Faith, and Healing*, pp. 7-12. New York: The Free Press.

FREED, STANLEY A. and RUTH S. FREED
1964 "Spirit Possession as Illness in a North Indian Village." *Ethnology* 3:152-171.

GOULD, HAROLD A.
1957 "The Implications of Technological Change for Folk and Scientific Medicine." *American Anthropologist* 59:507-16.

LEVI-STRAUSS, CLAUDE
1966 *The Savage Mind.* Chicago: The University of Chicago Press.

LEWIS, OSCAR
1968 *Village Life in Northern India.* New York: Random House.
MARRIOTT, MCKIM
1955 "Western Medicine in a Village of Northern India." In Benjamin D. Paul (ed.), *Health, Culture and Community*, pp. 239-268. New York: Russell Sage Foundation.
MURPHY, JANE M.
1964 "Psychotherapeutic Aspects of Shamanism on St. Lawrence Island, Alaska." In Ari Kiev (ed.), *Magic, Faith, and Healing*, pp. 53-83. New York: The Free Press.
OPLER, MORRIS
1958 "Spirit Possession in a Rural Area of Northern India." In William A. Lessa and Evon Z. Vogt (eds.), pp. 553-566. *Reader in Comparative Religion; An Anthropological Approach.* Evanston, Illinois: Harper and Row.
1963 "The Cultural Definition of Illness in Village India." *Human Organization* 22:32-35.
PELLEGRINO, E.D.
1963 "Medicine, History and the Idea of Man." In *Medicine and Society.* Philadelphia: Annals of the American Academy of Political and Social Science 346:10.
PLANALP, JACK M.
1956 *Religious Life and Values in a North Indian Village.* Ph. D. dissertation. Ithaca: Cornell University.
PRINCE, RAYMOND
1964 "Indigenous Yoruba Psychiatry." In Ari Kiev (ed.), *Magic, Faith, and Healing*, pp. 84-120. New York: The Free Press.
SHILOH, AILON
1969 "The Interaction of the Middle Eastern and Western Systems of Medicine." In Ailon Shiloh (ed.), *Peoples and Cultures of the Middle East.* New York: Random House.
SINGER, MILTON
1968 "The Indian Joint Family in Modern Industry." In Milton Singer and Bernard S. Cogen (eds), *Structure and Change in Indian Society*, pp. 423-452. Chicago: Aldine.
TORREY, E. FULLER
1972 *The Mind Game; Witchdoctors and Psychiatrists.* New York: Bantam Books.

JAMES M. FREEMAN

A FIREWALKING CEREMONY THAT FAILED

ABSTRACT. This paper is a description of the deep crisis of faith that both caused and was caused by the failure of an Orissan firewalking ceremony in which ten out of fifteen firewalkers were burned. In addition to describing the rituals of firewalking, this paper focuses on the social background and the symbolic significance of the ceremony; the power struggle between a magician and a shamanistic curer for control of the firewalking ceremony and its patron goddesses; and an analysis of the significance of religious faith and experience in the lives of devout Hindus whose beloved deity fails them.

'WE FEAR UP TO THE MOMENT WE STEP ONTO THE FIRE. WE FEAR our goddess Kali, and what might happen. Who knows? So we throw ourselves before her. We pray to her all day for seven days; we think of nothing else. Then, if we have followed the rules of ritual observance, we can walk over the fire without difficulty' (a firewalker who was burned while walking over hot coals on 15 April 1972).

Never in the memory of anyone in the village had there been a grotesque fiasco like this one. The annual firewalking ceremony

[1]I am grateful to several institutions for their generous support of my research, of which this article is one result. (1) in 1970-72 the American Institute of Indian studies granted me a Senior Faculty fellowship, during which I collected the data on firewalking. I revised this article during 1976-77, during which time the following institutions contributed to my support: (2) The Center for Advanced Study in the Behavioral Sciences, with funds from the Andrew W. Mellon Foundation: A Fellowship; (3) The Joint Committee on South Asian Studies of the Social Science Research Council and the American Council of Learned Societies: A Grant; (4) San Jose State University: A Sabbatical Leave. I am solely responsible for the conclusions and perspectives of this paper, which in no way necessarily reflect either the opinions or the policies of the institutions mentioned above. This paper is a revised and greatly expanded version of an article of mine that appeared in Natural History Magazine (1974).

was the most sacred event of the village of Sunderpur in the eastern coastal state of Orissa, India.[2] True, sometimes in past years a firewalker had been burned. But no one doubted that anyone who was burnt must have failed to carry out at least one of the preliminary rites of purification before embarking on the test by fire of his religious faith.

In 1972, however, ten out of fifteen of the firewalkers were burned, some severely. They refused to accept any explanation that would put the blame for the disaster on themselves.

When people perform rituals properly and the gods do not heed them, people may lose faith in either the rituals or in their gods. The extraordinary failure at Sunderpur caused an entire community of believers to display aspects of their religious faith that, although rarely seen, were nevertheless crucial to understanding the importance of religion in their lives.

While many anthropologists have written about Hinduism, few have focused on religious experience. Valuable as psychological, symbolic, and structural analyses of Hinduism may be, they do not by themselves adequately convey the significance of religious faith and experience in the lives of devout Hindus. Moreover, such studies provide no guidelines for understanding the limits of religious faith, the processes by which faith may become questioned, and the ways in which believers attempt to resolve fundamental religious conflicts.

In this paper, in addition to discussing the social background and symbolic significance of Orissan firewalking, I shall describe the deep crisis of faith that both caused and was caused by the failure of Sunderpur's firewalking ceremony, and how this crisis affected the religious outlook of the believers in this ceremony. My aim is to convey what this crisis meant to the anguished believers whose beloved deity failed them.

Jhammu Jatra : The Firewalking Ceremony

Each year thousands of Orissans in hundreds of villages, beginning a day before or on Pana Sankranti, a holy day that falls in mid-April, subject themselves to ordeals by fire in which they test their faith that the goddess Kali has the power to protect them.

[2]The names of individuals, locations, and shrines are pseudonyms.

The climax of the most frequently performed religious rite is firewalking, in which from one to 25 or more persons walk over hot coals; they are observed by up to 20,000 spectators. The paths of hot coals are from 20 to 60 yards in length, and firewalkers traverse their entire length back and forth from three to seven times.

There are, however, many other ordeals by fire. One of the most dramatic of these is fireswinging, in which devotees dressed in loin cloths are lifted to scaffolds, flipped upside down, tied by the ankles with ropes, and then swung, hanging face down, through blazing fires. After each swing, the attendants on the scaffolds hold the ropes fast and daub the fireswingers with sacred sweet water and aromatic sandalwood paste, and make the fire flare up by throwing pungent resin on it, while men chant, "Hail the name of God!," and women make ululating sounds as they do at all auspicious or holy occasions. After they have gone through the fire seven times in each direction, the fireswingers are taken down, usually unharmed.

In other villages, participants do not perform ordeals by fire; instead, they pass hot skewers through their tongues, lick boiling milk, or pass hooks through the skin of their backs. In some villages worshippers of Kali on Pana Sankranti day do not attempt any ordeals, but instead participate in or listen to a devotional chanting dance called the *patua*, the performance of which may continue for seven days (Das, 1953: 81-82). Ordeals are performed both by tribal peoples in the states of Bihar and Orissa as well as by nontribal residents in states such as Orissa and Madhya Pradesh, and in overseas Indian communities (Babb, 1975: 132-40; Das, 1953: 81-85; Kuper, 1960: 217-27; Rosner, 1966; Freeman, 1974).

While firewalking is performed only once a year, the worship of Kali, the patron of firewalking, occurs daily throughout the year. Kali, one of the forms of the mother goddess, is worshipped at numerous small village shrines by devotees who pray that she will help them overcome personal problems. At these shrines Kali is represented by numerous shapes and is known by many different names.

In paintings and sculpture, Kali usually is depicted as having a paradoxical character, representing at the same time two contradictory opposites. Zimmer (1946: 211-15: figs 67, 69) observes that Kali represents the dynamic force of the universe, the temporal aspect of the absolute. She represents simultaneously life and death, creation and destruction, which are part of the same process.

She often is represented dancing on Shiva, her husband, the eternal aspect of the absolute. While Kali usually is shown representing destruction, wearing skulls, holding a sickle and a freshly decapitated head, she also may be holding at the same time a bowl of life-nourishing food.

These contradictory themes are represented not only in art, but also in the firewalking and fireswinging ceremonies. The life-affirming aspects of the mother goddess as Kali are represented by green mangoes which are tied to the fireswinging scaffold, any by libations of sacred sweet water; death and the destructive aspects of Kali are represented by animal sacrifices at which shamanistic curers called *kalasi,* who represent the goddess, drink the blood.[3]

Finally, contradictory aspects of Kali are also represented in the personal worship of the devotees of Kali, who ask her for help, yet fear that she may punish them with disease or death if they displease her. Firewalking represents an extreme extension of these contradictory attitudes. Firewalkers usually have suffered great crises, such as illnesses in their family that they believe have been caused by Kali. They ask the goddess to cure those who are afflicted, and as a testimony to their faith in her power, they vow to walk over fire, often at each annual ceremony for five or more years. While firewalkers may come from any caste, women are not permitted to walk over the coals unless they are *kalasis.* In some communities outside Orissa, women frequently are firewalkers (see Kuper, 1960: 219).

Firewalking, like many Hindu ceremonies, is a *brata* (or *vrata*)—rite—a vowed observance. Historically, vows have been an important part of Hindu ritualism for centuries. Kane, for example, lists hundreds of vowed observances that are referred to in Hindu religious writings, particularly those known as *puranas,* which contain some 25,000 verses on vows (Kane, 1974: 57, 251-462). People take vows mostly to secure something in this world, such as progeny, wealth, good fortune, health, fame, or long life; sometimes people

[3]The term "kalasi" comes not from Kali, the mother-goddess, but from the word *kalasha*, the auspicious jar that devotees carry at auspicious or religious occasions such as weddings, establishing an idol, starting a new enterprise, or firewalking (see Kane, 1974: 280). Babb (1975:42) describes the *kalasha* as the concrete symbol of the deity during rituals. The *kalasha* is also important in firewalking. During the procession preceding the firewalking ordeal, devotees carried the auspicious jar of the goddess, which at other times remained at the mother-goddess shrines at which the kalasi-shamans worshipped.

take vows to gain something both in this world and in the next (Kane, 1974: 55; Das, 1952: 209-10). Some vows last only a day; others a lifetime, but whether they be long or short, failure to fulfil a vow, either personally or by proxy, is said to lead to dire consequences (Kane, 1974: 47-48). The puranas contain detailed descriptions of rules that vow-takers should follow. These include fasting, worshipping gods, frequent purificatory baths, sexual abstinence, avoidance of drinking water, chewing betel or sleeping during daylight hours, and many other injunctions (Das, 1952: 213). The proper performance of vows brings the vow-taker not only the rewards that he or she seeks, but also is said to invest such a person with great spiritual power. For example, a virtuous wife who properly performs particular vows is said to be able to gain the power to prevent the death of her husband (Kane, 1941: 567-68).

The key figures at firewalking ceremonies are the *kalasis*. The villagers believe that when the *kalasis* go into a trance, the soul of the mother goddess enters them. While in trance, the *kalasis* are believed to be the deity, and are addressed by the deity's name. The trance may occur at any time, but almost invariably occurs during religious ceremonies. Like shamanistic curers elsewhere in India, Orissan *kalasis* usually are very poor or are of very low caste (Berreman, 1964: 61, 62; O'Malley, 1929: 83-84). When they are not possessed by the goddess, *kalasis* are treated as ordinary villagers, but in their religious roles they have a large following of worshippers from all castes and economic levels. Throughout the year, *kalasis* give advice and perform faith cures in their role as the goddess, while on Pana Sankranti day they select those firewalkers whom they consider pure and lead them over the hot coals.

RITUAL PREPARATIONS

For the past 20 years the firewalking ceremony at Sunderpur had been led by two *kalasis,* both of whom were of a caste of untouchables called Bauri. (The life style of the Bauris has been described by Freeman 1977.)

One of these *kalasis*, an old woman, represented a mother goddess called Banadurga, whose shrine was located in a Bauri ward of the village. The other *kalasi,* a man, represented the mother goddess Chandi, whose shrine was in a field just outside of the village.

For years both of these *kalasis* had walked over hot coals without mishap.

Ten days before the firewalking ceremony was to begin, a magician, called a *gunia,* of Sunderpur challenged the Chandi *kalasi's* authority and powers by declaring that he would prove that he could walk over the coals without being burnt, even though he had not performed any of the seven-day ritual purifications and vows as required by the *kalasi* of firewalkers for their protection. Villagers fear magicians, who are believed to have malevolent powers. After going into trance, the Chandi *kalasi* replied with the voice and authority of the goddess: if the magician tried to walk over hot coals, the goddess would punish and burn him.

One week before the ceremony, eleven prospective firewalkers, including two who were attempting the ordeal for the first time, went to live at the Sunderpur village temple, where they prayed, performed ritual ablutions, cooked and ate one vegetarian meal a day, and drank water once a day with their meal. They were not supposed to swallow at any time during the day except during the time of their meal, and they were supposed to refrain from touching anyone. For the first six days, by a ruling of the chief firewalker, whose word was law on such matters, they were permitted to converse only among themselves, or with me, or with their *kalasi* leaders. For the final 24 hours, he imposed vow of total silence on them. Furthermore, during the entire week of ritual purification they were not permitted to leave the temple grounds except to visit their *kalasis,* who did not remain in the village temple but at their own shrines, where they prepared themselves for the coming ordeal. These activities and prohibitions, which were intended to purify them, were their sole preparations for firewalking.

Because I was able to converse with him in the Oriya language and thus gain his confidence, the chief firewalker invited me to remain in the temple until the final 24 hours before the ceremonies. During my stay in the temple, I was permitted to observe the rituals and even to interview the prospective firewalkers.

The chief firewalker, whose grandfather had founded the firewalking ceremony in Sunderpur 90 years ago, informed the two new firewalkers that they were supposed to pay for all their own expenses (about one month's wages for an agricultural field laborer), and he helped them to arrange the material items they would need: a gift to the deity, new clothes, turmeric paste and oil which they would daub on themselves after morning and evening baths, rice, lentils, and vegetables for the daily meal, the coals that they would walk over, the fan used to keep the coals hot, aromatic resin sprinkled on the glowing coals, and dried coconuts which they would carry while walking over the coals.

The daily ritual preparations of the firewalkers took only a few hours; the rest of the day they sat listlessly on the temple's cool, white-washed veranda and talked. A frequent topic was the impending confrontation between the magician and the *kalasi* who was their religious leader. The firewalkers said that they were worried. Some magicians are said to be so powerful that they can cause a deity to come under their control. When this happens, the deity becomes "silent," she is unable to appear in the form of a *kalasi*. Her powers are then used solely for the magician's malevolent purposes. The firewalkers recounted an incident of 50 years ago in which a magician caused the deity of the Sunderpur temple to become permanently silent; since that time, this deity has not appeared as a *kalasi*.

Although men of all castes may elect to walk the fire, all of Sunderpur's firewalkers except the *kalasis* were from middle castes such as goldsmith, confectioner, oilpresser, and cultivator. They ranged in age from 24 to 67, but several of them had begun firewalking when they were only 12 years old.[4] While most were literate, none had attended more than six years of school. All of them worked at their hereditary caste occupations except the chief firewalker, who worked for the railroad.

Most of the men walked over the coals to ward off their own or their children's illnesses, and many planned to carry their children with them if these children were too small to walk over the coals themselves. One 60 year old cultivator-caste man, who was preparing to carry his grandson for the seventh time, said that he started fire-walking 35 years ago in gratitude to the mother deity after she blessed his family with a child. He explained why he still walks the fire:

> After I completed my five-year vow, I decided to quit, but the mother goddess would not let me. Once she reminded me to walk by letting my son and daughter become very ill. Another time, when I was working in Calcutta, I dreamed that an old woman

[4]Elsewhere, observers have seen small children walk over hot coals. See, for example, Rosner (1966).

struck me with a cane and said, 'Why are you sleeping, with my festival only one week away?[5] Have you forgotten?' I awoke with a start, realized that the mother goddess was calling me, and returned home just in time for the festival. I hope to walk until the end of my days because the deity has given me whatever I asked for.

The Disaster

By noon on firewalking day, volunteers from many castes had finished digging 13 firelanes and filling them with coals. Each lane was 75 feet long and one foot deep, with pits at each end which were filled with sacred water to purify the feet of the firewalkers. The firelanes, which were located a few feet from the main temple of the village, were placed so that the firewalkers would begin their journey facing east, the auspicious and most sacred direction, associated with purity and the absence of sin.[6] After walking back and forth seven times, the firewalkers were supposed to finish facing west, the direction associated with the completion of auspicious rituals. The northern-most two lanes, which were the most sacred, were reserved for the two *kalasis*, while the remaining eleven lanes were allotted to the other firewalkers.

Two men of the untouchable Sweeper caste began beating drums, signifying that a *kalasi* was preparing to go into trance. Attendants shouted, "The deity is going to take the shape of a person!" A boisterous crowd of spectators rushed through the narrow lanes of the village to an untouchable Bauri ward. An old woman, the Banadurga *kalasi*, sat outside on the veranda of a mud hut. She was tiny, bowed, and wrinkled, a fragile looking silvery-haired woman of 70.

Although she was quite feeble and hard of hearing, the old woman was considered a more important *kalasi* than the Chandi *kalasi* because the deity of her shrine was considered to be more powerful than that of the Chandi *kalasi*. She went into trance, trembling, stretching, and yawning, accompanied by loud drumming, blaring bagpipes and horns, played by Bauri-caste musicians, and a twirling dancing boy, dressed in women's garb, performing the *patua* dance. The villagers believe that when the *kalasi* goes into trance, her human

[5]Kalasis in trance select those firewalkers whom they wish to accompany them over the hot coals by touching or striking them with their sacred canes.

[6]Some ceremonies begin facing north, also a sacred direction.

breath is expelled, and the breath of the goddess enters her; at that moment the *kalasi* becomes the goddess.

The devotees, jostling and swaying, with their living goddess among them, ran towards the fire lines. Suddenly Banadurga stumbled and collapsed, but she was caught by eager hands before she reached the ground. Later, the villagers wondered if the goddess's fall was the first sign of her declining powers.

At a sharp turn in the road, the Chandi *kalasi*, in trance, and his followers joined Banadurga's procession. Worshippers along the way threw themselves to the ground or bowed deeply with folded hands as the two living goddesses passed by.

As the noisy procession approached the firelanes, the firewalkers emerged from the nearby temple where they had spent the last 24 hours fasting, praying, and maintaining a total silence in order to further purify themselves for the ordeal. There were now 12 prospective firewalkers; the newcomer was a 12 year old boy. He had already gone through six days of ritual preparation in the temple of his home village several miles away before he joined the group in Sunderpur for the final night's vigil. Since he was young and this was his first attempt, the Banadurga *kalasi* would lead him across the coals on her fire lane.

The firewalkers stood, appearing drawn and dazed, with their hands folded in greeting. When they saw the two living goddesses, they threw themselves to the ground and rolled over and over, stirring up choking clouds of dust. They kept their clasped hands in front of themselves so that their chests did not touch the ground. These acts were their final demonstrations of faith and devotion to the mother goddess.

Prospective firewalkers must roll on the ground until the *kalasis* touch them with their sacred canes, indicating that they have been selected to walk the fire. Although *kalasis* may decide to forbid a prospective firewalker to walk over the coals, on the grounds that he is still impure, most devotees who perform the week-long purification rituals are selected.

The *kalasis* touched the 12 firewalkers with the sacred canes, lifted them to their feet, and led them to the village pond for the final rites of purification. While the firewalkers bathed in the pond, changed into new clothes, and daubed turmeric over their bodies (except the soles of their feet), Bauri attendants washed the clay pots that contained the sacred fire of the goddess. This fire is used to light the coals of the firewalkers. While the firewalkers sat quietly on the bank of the pond, a Bauri leader purified the goddess's wooden throne by daubing red paste and turmeric on it. This leader then lit the sacred fire inside the goddess's pots, and sprinkled them with aromatic resin. Because the goddess is said to like its smell, the Banadurga *kalasi* hunkered over to the pots and gulped the billowing smoke. The leader took one of the flaming pots over to the firelanes and lit the straw surrounding the coals; attendants immediately began fanning the coals to make them glowing hot. Near the village temple a Brahman lit a fire for a sacrificial fire ceremony, creating a sacred altar and a sacred space, uttering incantations in which he invited all of the deities and sacred spirits to be witnesses to the sacred event which was to follow. This fire, too, was used to light the firelanes. The *kalasis*, the firewalkers, and many of the spectators remained near the pond; the Banadurga *kalasi* sat in trance with her cheeks sucked in and her eyes bulging, while the Chandi *kalasi* shrieked and hopped through the crowd of spectators.

Suddenly the Chandi *kalasi* slapped his cane across the shoulders of a smooth skinned brooding man with piercing eyes. With a slight nod the man stepped forward, peeled off his shirt, accepted a new cloth someone handed him, and took a dip in the pond. A *kalasi* may select any person to walk over coals, whether or not he has prepared, and when the villagers saw who had been selected, they gasped: it was the magician. The chief firewalker appeared upset as he waited for the magician to finish his ablutions.

The two *kalasis* and the 13 other firewalkers, bedecked with garlands, carrying children, and clenching pieces of straw in their teeth to maintain their vows of silence, walked quickly to the firelanes. The coals were blisteringly hot. The spectators shouted as the firewalkers twice circled the lanes and then stood in a row in the pits of sacred water. The Chandi *kalasi* motioned to his rival, the magician, to stand behind him and follow him on the second lane. The Banadurga *kalasi*, the leader on the north lane, started first, leading the 12-year-old boy on his first journey over coals. They walked without difficulty, but the others who followed were not so fortunate. The magician frequently stepped off the coals, while others, including the Chandi *kalasi*, faltered and grimaced as they scampered on and off the coals. After only four trips instead of the required seven, the Banadurga *kalasi* stopped abruptly; the others also stopped. As attendants led the firewalkers to the village temple for further prayers, the chief firewalker murmured, breaking his vow of silence, "It was too hot, the fire has never been so hot." The spectators should have realized that something was wrong, but in the excitement, they appeared not to notice; women rushed forward and grasped the smouldering embers, dipped them in the pits of sacred water, and tucked them in their saris as sacred souvenirs. Others smeared the ashes from the sacred charcoal across their foreheads.

The disruption of the ceremony continued. The two *kalasis* were led to a small clearing between the fire lanes and the village temple where goat sacrifices were to be held. The villagers believe that on Pana Sankranti day the goddess Kali needs blood, and her *kalasis* drink the spilled blood of sacrificed goats and chickens. The two Washerman caste men who sacrifice the goats stepped forward. One of them carried the wooden handled sacrificial knife. They looked around the clearing, saw no goats, and shouted with dismay, "Where is the goat?" A Brahman devotee of the Banadurga *kalasi*, who helps to organize the ceremony, said, "No one offered a goat for sacrifice this year." He handed the Washermen a broken pot which is used for catching the blood, and told them to behead the chickens. The Washermen, quite disturbed, refused, "Why should we use this broken pot? It's not needed for chickens, only for goats." The spectators stirred uneasily as the Brahman replied, "Preserve the custom nonetheless. Pour the blood on it, even if there is no goat."

Although clearly upset by this break in tradition, the Washermen decapitated two chickens, poured the blood into two broken pots, and handed one to each of the *kalasis*. As they drank, irritated spectators shouted, "There's no need for those pots, the deity won't get enough blood that way and will not be satisfied." The Washermen decapitated the remaining chickens and handed them directly to the *kalasis*, who drank deeply from the severed necks.

The firewalkers rejoined the *kalasis* near a great mango tree where the *kalasis* offer advice, faith cures, and divine favors to their worshippers. The Banadurga *kalasi* struck a firewalker with her sacred cane, indicating that he was to be the first beneficiary of the divine favors. The firewalker said nothing, but pointed at his feet; huge blisters had formed. The spectators gasped. The Chandi *kalasi* called out angrily, "Why are blisters forming on your feet? Go and ask your wife why she ate fish on the day before the ceremony when it was prohibited. That's why you were burned."

The Chandi *kalasi* then touched another firewalker with his cane, but to the shocked surprise of the spectators, this man's burns were even worse than those of his predecessor. Once again the Chandi *kalasi* had an immediate answer: "Why did your wife touch your ceremonial articles of cloth, coconut, and turmeric when she was menstruating and impure? That's why you were burned."

One after another the *kalasis* inspected the firewalkers as the dismayed spectators looked on. The magician, the Banadurga *kalasi*, and the 12 year-old boy were unharmed, but 10 of the firewalkers were burned. The chief firewalker's feet were swollen so badly that he could barely hobble. The Chandi *kalasi's* feet also were blistered. When the Chandi *kalasi* saw this, he remained silent; the speechless spectators dispersed, bewildered, frightened, and angry.

The Hearing and Trial : Kalasis Versus the Magician

The day after the disastrous ceremony, about 70 of the villagers assembled at the shrine of the goddess Chandi and asked the Chandi *kalasi* to go into trance to tell them why the firewalkers were burned. The magician did not attend, but he sent his 20-year-old son. The Chandi *kalasi* agreed to help the villagers, and he invited me to witness this demonstration of his divine power.

After bathing, he perched rigidly on the stone slabs near his shrine. As drums rolled he trembled, and as the tempo of the drummers increased he jerked his arms and shoulders rapidly. Then he stretched and yawned widely, the sign that the deity had entered his body. While men shouted the name of God, and women made their holy, shrill ululations, the Chandi *kalasi* slowly fell backwards off the slabs, uttered the characteristic frenzied shrieks that he makes while in trance, and twitched and rolled his way to the shrine in time to the drums. The devotees inched forward to catch the Chandi *kalasi's* words, but to their surprise none were forthcoming. Instead of replying, the Chandi *kalasi* rocked wordlessly back and forth on his heels as he hunkered before the formless lump of stone that was his deity. As minutes lengthened into hours, the anticipation of his disciples turned to exasperation and finally to anger and contempt at his silence.

Suddenly the devotees were startled by an angry voice. A powerfully built man was shaking his fist at the *kalasi*; it was the *baistamba*, the hereditary religious leader of the untouchable Bauris:

You are a fraud and a fake! How could ten people who had carried out every ritual preparation be burned by the fire unless you were a fraud? And why were *you* one of those burned unless you were a fraud? I don't think that the goddess ever entered your body. You make the sounds of the deity but you never answer anything. How many more hours do you think we're going to wait to find out what happened? I'm through waiting. Either you explain this—right now—or I say that you're nothing but a faker! Neither I nor anyone else will obey you or the goddess every again!"

The Chandi *kalasi* responded with a series of high pitched stacatto shrieks. Then he turned grinning, his mouth a black hollow of betel reddened teeth, staring with his one good eye at his principal accusor.

The spectators heard shouts in the distance. The Banadurga *kalasi*, clutching her billowing purple sari, dashed down the narrow path towards the shrine, leaving choking clouds of dust that enveloped her straggling followers. Her arrival was a surprise. Because she was considered the most powerful *kalasi* in the area, other *kalasis* customarily visited her. A man near me muttered, "Why has she come here? Is she losing her powers!"

Four burned firewalkers, including their spokesman, the chief firewalker, hobbled forward, grimacing with each step. The chief firewalker asked the old woman why the firewalkers were burned. She pursed her lips but said nothing. She was partially deaf and probably never heard the question. The chief firewalker then demanded an answer from the Chandi *kalasi*. For the first time in the several hours that we had been sitting there the Chandi *kalasi* offered an explanation, "One of the women of your house was impure. She ate forbidden food on firewalking day."

The chief firewalker shook his head, "No! The women of my house fasted."

The Chandi *kalasi* said, "Well, you didn't perform a sacrificial fire ceremony at the village pond and sprinkle cow dung mixed with water to purify the path to the firelanes. That's why you were burned."

The chief firewalker replied angrily, "We never performed these ceremonies in previous years; why do you make them up now?"

The Chandi *kalasi* said, "Well, then, why did you accept prospective firewalkers into the temple only three days before the ceremony without consulting me?"

The chief firewalker shook his head, "I never did that. Rather, you ought to remember whom you called to walk at the last moment--that skin cutter whose caste occupation is removing corns from people's feet!"

The spectators laughed at the chief firewalker's insulting reference to the magician, who is a member of the low-standing Barber caste, one of whose degrading hereditary tasks is removing corns from people's feet.

The chief firewalker now recounted the humiliation and painful events of the previous day, "We who observed the sacred vows for seven days were burned, but nothing happened to the person who didn't follow any rules, who ate anything and everything. Tell us why this happened or we'll drive you out! If your own firewalkers are burned, how can the ceremony continue?"

The Chandi *kalasi* asked, "Do you think that the people who were burned didn't know why?"

The chief firewalker replied impatiently, "Of course we didn't. If we had known that we were doing something wrong, we wouldn't have done it. You are the goddess—you know everything—so you tell us. If you don't, we'll know that you are a fake, sitting here with no goddess in your body—and we'll beat you so hard that you'll really straighten up!"

The Chandi *kalasi's* face twisted into a grin, "Oh, do you want to beat me? Go ahead. You are my son. If you want to beat your mother, I don't care—beat—beat."

The chief firewalker shouted, "I'm not just threatening, I'll really do it! If you are really the goddess, say so. I don't believe you are—you're just a man like me. We're the same."

He snatched the two looped canes from the *kalasis* and placed them around his neck, as if he were a *kalasi.* He turned to the crowd, mimicking the Chandi *kalasi's* trance voice, "Do you know who I am? I am Jageswari, the village goddess of Sunderpur. I am the eldest and most powerful goddess of all. Whatever you want to know, just ask me."

He turned to the two *kalasis,* grabbed their shoulders, and shook them roughly as he shouted, "I order you, tell us the truth or I'll purify you both with a beating! Tell us! Tell us! If you don't, we'll stop your ceremony forever ! I'll beat you with these!"

He shoved them and raised the canes threateningly over their heads.

The Chandi *kalasi* replied with an air of indifference, "Yes, let it stop. I don't mind. My ceremony is with my children. You are all my children. If I am true—if I am Chandi—and all my children are true, then I don't need a ceremony. I don't want one. Go and stop it."

The *baistamba* said, "What kind of goddess is this? He's a cheat—he can say nothing, so why is the chief firewalker trying to get answers out of that man? Why should we stay here any longer? He should be beaten!"

A few people stood up to leave. The Chandi *kalasi* looked around as if he were searching for someone. He asked softly, "Where is he, where is that youth?"

The spectators became quiet. Finally, he motioned to the magician's son to come forward and sit by him. As he reached the platform, the magician's son tucked in his dhoti in the manner considered suitable for entering shrines, but he insultingly did not greet the *kalasi.*

The Chandi *kalasi* spoke first, "Will you explain what happened?"

The magician's son replied, "How should I know? You tell me; you are the goddess."

The Chandi *kalasi* smiled, "Don't you know who did it? You know, someone in your family."

The magician's son screamed, "You are an uncivilized fake! By nodding your head pretending to be in trance you insult the goddess. The real goddess is on the stone throne. If we worship her everything will be all right. But you tell lies and destroy the truth. I'll finish you now with a beating!"

He grabbed one of the Chandi *kalasi's* canes and hit him several times on the head. As he struck he shouted, "I'll see what kind of goddess you are. I'm beating you and everyone is watching. If you really are the goddess, strike me down or kill me now where everyone can see!"

There was silence. The magician's son looked at the spectators, spread his arms wide, and shouted triumphantly, "See! There is no goddess in them. The two of them are making a farce of religion. This old lady who pretends to be the goddess Banadurga is no better."

He turned to her and said, "You're at the bottom of all this. Did you really become possessed by Banadurga? If not, I'll beat the skin off your back!"

He grabbed one of her canes with his left hand and one of the Chandi *kalasi's* with his right. The two canes snapped. He struck both *kalasis* with the broken canes. Then he slapped the old woman's face four times, hard. As he shouted and scuffled with them, the spectators sat shocked and silent. The women of the Chandi *kalasi's* household broke into tears and were still softly sobbing when two spectators finally pulled the magician's son away from the *kalasis.*

The Chandi *kalasi* saw his wife and his brother's wife crying, and he said, "Why do they cry? Nothing has happened to the *Kalasi*—he's never in danger. What are they afraid of? Tell them not to cry." He uttered his sacred shrieking sounds; several devotees responded by shouting the sacred names and sounds of God.

The *baistamba* scowled, "Why utter the names of God? These two are not genuine *kalasis.* No one should pay any attention to them."

The chief firewalker called to the crowd, "Why do you people stay here? Why don't you go home and take care of your daily chores? No one should stay here any longer. From this day none of you should consult these *kalasis.*"

Most of the villagers shuffled away slowly. The people of the Chandi *kalasi's* caste (Bauri) remained at the shrine with the two *kalasis.* For a moment there was silence. Then the *baistamba* spoke, "Why keep the image of the goddess? Let's bring our stone cutting tools and dig her up. We'll break her into pieces and throw her into the village pond. From today the goddess Chandi will be no more!"

The Chandi *kalasi* said, "Do you think that the guilty won't be punished? They will—certainly."

The *baistamba* replied, "But when? Within how many days? If you can tell us, then we'll believe that you are genuine."

The Chandi *kalasi* said, "Why are you so worried? You'll see what heppens."

The *baistamba* dismissed him impatiently with a wave of his hand, "Why don't you get the goddess to leave your body now?"

The Chandi *kalasi* nodded, "Yes, let me return. Please hold me."

The villagers believe that a deity cannot leave a *kalasi's* body unless attendants stand and catch him as he falls. The Chandi *kalasi* yawned three or four times, stretched widely, held onto a small tree and collapsed to the ground. He twitched at the moment that the goddess was said to have left his body. He tried to stand, but he staggered, and two men caught him before he fell.

The chief firewalker snapped, "Huh! You should never become a *kalasi* again. Who ever heard of a goddess allowing herself to be beaten! Get up and go home! Who entered your body—this goddess here? You heard our leader, the *baistamba*, today we'll take her and throw her into the pond. Oh children, let's bring our pickaxes and finish the job! The goddess should know that no one believes in her."

Two people helped the Chandi *kalasi* walk to his house while the Banadurga *kalasi* trailed behind them looking dazed and lost. She was still in trance. As the Chandi *kalasi* slumped heavily on his veranda, his followers repeated, "Let's dig up that image and throw it away today."

The Chandi *kalasi*, now fully conscious, cried out in alarm, "What happened? What happened?"

The chief firewalker replied angrily, "Hey, 'brother-in-law,' don't you know anything?[7] Don't you know on how many places you were beaten?"

The Chandi *kalasi* asked, "Who beat me? Why would anyone beat me? What happened? Why is everyone shouting? I don't understand."

The chief firewalker replied contemptuously, "What would you understand? You are the all-knowing goddess and the powerful *kalasi*. Well, today, after we dig her up, we'll *see* when she returns again to your body!"

The Chandi *kalasi* said weakly, "Let me go inside my house." He stood up, trembled and sat down heavily.

The Banadurga *kalasi* saw him move and asked, "Who will help the deity leave my body?" Nobody moved.

She spoke again softly, "Someone should help the goddess leave my body. Then I'll go."

One man offered this hand, and called for others to hold her. No one else stepped forward.

The chief firewalker said, "Why should we hold her? What kind of return journey will she make? She's pretending. She doesn't need attendants to release the goddess because she's not genuine. Let her go home. The road is straight ahead—she can walk."

The *baistamba* said to her, "Since you cannot tell us when the magician's son will be punished, we don't accept you as a goddess."

The old woman twitched her mouth angrily. Then she replied,

[7]The term "brother-in-law" is a commonly used insult in Orissa and elsewhere in Northern India; in this context it connotes having sexual relations with a man's sister.

"He beat us, he attacked the prestige and fame of our deity. Do you think that he won't be punished?"

The exasperated leader shouted, "But when? We asked the Chandi *kalasi* and now you. If you two cannot punish the magician's son within three days, we'll smash your images and throw them away!"

The old woman replied, "Be patient! Be patient! The day will come; the tree will bear fruit. Think about that, or your fate will be very bad."

She implored them once again, "Help me to get rid of the goddess!"

The men ignored her. After a few moments the old woman rose hesitantly and started off alone down the dusty road to her home.

The villagers waited for three days, but the deity did not punish the magician's son. Since the *kalasis* appeared to be ineffective, the villagers conducted an informal trial of the magician and his son, at which leaders from the surrounding villages served as judges. The leaders invited me to be a judge, but anticipating that they would condemn and punish a man for doing witchcraft (malevolent magic), I refused their offer, saying that I did not know enough to make decisions about such a case.

To no one's surprise, the judges found the magician and his son guilty, and forced them to pay a fine of 1000 rupees (several months' wages for an agricultural laborer) which was to be used for the maintenance of the shrines they were said to have desecrated. The magician swore that he was innocent, "If I am not," he said, "let me lose my only son within six months!"

Many villagers accepted his oath and argued furthermore that there was no way to prove whether or not he disrupted the ceremony with magic. They said, however, that his son could not be permitted to assault people. The magician was considered responsible for letting his son misbehave, and therefore the judges hoped that the fine would prompt the magician to try to control his quick tempered son. The *kalasis* were left to vindicate themselves.

An Interview with the Chandi Kalasi

On the day of the trial I talked at length to the Chandi *kalasi* about his faith in himself and in the deity to whom he had devoted his life. The Chandi *kalasi* invited me into his caste community house: crumbling gray mud walls, windowless, cool and dark, with a high thatch roof pierced by dust-mote filled shafts of light. There were no mats to sit on since my host could not afford them. He gave me the seat reserved for guests—wooden planks that were the remnants of an old door. The Chandi *kalasi* and his friends sat on the hard mud floor, using the walls as backrests.

The Chandi *kalasi's* demeanor impressed me immediately. Although some of my questions were new to him and puzzling, once he understood them he answered in a straightforward manner, attempting neither pretense nor subterfuge. He maintained his composure during a time which must have been one of the most trying of his life.

The Chandi *kalasi* said that like other men of his untouchable caste his earnings came primarily from working as a landless wage laborer in the fields of high caste landowners. He performed as a holy man in his spare time. At my request he described how he became a holy man:

> About twenty years ago, on firewalking day, I returned from a journey and was very hungry. My family was preparing sacred food, but I could not wait. I roasted and ate some food that was forbidden on that sacred day—dried prawns. My relatives scolded me angrily, but I did not listen to them. That afternoon, all of us went to pray at the shrine of Chandi. As I stepped forward, I was suddenly thrown to the ground. At first nobody realized that the deity had entered my body. They thought that she had just knocked me down to punish me. I stepped forward and again was thrown to the ground. I do not know what happened. When the goddess enters me I lose all sense of being conscious. Later I was told that when people saw that I became the living goddess, they gathered around me uttering the sacred names and sounds of God.

The Chandi *kalasi's* followers believed that he had the power to perform faith cures, and they implored him to use it. Since his initial attempts appeared to be successful, his fame spread. The Chandi *kalasi* and his friends told me about many patients whose cures they attributed to the power of the goddess working through him: previously barren women who bore children, sufferers from dysentery, lepers, and hysterical girls who were said to have been cured of being inhabited by evil spirits. The Chandi *kalasi* did not claim to possess unique powers. He said, "I am a small man, a small disciple of a small goddess. I have no personal ability or knowledge. I do not even know what kind of spirit is within the patients I cure. Anything I do comes from the sacred cane of the goddess. It is her power, not mine, that cures."

I asked, "Are there times when the goddess refuses to help or does not fulfil her promise?"

The Chandi *kalasi* replied, "It happens often, and then people become very displeased with the goddess. Sometimes people do not follow the vows that they must make if the goddess's promise is to be fulfilled. Sometimes their fortune is bad. But the goddess never lies. If a barren woman does not have it in her fortune to have children, the deity will not give her children. If she doesn't like you, she won't help you."

I asked, "How does she feel about you?"

He replied, "She doesn't like me and so I don't like her. I have prayed, but she never helps me, only others. The people of my house often go without food, but what does she care! She cures others of diseases, but look at me—blind in one eye and carrying around a big basket!"

He pointed to a large lump under his dhoti—his painful, filaria-swollen scrotum. "She sees my condition, so I know that she doesn't like me. If I ever meet her I'll give her a beating that she'll never forget! But what can I do? Whenever she appears my eyes are closed (in trance) and I am unable to see her."

I asked, "How do you feel about continuing to worship the goddess or becoming the goddess again?"

He replied: "When I heard that the goddess was beaten while she was within me, I became very angry. That evening, I brought an axe to the goddess's throne and the sacred tree around it. I tried to cut down the tree, but although no one else appeared to be there, someone prevented me from striking. I tried once again, but the blade turned on its side, rebounded and struck my forehead. A little blood came out. Then I heard someone whisper in my ear, 'Don't do that—wait for further action. Don't be angry with me.' I thought that this was the goddess's voice, so I prostrated myself and then returned home. Now I wait. I never wanted to become the *kalasi*. She pulled me into it; I don't know why. I didn't know any prayers or anything else to please the goddess. The only thing I ever did was to greet her every morning after bathing. I do not know whether she will drag me to follow her commands ever again or not."

Three months later, when I left India, the Chandi *kalasi* still was waiting in patient anguish for the day that he and his goddess would be vindicated.

SUMMARY AND CONCLUSION

Firewalking ceremonies reveal at least six important aspects of Hindu culture. First, firewalking is one of many ceremonies devoted to the worship of the mother goddess, of whom Kali is one of the most popular forms. Orissan folk art representations of Kali dancing with her consort Shiva, are compact symbolic messages which refer simultaneously and paradoxically to several contradictory themes—time and eternity, life and death, creation and destruction, blind energy and ordered control, purity and pollution, the one and the many. These representations are attempts to depict, in visual form, the contradictory totality of the universe, and the place of humans in it.

Second, the ritual symbolism of the firewalking ceremonies is shared with many other Hindu ceremonies. The important themes that are repeated are those of the opposing themes of purity and pollution. Purity is associated with "good" or auspicious rituals that require participants to acquire a high degree of ritual purity, that is, to eliminate pollution to a greater degree that is usual. Water and fire symbolize purifying substances and usually are used in auspicious ceremonies.

Pollution is associated with "bad" or inauspicious ceremonies that require an individual to eliminate excessive pollution from himself. A Hindu's ordinary ritual condition is somewhere between these two extremes. Although worshippers in Sunderpur often cannot explain the symbolic significance of the rites they perform, they are well aware of the symbols of pollution and purity, which are central to their social and ritual behaviors.

Examples of auspicious ceremonies include marriage, sacred thread, and many calendrical rituals of deities. All of these ceremonies begin facing east or north, auspicious directions, and conclude facing the west.

Examples of inauspicious rituals are funerals, rites of exorcism, fly larvae infection ceremonies, and rites expiating guilt for the death of a cow. These rituals are begun with participants facing south, the least sacred direction, which is associated with sin, death, and the deity of death. Many of the procedures of inauspicious rituals are reversals of the procedures of auspicious rituals.

The firewalking ceremonies are unusual in that they contain both purity rites (walking or swinging through sacred fire), and pollution rites (blood sacrifice) in the same ceremonial sequence.[8]

Third, the firewalking ceremonies portray the caste hierarchy and its relation to the symbols of ritual purity. Because they have a high degree of ritual purity, hereditary Brahman priests sanctify the fire and transform the ritual arena into a sacred space, reciting incantations that invite all the deities and spirits to witness the sacred event. Because they are untouchables and are associated with pollution, men of the Washerman caste are given the task of decapitating the animals offered to the goddess Kali. The predominantly low caste shamanistic *kalasis* represent both the pure aspects of the goddess (through firewalking) and the impure (through drinking blood).

Fourth, firewalking and blood sacrifice are rituals that villagers use to achieve immediate needs which are usually tied to severe personal or group crises, particularly illnesses. Sunderpur is located in an area which is noted for the frequency as well as the ferocity of its sudden natural disasters: cyclones, floods, epidemics, and droughts, or a combination of these, which occur on the average of six out of every 10 years (Census of India, 1961: 11-12, 28). During these crises, the villagers turn to their local mother goddesses and *kalasis* for help, and they expect an immediate return for their offerings and prayers; if they are not forthcoming, they may angrily insult and curse their deities abandon them, and seek help from new deities and *kalasis*. Thus the relationship between worshippers and their deities is an ambivalent one: deities are said to punish worshippers who disobey their rules, but worshippers in turn punish their deities who disobey them.

Fifth, as in other areas of Northern India, mother goddess priests and shamans are recruited primarily from among the Shudra, low and untouchable castes. Some of the reasons for this have been summarized by Henry (1975: 16-28), who cites several studies

[8]Beliefs about bodily pollution are widespread throughout India. People believe that they have differing degrees of pollution at different stages of their lives, and that many rituals focus on the elimination of pollution. See, for example, Harper (1964: 158-61, 170), Babb (1975: 47-51, 80-81, 98), and Kane (1941: 583-85).

supporting these conclusions. Both low castes or untouchables, and non-Sanskritic mother-goddess cults frequently originated in aboriginal cultures; hence aboriginals or low or untouchable castes frequently were commissioned to propitiate these non-Sanskritic mother deities. Lower castes thus are assumed to have greater power to control such deities. Lower castes also are less pure than higher castes, so they can deal with the impure aspects of the mother goddess, such as meat eating, blood sacrifice, or disease. Citing Berreman, Henry observes that low caste persons might benefit as shamans and mother-goddess priests when they do not have adequate and other reliable means of support (Berreman, 1964: 61. Citing Planalp, Henry notes that untouchables may take advantage of crises such as smallpox epidemics to cause fear among high caste people by threatening them, saying that the smallpox goddess will infect them if they do not worship in a particular way which provides economic benefits to the untouchables (Planalp, 1956: 730). Citing Opler, Henry notes that spirit possession by a mother goddess gives a person of low status "licensed aggression" against social superiors who consider the possessed person to be the goddess and thus must give deference to that person (Opler, 1958: 558). Citing Kolenda, Henry concludes that the ability of untouchables to control non-Sanskritic deities enables low and untouchable castes to gain fame, income, some power over high castes, and compensation, for their low rank (Kolenda, 1968). Berreman's statement aptly characterizes these views. "There can be no doubt that low caste people derive considerable satisfaction, personally if they are practitioners and vicariously if they are not, from the power non-Brahmanical practitioners exercise in overtly manipulating their caste superiors" (Berreman, 1964: 62).

No doubt, low caste and untouchable practitioners and observers derive some economic benefit from goddess-possession ceremonies that are attended by high castes. In many Orissan villages, for example, in addition to receiving gifts, low-caste *kalasis* receive portions of the animals that are sacrificed, and they usually distribute this meat to people of their caste. Significantly, large numbers of goats and chickens are sacrificed at two mother goddess ceremonies during the year, the Durga Puja and the Jhammu (firewalking) ceremonies. Durga Puja occurs usually in September or October, just before harvesting, when food stores are low, especially for the landless low caste and untouchable laborers who perform most of the heavy farm work. Similarly, the mid-April Jhammu traditionally occurs at about the time of the harvesting of the winter pulse crop in some fields, and the time when the untouchable landless laborers begin the first of several ploughings to prepare the fields for the sowing of the following season's winter rice (O'Malley, 1929: 170, 172). The untouchable laborers who perform these arduous tasks not only have virtually no animal protein or fats in their diet except during these two physically demanding times of the year, they frequently suffer from food shortages. The redistribution of meat at these times thus may be of considerable nutritional significance (Care, 1972: 3, 5-10; Appendix 15, pp. 1-4). During sacrifices at mother goddess ceremonies there are frequent disputes, and sometimes violent clashes between high caste donors and low caste recipients over what percentage of the meat belongs to the *kalasis.*

Nevertheless, possession by mother goddesses cannot be explained simply as a political and economic retaliatory power play that low castes exert on high castes, for two reasons: (1) during crises such as smallpox or cholera epidemics, both high caste and low caste persons become possessed by Sitala, the smallpox goddess, or by the cholera goddess who is, in Sunderpur, one of the forms of Kali. Traditionally, anyone who had smallpox or cholera was said to be possessed by Sitala, used "licensed aggression" against the people around them, and while doing so was considered to be the goddess whose orders must be obeyed. Such behavior, then, was not simply associated with low castes, but also with the high.

(2) More importantly, an affliction with cholera frequently led individuals through traumatic initiatory experiences which led to their first possession by the goddess, after which they became *kalasis.* In one typical episode, a high-caste temple priest prayed to the goddess Kali to save one of this relatives from cholera, but when the relative died, the disillusioned priest cursed the goddess and defiled her image with dung. Soon afterwards, the priest became ill with cholera, during which the goddess appeared to him as a terrifying apparition. She announced that she had chosen to appear through his body, that he would be cured, and that henceforth he would obey her orders. Such events were viewed as terrifying initiatory transformations that a person does not experience lightly, nor consciously wish upon himself.

While most of the persons who become *kalasis* are of low or untouchable caste, and while high-caste *kalasis* usually come from families with little economic or political power, the actions of these *kalasis* in three ways involve more than simply overt or conscious manipulation of higher castes, even though as the struggle between the *kalasi* and the magician of Sunderpur shows, some sort of manipulation may occur.

(1) Such manipulation usually occurs while *kalasis* are possessed, that is, considered to be the goddess herself. *Kalasis* say that they have no recollection whatsoever when they are in such a state. If they are telling the truth, then they are not involved in conscious or overt manipulation at all. Of course, deliberate fakes exist, and no doubt they consciously manipulate people.

(2) People give respect to the goddess, not to the individual whose body she temporarily happens to ocupy. The villagers of Sunderpur are very explicit about this; if the *kalasi* is an untouchable, he remains an untouchable, even when possessed, and is not permitted access to the main temple of the village, which is used by the high castes.

(3) I am inclined to believe many of the people who say that they had no recollection of what they do while possessed by the goddess, since people describe the *experience* of being possessed as a powerful, terrifying, and disintegrative experience, or one that is viewed ambivalently, as with the Chandi *kalasi*. In their reports of shamanistic activity, Berreman, Opler, Planalp, Kolenda, and Henry greatly underplay the shamanistic experience itself. While the effects of goddess possession clearly may lead to temporary control over higher status people, possession itself, as reported by many people who have experienced it, is hardly a lark.

Sixth, and finally, the failure of the firewalkig ceremony and the humiliation of the *kalasis* and goddesses of Sunderpur provides a unique opportunity to glimpse what happens when the religious faith of villagers becomes questioned. Despite fining the magician, the villagers reluctantly agreed that the magician had won his battle for control of the goddesses of the *kalasis*. Significantly, the villagers did not question their faith in the mother goddess, but in the two representatives of the goddess that had been insulted. The failure of the *kalasis* did not lead to secularization, that is, the loss of a religious outlook or world view.

What caused the Chandi *kalasi* and his followers to be burned? Preparations for walking over hot coals involve a week-long psychological build-up through prayer and rites of purification. Yet even before the ritual preparations began, the magician challenged and threatened the *kalasi* and his firewalkers, damaging their concentration, and possibly their faith in the deity's powers to protect them. On firewalking day, whatever concentration or self-control the firewalkers might still have had, was shattered by two psychological shocks: the Chandi *kalasi* selected the magician to walk over the coals, even though he had not performed the rituals; and the Chandi *kalasi* delayed the firewalking ceremony so that the magician could participate. Once burned, the firewalkers refused to accept responsibility; they blamed the *kalasi* for failing to protect them, and the magician for deliberately disrupting the ceremony.

Another possible cause of the failure was my presence at the ceremony. While I would not rule out this possibility, I consider it unlikely for two reasons. (1) The firewalkers were accustomed to being observed and photographed by outsiders. I was not the first Westerner to witness firewalking ceremonies at Sunderpur; in the past decade, many had done so, and their presence had not disrupted the ceremony. (2) The Chandi *kalasi* clearly could have accused me during the meeting at his shrine; instead, while in trance as the goddess, he invited me to take photographs of his performance, in which he accused the magician, who had challenged his powers and had openly threatened to disrupt the ceremony.

Walker has suggested that the success of firewalkers may be due to a simple and widely-known physical process. Water dropped on very hot surfaces forms a layer of water vapor between the hot surface and the water drops, and this enables the water drops to last for a surprisingly long time. When a firewalker steps on coals that are hot enough, sweat or water on the soles of his feet will form long-lasting drops (Leidenfrost drops) that protect his feet (Walker, 1977: 126-31). This explanation is particularly plausible for the Sunderpur ceremony, since the firewalkers stand in pits of sacred water before each journey they take over the coals. Significantly, the Banadurga *kalasi* and the 12-year-old boy she led over the coals walked only on the northernmost firepath, and neither of them was burned, while many of those walking on other lanes suffered burns. Paradoxically, the others may have been burned, not because the firelanes were too hot, but because they were not hot enough. Unlike most of the others, the Banadurga *kalasi* and the boy walked fairly slowly over the glowing coals. Walker observes that a person who walks slowly over hot coals will preserve Leidenfrost drops for a longer period than a person who runs. With their concentration shattered by the magician's presence, many of the disconcerted firewalkers ran over the coals instead of walking, thus involuntarily insuring that they would be burned. Those who lack faith in the goddess's powers to protect them might also tend to run over the coals and thus injure themselves. Thus the native interpretations of the success of the firewalkers—that they have faith—fits neatly with the scientific explanation of the physical properties of water on very hot surfaces. Both perspectives require that, to be successful, the firewalker act in a way that goes against common sense—by walking slower rather than faster over surfaces that are hotter rather than cooler. Whether acting from scientific knowledge or from religious belief, a firewalker requires strong faith in the rightness of the explanatory framework he uses.

It is not surprising that the Chandi *kalasi*, the firewalkers, and virtually all of the villagers blamed the magician for disrupting the ceremony, since he had openly threatened to do so. Moreover, the villagers fear and loathe magicians, believing that magicians cause evil spirits to possess young women who, if not treated, will die. Magicians, however, not only afflict people, they are the only ones who can cure them. People thus fear magicians, but must placate them. Magicians thus control their neighbors through terrorizing them, while at the same time earning substantial fees curing them.

Magicians not only cause harm to people, but to deities whom they bring under their control. Villagers view magicians as deliberate trouble makers and rule breakers. Sensing that the magician was threatening their deities, the villagers sought to prevent further damage to their deities and shrines. Ordinarily villagers do not oppose magicians because they fear retaliation. The villagers rose as a group to stop the magician only because his threat to the foundation of their religious faith was more than they could bear.

The failure of the firewalking ceremony of Sunderpur highlights the lonely lives both of an Indian *kalasi* and a magician. Unlike hereditary Brahman priests, neither a *kalasi* nor a magician inherits his religious role. Both acquire their position through their own abilities, but the ways they achieve their positions are quite different; a *kalasi* undergoes an initiatory experience in which he becomes possessed by the goddess, who works through him; a magician deliberately learns his techniques and spells from other magicians or from books on magic. The greater the success *kalasis* and magicians achieve, the greater the potential for outraged retaliation by their clients if they lose their powers: a magician whose exorcistic cures fail is ridiculed and insulted, and his reputation is ruined; a *kalasi* who fails is insulted and beaten by his infuriated followers, who may defiantly desecrate his shrine, smash the image of his goddess, and seek another goddess and *kalasi* who can more successfully fulfil their deep religious needs.

REFERENCES

BABB, LAWRENCE

1975 *The Divine Hierarchy.* New York: Columbia University Press.

BERREMAN, GERALD

1964 "Brahmins and Shamans in Pahari Religion." *The Journal of Asian Studies* 13 (June): 53-69.

CARE-ORISSA

1972 *Planning for Better Nutrition in Orissa.* Care: Orissa.

CENSUS OF INDIA, 1961

1966 *Orissa. District Census Handbook, Puri.* Cuttack: Orissa Government Press.

DAS, KUNJABEHARI

1953 *A Study of Orissan Folklore.* Shantiniketan: Shantiniketan Press.

DAS, S.R.

1952 "A Study of the Vrata Rites of Bengal." *Man in India* 32 (October-December): 207-45.

FREEMAN, JAMES M.

1974 "Trial by Fire." *Natural History Magazine* 83 (January): 54-63.

1977 *Scarcity and Opportunity in an Indian Village.* Menlo Park. California: Cumming Publishing Company.

HARPER, EDWARD B.

1964 "Ritual Pollution as an Integrator of Caste and Religion." *Journal of Asian Studies* (*Aspects of Relgion in South Asia*) 23 (June): 151-97.

HENRY, EDWARD O.

1975 "The Mother Goddess Cult and Competition Between Little and Great Traditions." Paper presented at a Symposium "Anthropological Inquiries into Mother Worship." Annual Meeting of the American Anthropological Association, San Francisco, December 1975.

KANE, PANDURANG VAMAN

1941 *History of Dharmaśāstra.* Volume 2, Part I. Poona: Bhandarkar Oriental Research Institute.

1974 *History of Dharmaśāstra.* Volume 5, Part I, 2nd edition. Poona: Bhandarkar Oriental Research Institute.

KOLENDA, PAULINE MAHAR

1968 "Functional Relations of a Bhangi Cult." *The Anthropologist.* (Special Volume 2.)

KUPER HILDA
1960 *Indian People in Natal.* Natal: University Press.
O'MALLEY, L.S.S.
1929 *Puri District Gazeteer.* Patna: Government Printing Press.
OPLER, MORRIS E.
1958 "Spirit Possession in a Rural Area of Northern India." In William A. Lessa and Evon Z. Vogt (eds.), *Reader in Comparative Religion; An Anthropological Approach,* pp. 553-66, Evanston, Illinois: Row, Peterson and Company.
PLANALP, JACK
1956 Religious Life and Values in a North Indian Village. Ph.D. dissertation, Cornell University, Xerox University Microfilms No. 56-979.
ROSNER, VICTOR
1966 "Firewalking the Tribal Way." *Anthropos* 61: 177-90.
WALKER, JEARL
1977 "The Amateur Scientist." *Scientific American* 237 (August): 126-31.
ZIMMER, HEINRICH
1946 *Myths and Symbols in Indian Art and Civilization.* New York: Bollingen.

LORNA RHODES AMARSINGHAM

THE SINHALESE EXORCIST AS TRICKSTER

ABSTRACT. Sinhalese exorcists combine a power to remove demonic forces with a reputation for trickery. Exorcists themselves cultivate an image of cunning and deception. This paper explores the relationship between the style of the exorcist as trickster and the meaning of illness in the Sinhalese context. It is concluded that the use of ambiguity and deception is central to the exorcist's ability to "deflect" the demonic through wit, persuasion and social manipulation.

THE WESTERN DOCTOR, BOTH IN THE WEST AND IN NON-WESTERN countries, is a figure who commands a high level of respect and whose prestige is generally unquestioned (see, for example, NORC, 1953). In Sri Lanka, however, there is a category of ritual healer whose public image is far from that of the Western doctor. These specialists are of low status in the social hierarchy and are often referred to as greedy, cunning and untrustworthy.

This negative image is not confined to the villagers who constitute the "public" of the ritual specialists; healers themselves tell stories about their own cunning and take care to cultivate an impression of mystery and canniness. Further, an examination of their role in ritual reveals that tricks and cunning are an integral part of their style in dealing with the forces that cause illness. This suggests that we should examine the relationship between the "style" of the healer and Sinhalese conceptions of illness and cure. An understanding of this relationship should clarify the role of the specialist while also providing an interesting contrast to the orientation of Western medicine.

The Sinhalese, who make up 70 per cent of the population of Sri Lanka, are Theravada Buddhists. The majority of Sinhalese live in agricultural villages centered on wet rice cultivation. For most villagers, there are several alternative treatments for illness, including Western Medicine, practiced in clinics staffed by apothecaries or doctors, and Ayurvedic medicine, practiced by specialists *(vedu-*

ralas) in Ayurveda (see Obeyesekere, 1976 for a discussion of the interrelationship of Ayurveda, Western Medicine, and ritual practice).

The treatment I will focus on here can best be labelled exorcism, for it involves the removal, through ritual, of "supernatural" forces believed to cause illness.[1] Chief among these forces are demonic beings, or *yakas*, which are malevolent, ugly and ferocious creatures dependent on human beings for their source of food.[2] Illness is caused when one of these beings gains access to a person and attacks him; it can be cured by luring the demon away with offerings of food which substitute for the flesh of the person attacked.

The demons are by no means alone in the supernatural world, which is heavily populated with beings which exhibit various degrees of purity and power. Most important of these is the Buddha himself, who gave men the potential for controlling demons before he passed into *nirvana* and left the world of sentient beings altogether. Next in importance, and prominent in all healing ceremonies, are the gods (*deviyo*), potent beings who directly control demons and who can be persuaded with offerings to intercede on the behalf of men. The demons are below the gods in power and are also impure and wicked; they are also below men in terms of their potential for salvation. Finally there are ghosts (*pretayo*) and assorted apparitions which are frightening and impure but not particularly powerful.

The "glue" which holds this supernatural domain together is the doctrine of *karma*. All beings are nearer or farther from salvation according to their deeds in past lives; thus demons are the result of excessive greed which has led them to a sorry dependence on human flesh in their present existence. The exorcist's task is to

[1]The research on which this paper is based was carried out in the Kotmale area of Sri Lanka (formerly Ceylon) from November 1971 to June 1972 and was supported by an NIH traineeship grant administered through Cornell University. The author and her assistant interviewed between 10 and 20 people for whom rituals had been or were about to be performed and discussed ritual exorcism with members of the three exorcist troupes who practiced in the area. The rituals which were performed by these troupes during the author's stay in the area were observed (five all-night and several shorter rituals). The author also met with ritual specialists in the Kandy and Colombo areas. Unless otherwise indicated, quotes are taken from field-notes.

[2]Sinhalese exorcism involves numerous rituals of varying complexity. In this discussion I will limit myself to those in which the demonic forces believed to cause illness are dramatically portrayed by the exorcists.

act as mediator, enlisting the aid of the gods on behalf of the patient and "persuading" the demons to leave the patient alone. He is concerned with what Mandelbaum (1970) has called the "pragmatic" aspect of religion, intervening at those moments when demonic forces are felt to be impinging directly on everyday life.

An exorcist *(kattadiya, yakadurā, yakdesa)* usually works in a troupe consisting of a leader and several dancers, drummers and assistants. The size of the troupes, which is usually a group of kinsmen and apprentices, varies with the type of ritual and the ability of the patient *(āturayā, leda)* to pay. The process of diagnosis and treatment is highly variable. Sometimes a villager behaves in a manner clearly indicative of demon-caused illness *(yak-dosa, tanikama)* (shouting, threatening people, demanding offerings) in which case the family may arrange immediately for a ritual. Sometimes a villager with recurring symptoms tries Western and Ayurvedic medicine first, going to the exorcist only after an astrologer, monk, or fortune-teller has recommended a ritual cure. Exorcist rituals *(tovil, yaktovil)* are by far the most expensive of the treatments available to the villager and it often takes considerable time and preparation before one can be held.

Sinhalese society is organized into ranked, endogamous castes; culturally, the pollution-complex is similar to that of India. However, the hierarchy of castes differs somewhat from Indian caste systems in that the highest cast, the cultivators, is also the most numerous. Lower castes make up less than half the population. Exorcists come from several of the lower castes, most generally the potter or drummer castes. This means that often the exorcist is lower and thus polluting to his high-caste patient; he must observe certain precautions in using the house and utensils of the patient, and must follow ritual forms (such as sitting at a lower level) when interacting with the patient and his family.

Although rituals vary depending on the situation of the patient and the specific demons believed to be involved in the illness, their basic structure is consistent. Once the ritual arena *(simuva midula)* has been set up in the patient's house, there is a long period of dancing and invocation (usually lasting from evening to midnight) after which masked dancers representing demons appear in the arena and "threaten" the patient, who sometimes becomes "possessed" at this point and interacts with the exorcists and dancers (see Obeyesekere for descriptions of Sinhalese possession). Gradually, using jokes and comic drama, the chief exorcist "subdues" the demons into agreeing to leave the patient. Usually this process of submission on the part of the demons takes the form of their transformation from frightening figures into rather ineffectual buffoons. As Kapferer has pointed out, the division of the ritual into a "serious" and a comic half serves to set up the reality of the demonic world and then to undermine it, thus providing the patient with "essential symbolic reversals" of his experience of his illness (1974:2). Ritualists and patients, in talking about the process of cure, point out the psychological effect on the patient of the "fear" and "laughter" brought about by representations of the exorcists.

As I said at the beginning, the reputation of the ritual specialist is often in harmony with his low status. The low esteem in which he is held is mentioned by several writers on South Asian religion. Harper, for instance, discussing shamanism in a South Indian village, says that there was only one shaman in the area "whose motives and ability were never questioned" (1957: 269). Similarly Wirz, in his *Exorcism and the Art of Healing in Ceylon*, says that the exorcist "is no less prominent than the *vedurala* (ayurvedic specialist), although by no means so respected a personality" (1960:2). One name for the ritual specialist is *kattadiya* which, according to Raghavnan, means "disguised dancer" (1974). The *kattadiya* is a person who can disguise himself, make himself into something other than what he is. Sinhalese villagers say that someone is "clever as a *kattadiya*" when he can outwit others in the confrontation of daily life. An anthropologist hoping to study curing rituals receives many warnings about the tendency of ritualists to "tell lies" *(boru)* and to be greedy.

Ritualists tell stories about themselves which reveal that they consider this kind of cunning to be important in their work and an important part of their self-image.

> Once upon a time there was *kattadiya* whose wife developed a craving for a certain kind of grain. The only person who had any was a certain rich man, but he refused their request. After awhile the rich man got sick and called on the *kattadiya* to perform a ritual. Seeing his opportunity for revenge, he told them that for this ritual a special kind of image, made out of this particular grain, would be necessary, and that after the ceremony the image must be placed in a certain tree. The only tree of this kind was in

the *kattadiya's* yard, so after the ceremony he collected all the grain and kept it for himself.

In this story the cunning of the *kattadiya* is justified by the greediness of the rich man, but it is also a result of his own (his wife's) craving.

Once there was a *kattadiya* who wanted a particular vegetable. When he asked a man who had some in his garden, he refused. A few months later someone in that family needed a ritual performed and the *kattadiya* took revenge. When they finished the meal given them before the ceremony, the *kattadiya* threw his leaf into the garden. The drummer threw his leaf on top of it. The *kattadiya* asked him 'How dare you throw your leaf on top of mine? You are only a drummer.' They pretended to have a violent 'fight', rolling all over the garden and destroyed it.

Two themes recur in *kattadiya's* stories: a craving (especially for that possessed by someone higer in status) which is unsatisfied and an act of revenge through trickery. In other stories, *kattadiyas* arriving at a house for a performance discover that the family of the patient is eating better food than is offered to them; by inventing ritual poems which demand that particular food for use in the ritual itself, they succeed in obtaining it for themselves.

Two other stories show how the tendency to use trickery extends into the acquisition of ritual knowledge.

One ceremony calls for a small clay image (*baliya*); this is supposed to be modeled the day before the ritual. The reason for this is that when these rituals were performed in the past the image had to be made in the likeness of the patient. In order to get a glimpse of the patient, the specialists insisted on coming to the house the day before, during which they chanted all sorts of things which were simply made—up to give an impression of authenticity.

In the old days the specialists for certain kind of ritual had to be imported from India, which was rather expensive. Then one day two monks entertained a visitor from India who told them how to perform the ceremonies. While one was listening, the other sat in an inner room and wrote down everything he said. When he asked them whether they already had all the information he was giving them, the monk who had written everything down brought out his palm leaves and showed them to the visitor, saying that everything he had said was already known to them. Thus, they could begin the tradition of the ceremony in Ceylon without having to pay for the ceremonial material.

Here the performers are people who know how to get knowledge without seeming to, and who fool people into giving them what they want without realizing it. These stories which the performers tell about themselves show them as people who can make things appear other than what they are and who know how to use ritual material for their own ends. In the exorcist rituals themselves, much of the performer's activity is devoted to a manipulation of time, space, his body and language itself to produce a series of impressions which call into question the reality within which the patient manifests his illness.

Because the exorcist must create a special setting within the ordinary atmosphere of the patient's home (in contrast to the medical or ayurvedic practitioner who can set up a permanent office), the management of image, time and spaces particularly important to the effectiveness of the ritual. The performers engage in some elementary stage-management which provides, from the outset of the ritual, for a "backstage" area to be used for costume change and for eating and socializing with each other. Besides the protection from pollution which this affords to the patient's house, this area also provides them with a way of keeping their ordinary selves hidden from the patient and audience.[3] The ritual space is also bounded in various magical ways to protect the performers and patients; this enables the performers to indulge in episodes of anger or unconsciousness and to exercise their authority over the patient within a clearly bounded space. Similarly, the ritual time is sharply delineated, with drumbeats, chanting and megical performances, so that what happens within it is marked off from ordinary time and can transcend the conventions of daily life without threatening them.

The ritual specialist also manipulates his own body. The masks which he uses to represent the demons are large and menacing and

[3]Even when performers are of the same caste as their patient, they set up a private place within the patient's house, which functions as a "backstage" area.

effectively hide the wearer's face. By using masks, a small troupe of performers can manifest a number of different aspects and personalities in the course of a ritual; masks also make the transition from the earlier, "serious" part of the ritual to the later dramatic episodes more complete in its effect.[4]

In addition to masks which enhance the mutability of the bodily form of the exorcist, some of the dialogues in the comic episodes make explicit an image of his body as fluid, uncertain in form and ambiguous in its relation to other objects in the world. For instance, in one ritual dialogue, the parts of the body are humorously compared to various objects, and each time the chief exorcist must point out the correct identification.

> *Dancer* (pointing to actor representing a demon): See this fence around a paddy field?
> *Chief exorcist:* That is not a fence around a field, it is the teeth in the mouth.
> *Dancer:* What is that heap of fruit?
> *Chief exorcist:* That is not fruit, but what you call a neck.
> *Dancer:* And what are these two ticks?
> *Chief exorcist:* Those are the nipples.

In some rituals the performers act the part of women, while in others they squeeze themselves into tiny enclosures, or make jokes about having polluted themselves by oral or sexual contact with low things. In all of these ways they indicate that their bodily existence is somehow unstable, that they can allow intrusions, disjunctions and absurdities which would be intolerable to an ordinary person.

Another technique which the exorcist can use to make a similar point and at the same time create a highly charged atmosphere is the ritual trance. Using a powerful drumbeat, the sharp smell of incense and rhythmic dancing and chanting, he goes into a trance-like state in which his voice and demeanor are markedly different from his usual manner. Using archane language and a peculiar, jerky style of speech, he speaks in the "voice" of the demon being invoked (see Jones, 1968, for a discussion of the relation of possession to shama-

[4]Not all exorcist rituals involve masks, but even when masks are not used there is some device of costuming and manner which hides the everyday personalities of the actors.

nism). In this state the performer can say and do things he would not be able to ordinarily. In one ritual, the performer while in a trance announced that there was someone in the room who was polluting it; the audience and patient tensed in expectation that he would expel a menstruating woman or reveal someone's recent sexual activity. At another ritual, the performer discovered that the incense which had been provided by the patient's relatives was not smoking properly. He went into a rage, accusing the patient's family of trying to sabotage the ritual by leaving him open to supernatural harm. His freedom, in this situation, to express open and direct anger contrasts with the normal emphasis on control in Sinhalese society and gives him a great deal of power in manipulating the ritual scene.

When performers enact comic dramas, they have a further means of creating illusion and changing their image, for these dramas usually depend on the use of word-play and obscenity. The "demons," suitably masked, often enter the ritual arena as frightening figures, but as the drama proceeds their buffoonery reaches such a pitch that even the patient laughs. The transformation is achieved by means of words and actions that portray the demons as completely unable to see "reality" as it is, unable to understand ordinary words or the context of ordinary language. This world, as portrayed in the comic dramas, is a slippery, unreliable but hilarious place where even illness cannot be taken too seriously.

Dancer: I am ill.
Chief exorcist: What do you have?
Dancer: I can bend my arm but not unbend it. When I eat I have to finish one bite before I can swallow another.
Chief exorcist: If you would stop breathing, you would be just fine!

Many of the jokes rest on puns or twists of meaning, and they often make fun of sacred or high-status people and things.

Drummer: An umbrella and a flag should now be presented.
Actor: What is an umbrella?
Drummer: An umbrella protects you from the sun and rain.
Actor: It cannot do two things at once.... Where can I find one.
Drummer: The schoolmistress has one. You know, the one that

breaks into two or three bits and is carried under the arm.
Actor: Are you going to break up the schoolmistress?
Drummer: If you did that her teacher husband would break your neck. I am talking about modern umbrellas, not those ancient ones....
Actor: Really! When I talk of an umbrella I mean the umbrella which is held over the sacred tooth relic. The actor twirls the umbrella until it breaks (Kapferer, 1974 : 21).

In addition to these techniques in which the healer disguises himself and manipulates language to create "special effects" for the patient and audience, there are episodes in the rituals in which the exorcist tricks the "demons" themselves. Sometimes this takes the form of a made-up "letter" which is supposed to come from the Buddha and which frightens the demons into submission (Obeyesekere, 1969). More devious still is a technique in which the exorcist pretends to be the "dead" patient and has himself carried to a nearby cemetery where, presumably, the demon follows him. The demon is tricked into "leaving" the actual patient, and when he discovers the ruse it is too late to go back, for his way has been blocked by various magical barriers. A similar trick described by Hildburgh involves "devils who are afflicted as the patient is afflicted and are invoked to suggest to the afflicting devil that he will transfer his malignant influence to them, in the expectation that he will have a sort of brotherly compassion for them and after leaving the man, will inflict neither them nor him" (quoted in Wood, 1934, 488).

Finally, the ritualist uses language in a fluid and unconventional way which allows him to "wander all over" the social and supernatural hierarchy. In addressing and dealing with the patient, he ranges from respect and humility to outright insult, as when battling directly with the demon manifested in the patient (Obeyesekere, 1973). Similarly with the demons, the ritual language extended to them is sometimes respectful and, at other times, extremely insulting. Demons can be addressed as gods and their sometimes princely origins emphasized, or in other contexts they can be contemptuously referred to as fools and compared to animals.[5] Even the gods are not

[5]Peter Claus, writing about India, points out that the attributes of beings in the local Hindu pantheons are relative and depend to some extent on the social situation in which they have relevance; the gods, for instance, can provide protection *or* inflict disease. This is to some extent true for the Sinhalese pantheon.

free from insult; although they are addressed with respect in many of the invocations, they are also made fun of and treated to all kinds of insulting analogies in the joking episodes. Movement from "high" to "low" language is not confined to supernaturals, in many episodes, especially joking ones, jokes are made at the expense of people in various social categories, and monks, for instance, who are normally respected, come in for a share of insult. Sometimes the patient too is made fun of and his condition mocked.

Thus, the ritual specialist exhibits a fluidity and unpredictability in dealing with normally fixed situations of hierarchy, bodily integrity and language. He is able to disguise himself, not only with masks, but with a more basic ambiguity of self-image. He can manipulate space and time, make outrageous jokes at the expense of those higher than he is, and verbally undermine his own bodily boundaries.

These characteristics of the healer are similar to those of the "trickster" figure who appears in many mythologies. Paul Radin, in his classic on the trickster, describes two aspects of the Winnebago trickster figure; first, he is in the process of moving from an undifferentiated existence to a more social and self-conscious one,and secondly, his is an embodiment of deliberate social satire. Jung, in his commentary on Radin's work, explicitly compares the shaman with the trickster. "There is something of the trickster in the character of the shaman and medicine man, for he, too, often plays malicious tricks on people" (1956: 196). This comparison can be elaborated in the case of the Sinhalese *kattadiya.* For example, the trickster has an amorphous and ambiguous body, which is not integrated around a core or self but is rather separable and manipulable. In the Winnego trickster cycle, trickster goes to sleep and leaves his anus to guard his food (Radin, 1956 : 16); when it fails in this task he burns it and is surprised when he feels pain. Similar incidents occur in the joking episodes of Sinhalese rituals, where the specialist acts out a comic inability to comprehend the connections among his various body parts ("if you stop breathing, you will be cured"). The disconnectedness of the exorcist's body is apparent during trance episodes, when his movements and speech are uncoordinated and (supposedly) unconnected to his consciousness, and is explicitly brought out in

Although the demons are consistently malevolent, the lower gods who must be called upon to control them have both benevolent and malevolent potential and this constitutes one of the complexities which engages the skill of the exorcist (see Claus, 1973: 231).

many joking episodes where parts of the body are given separate and absurd identities.

The trickster is also socially defiant, acting in an apparently non-deliberate and absurd way to mock and undermine social convention. The Winnebago trickster shows disrespect to the most sacred customs of the tribe by throwing away valuable magical objects, and by acting with great disrespect toward sacred positions in the society (Radin, 1956 : 6). Similarly, the exorcist mocks all social and religious convention. Much of the dialogue in the joking parts of the rituals deliberately points out the absurdity of social positions, making fun in turn of each category in the social hierarchy. Supernatural forces, not only demons but the gods and Buddha as well, are made fun of and explicitly connected to polluted or dangerous things.

The dramatic style of the exorcist allows him to point out the absurdity of the world by being absurd himself. Within the bounded comic episodes of ritual, the exorcist gives a droll portrayal of unself-consciousness and social ignorance. With his slips of the tongue, misapprehensions of words and things, and insulting yet naive remarks, he conveys an irresponsible, marginal quality. But this style is far from self-defeating; through it, the exorcist creates demonic figures who are also droll, stupid and clever at the same time. Using these qualities in dealing with them, he succeeds in outwitting them to the advantage of the patient and the entertainment of the audience.

Why does Sinhalese exorcism require a performer who embodies, in the course of the rituals he performs and in his public image, a slyness and cunning reminiscent of mythological trickster figures? What is it, in the situation of Sinhalese curing, that makes these qualities appropriate?

First, the relationship between the body of the patient and the demonic force attacking it is not a clear-cut one. Demons are able to attack people and feed on them because they have been given "permission" to do so by the Buddha on the condition that they desist when ritually presented with offerings. However, the Buddha has also banished the demons to a demon-world from which they can only look at the earth, not actually inhabit it. Thus, they can attack people only by "looking" at them, and the ritual is designed to remove this "look" (*bálma, yaksha dishti*). But, at the same time, the ritual often treats the patient as though the demons were actually inside him; the patient sometimes speaks with the "voice" of a demon and exhibits demonic characteristics such as insensitivity to pain. The actual vulnerability of the patient's body is an ambiguous point which the ritual does not clarify; if anything, the ritual itself presents contradictory images of the bodily relationship between the patient and his illness.

Further, the relationship between the patient's mind or "self" and the attack of the demon is not clear. Although it seems at first glance that the removal of the demon could be done magically without the cooperation or even the consciousness of the patient, exorcists tend to describe their cures in terms of the patient "feeling happy" or "believing" that the demons have gone. They emphasize that the patient should stay awake and be attentive throughout the entire performance. This attitude suggests that part of what is going on in the ritual is a demand on the patient that he gain conscious control over his illness, that he be made aware of the true nature of what is bothering him. On the other hand, the patient during the ritual often becomes "possessed" and goes into a trance in which he behaves like the demon which is "residing" in him, shouting, shaking, and defiantly demanding his own way. During these episodes the patient unleashes a great deal of aggression, and the fact that he is so far out of conscious control is a demonstration, within the meaning of the ritual, that demonic forces do actually possess him. Thus the exorcist must deal with a situation in which the locus of the patient's "self" is ambiguous or uncertain; the exorcist is responsible for controlling the defiant demon/patient, and for returning, the patient's self to him at the end of the ritual.

In addition to this lack of certainty surrounding the nature of the demonic attack itself, there is, secondly, a considerable ambiguity about the hierarchy within which both demons and exorcists exist. The higher figures in the Sinhalese pantheon are both pure and powerful, and thus consistent with an ideology of castes which links purity and social and magical power. Similarly the very lowest figures, the ghosts, link impurity and powerlessness in a logically consistent way. Demons, however, are impure but powerful. That their power is limited in scope and subject to higher authority is the task of the exorcist to prove at every curing ritual. In other words, he must, without denying their power to create illness, use their impurity and low status against them by invoking the power of the gods over them. He must also retain the respect of the gods (that is, exhibit sufficient purity himself to command their attention) while dealing with demons who are unclean and irreverant.

In the human social world, the exorcist faces a similar ambiguity. In the ordinary social hierarchy, he is lower, and more impure, than his patient. Yet, in the context of the ritual, he wields considerable power over the patient, both because of his capacity to banish demons and because of the corollary capacity to enlist them against his enemies. While performing, the exorcist controls the patient and audience in ways not available to the ordinary villager, reversing the normal direction in which power is distributed.

Finally, the Sinhalese Buddhist position on illness is itself related to this question. In Buddhism, a primary truth is that "everything is suffering." This means that everything that exists is transitory and impermanent and that attachment to impermanence is the source of all ill. Even things which appear to be good (such as family life, or charity) contain the seeds of dissolution and are thus a form of "sorrow." Within this approach, illness is not a radical intrusion into a world which is "normally" orderly and good, but rather it is simply a manifestation of a basic truth about the world. Illness cannot be permanently removed, for it is an aspect of the very nature of the world (Boyd, n.d.:8). Thus, illness, whether manifested in demons or in germs, can only be forestalled temporarily through magical manipulation or medicine.

Buddhism further provides that the root of all suffering is craving, or attachment to the things of the world. Demons, with their desire for human flesh, are clearly gross manifestation of craving, and thus are particularly suited to be representations of "ill." Some of the episodes in curing rituals seem to indicate that the patient is also temporarily manifesting excessive craving, and that he can be persuaded to "give up" his illness just as the demon, by analogy, "gives up" human flesh. Finally, as we saw in the stories of the exorcists, they too are manifestations of greed and attachment, cunningly getting what they want from an unsuspecting (but also greedy) public. The exorcist thus deals on several levels with the forces of craving and greed which underly illness itself. This requires a movement on his part from attachment to giving up; and the entire ritual can be seen as an intricate expression of the Sinhalese concern with receiving and giving up.

The duplicity and the slipperiness of the exorcist clearly aid him in dealing with all of these aspects of the curing situation. In his bodily ambiguity he mirrors the physically ambiguous situation of the patient; by stressing the idea of physical disconnectedness he can deal with the uncertain quality of the demonic attack. Many of his jokes and manipulations raise the question of where the "inside" and the "outside" of the body are and of who is in control of the self of the patient; he takes the concern with body boundaries which inheres in the pollution complex and makes of it something both funny and potentially useful for cure.

The cunning and trickiness of the exorcist allows him to deal with the ambiguous power situation manifested in the demonic attack and in the ritual. He is both magically powerful and low in status; he is also both stupid and clever. Thus, he can manipulate gods and demons into doing what he wants, shifting constantly from "high" to "low" language and demeanor. He can be obscene and witty with the demons, solemn and obscure with the gods. And, by moving back and forth among supernatural modes, he can also control the social situation. His "stupidity" in the joking episodes makes him seem harmless and incompetent, and this offsets his connections with the gods demonstrated in other parts of the ritual. In other words, he is just smooth enough, and deceptive enough, to move around freely in an otherwise difficult and uncertain set of relationships.

If part of the task of the exorcist is to make his patient and audience see that illness is basic to the nature of the world, then his undermining of social and linguistic convention is a way of accomplishing it. As he plays with social roles and with language, he demonstrates an inherent instability in these forms. He shows how easily they can be distorted and made into objects of fun. Thus he throws into question the whole edifice of social normality. Illness, instead of threatening a well-established whole, becomes another manifestation of absurdity. It is less serious if that which it threatens (that is, ordinary social life) has lost its solidity, and becomes fluid and uncertain.

The exorcist, far from "conquering" illness, is a deflector of illness. There is no thought of eliminating demons from the world; the task is simply to make them temporarily less harmful.[6] Deviousness and ambiguity are well suited to this, for the essential skills are persuasion, wit and social manipulation. The kind of "attack"

[6]As Sherry Ortner points out in her article on "Sherpa Purity," the momentary defeat of the demons is simply a temporary stand off . . . the demons are never defeated once and for all (this eventually would represent the final purification of the world) (1973:60).

which a demon makes, and the responses of the patient, are not subject to straightforward intervention but must be dealt with through subterfuge and by undermining the assumptions which make such an attack possible.

Clearly the exorcist's image as a trickster is of use to him in his role as deflector. And this role, which is a necessary corollary of Sinhalese theories about the nature of illness, shapes the form of the rituals themselves, for the exorcist uses his freedom of movement to create boundaries, devise joking dramas and manipulate the beliefs of the audience, all in order to create an atmosphere in which the demonic is both possible and manageable.

An association between publicity and healing is thus embedded in the figure of the exorcist himself and in many aspects of the rituals he performs. A further exploration of the contrasts between "deflection" and "conquest" might clarify some of the conceptual differences between Western Medicine and ritual practice in Ceylon and illuminate the kinds of choices which are made by villagers as they seek treatment for both mental and physical illnesses.

REFERENCES

BOYD, JAMES W.

n.d. "Satan and Mara: Christian and Buddhist Symbols of Evil." Unpublished paper.

CLAUS, PETER J.

1973 "Possession, Protection and Punishment as Attributes of Deities in a South Indian Village." *Man in India* 53:231.

HARPER, EDWARD B.

1957 "Shamanism in South Asia." *Southeastern Journal of Anthropology* 13:267.

JONES, REX L.

1968 "Shamanism in South Asia." *History of Religion* 7:330.

JUNG, C.G.

1956 "On the Psychology of the Trickster Figure." In Rosin (ed.), *The Trickster: A study in American Indian Mythology*, pp. 195-221. London: Routledge and Kegan Paul.

KAPFERER, BRUCE

1947 *First Class to Maradana: The Sacred and the Secular in Sinhalese Exorcism Rituals*. New York: Wenner-Gren Foundation for Anthropological Research.

MANDELBAUM, DAVID G.
1970 "Curing and Religion in South Asia." *Journal of the Indian Anthropological Society* 5: 171-86.

NORC
1953 "Jobs and Occupations, A Popular Evaluation." In R. Bendix and S.M. Lipset (eds.), *Class, Status and Power*, pp. 411-26. Glencoe, Illnois: Free Press.

OBEYESEKERE, GANANATH
1969 "The Ritual Drama of the Sanni Demons: Collective Representatives of Disease in Ceylon." *Comparative Studies in Society and History* 11: 174-216.
1970 "The Idiom of Demonic Possession: A Case Study." *Social Science and Medicine* 4: 97-111.
1973 "Psycho-cultural Exegesis of a Case of Spirit Possession from Ceylon." Unpublished paper.
1976 "The Impact of Ayurvedic Ideas on the Culture and the Individual in Sri Lanka." In Charles Leslie (ed.) *Asian Medical Systems*, pp. 201-26. Berkeley: University of California Press.

ORTNER, SHERRY B.
1973 "Sherpa Purity." *American Anthropoligist* 75:1.

RADIN, PAUL
1956 *The Trickster: A Study in American Indian Mythology*. London: Routledge and Kegan Paul.

RAGHAVAN, M.D.
1974 "The Ceremonial and Ritual Dances in the Kohomba Kankariya." *Souvenir of the 17th Natyakala Conference*. Madras: Indian Institute of Fine Arts.

WIRZ, PAUL
1950 *Exorcism and the Art of Healing in Ceylon*. London: E.J. Brill.

WOOD, CASEY A.
1934 "Sinhalese and South India Ceremonials in the Prevention and Treatment of Disease." *Annals of Medical History* (new series) 6: 483.

INDEX